Scott A Perry

W9-ARU-608

551
W. 91

Science and the Human Spirit

GLG BNAF   FTP
HW WSP   TFS
H BC   NBM- NBGB

One's One   we're havin' some fun
            in the Bedroom · all day's all of the
                        night
Two's Two   she took off her shoes ...
Three's Three she undressed me ...
Four's Four we F..... on the floor...
Five's Five she pulled up her thigh ...
Six's Six   the bitch socked my dick ...

FRED D. WHITE *Santa Clara University*

Science and the Human Spirit

Contexts for Writing and Learning

WADSWORTH PUBLISHING COMPANY
Belmont, California   A Division of Wadsworth, Inc.

Production Editor: Jane Townsend
Managing Designer: Donna Davis
Print Buyer: Barbara Britton
Designer: Adriane Bosworth
Copy Editor: Evelyn Mercer Ward
Cover Designer: Donna Davis
Cover Painting: Albrecht Dürer: *The Great Piece of Turf,* 1503.
Watercolor. Graphische Sammlung Albertina, Vienna. Photo: Art
Resource, New York.

Acknowledgments are listed on pages 371–373.

© 1989 Wadsworth, Inc. All rights reserved. No part of this book may
be reproduced, stored in a retrieval system, or transcribed, in any
form or by any means, electronic, mechanical, photocopying, recording, or otherwise, without the prior written permission of the
publisher, Wadsworth Publishing Company, Belmont, California 94002,
a division of Wadsworth, Inc.

Printed in the United States of America   49

1 2 3 4 5 6 7 8 9 10—93 92 91 90 89

Library of Congress Cataloging-in-Publication Data

Science and the human spirit: contexts for writing and learning /
   [compiled by] Fred D. White.
         p.   cm.
      Includes index.
      ISBN 0–534–09666–2
      1. Readers—Science.   2. College readers.   3. Technical
writing.
      4. English language—Rhetoric.   5. English language—Technical
English.   6. Science.   I. White, Fred D., 1943–
   PE1127.S3S414 1989
   808'.0665—dc19   88–19051
                                                                CIP

ISBN 0–534–09666–2

For BEVERLY, MICHAEL, and LAURA

Contents

PART TWO

The Discovery Dimension: Scientists Who Have Revolutionized Our Understanding of Nature   77

PART THREE

The Social and Ethical Dimension: Issues in Science and Technology   141

PART FOUR

The Literary Dimension: Short Stories, Poetry, and Personal Essays on Scientific Themes 239

APPENDIX A

Researching a Scientific Topic   351

APPENDIX B

Important Scientists in History   359

Preface

This anthology of readings in the sciences attempts to fill a conspicuous gap in both technical and liberal arts education by providing students with an opportunity to read about science in a broad cultural context. By striving to understand the ideas and activities associated with scientific activity, students develop learning skills that are important to writing, as well as to any disciplined inquiry. The poet C. Day Lewis said it most succinctly: "It is by searching for means of communication that we sharpen our powers of observation. The discoveries of the artist and the scientist are exactly alike in this respect."

Few would disagree that science has been elemental in shaping our culture or that science literacy is a vital element in undergraduate education—yet, ironically, misconceptions about science abound. They are evident in our language—for instance, in the way we distinguish between "science" and "the humanities," as if science were not a humanistic activity. Science, contrary to being dehumanizing, enriches human culture by providing a way of distinguishing between truth and mere conjecture or falsehood. Science is the *quest* for knowledge, not just the accumulation and advancement of it, and as Carl Sagan reminds us, it is no accident that *quest* and *question* share a common etymology. Every question we ask about the nature of things launches us on a journey of exploration. Science combines intuition and imagination with incisive logic and analysis. Good science, like good writing, requires close and accurate observation, clarity, the ability to support assumptions with sufficient evidence (indeed, science nurtures an understanding of the nature of evidence itself), and a sensitivity to oversimplifications and faulty generalizations. These are the valuable learning tools with which science equips all students, regardless of their fields of interest.

COURSES FOR WHICH THIS BOOK IS INTENDED

This book may be used in three types of courses:

1. Any first-year writing course that stresses the importance of writing in the disciplines, yet does not restrict the scope to purely practical or narrowly professional discourse aims—or, conversely, attempt to represent every major discipline. To be sure, *science* embraces many disciplines, several of which have roots in traditionally humanistic areas (anthropology in language study, psychoanalysis in literary theory, archaeology in history, and so on).

2. Sophomore- or junior-level science writing courses, especially those that emphasize writing about scientific ideas for popular audiences.

3. Humanities courses that explore the nature and range of scientific activity in Western civilization or that wish to investigate the relationship between science and literature, perhaps focusing on the "Two Cultures Debate" launched by novelist-physicist C. P. Snow in 1959.

SPECIAL FEATURES OF THIS BOOK

Each of the four sections of this anthology offers a unique perspective from which to examine science's impact on our daily lives: 1) science's role in education and its influence upon the way we learn; 2) science's impact, through revolutionary discovery, on our understanding of reality; 3) science's influence on our values and our ability to make ethical decisions on matters of great complexity; 4) science as a wellspring of artistic expression. The sections may be taken up in any order, depending on the instructor's design for the course.

Each selection is preceded by a brief *Reading Introduction,* and accompanying each introduction is a list of *Terms to Learn*—beforehand (so that the student's concentration on the material need not be disrupted). Each selection is followed by a series of exercises and projects arranged by the following headings:

   • *Checking Your Comprehension*—questions for quickly checking the student's grasp of the selection.

- *For Discussion and Debate*—questions to stimulate in-class discussion or debate of issues raised by the selection.

- *For Your Notebook*—"brainstorming" types of writing tasks that engage students in the ideas at hand, as well as help them acquire a facility for using writing to explore and "flesh out" ideas.

- *For Writing*—a variety of writing exercises, many of which include suggestions for getting started and for organizing the writing task.

Suggestions for Further Reading appear at the end of each part.

To facilitate research projects, Appendix A presents guidelines for researching a scientific topic, along with a student research paper. Appendix B provides brief biographies of important scientists from ancient times to the present.

ACKNOWLEDGMENTS

I wish to acknowledge the valuable assistance of those who have provided me with detailed and insightful reviews of the manuscript in its various stages of completion: John Boe, University of California, Davis; Douglas M. Catron, Iowa State University; Mary Jane Dickerson, University of Vermont; Elizabeth Flynn, Michigan Technological University; Jeanette Harris, Texas Tech University; William Dennis Horn, Clarkson University; Laurie Kaplan, Goucher College; Marianthe V. Karanikas, University of Illinois at Chicago; Paul Plouffe, University of California, Berkeley; Barbara W. Rogers, Nashville State Technical Institute.

I also wish to thank Professor Judith Dobler, Loyola College of Baltimore, for her valuable suggestions regarding content and style. Likewise, my Santa Clara University colleagues, Professor Terry Beers, Professor Lois Rosenthal, and Professor Cory Wade, have graciously listened to my ideas and offered insightful responses.

To my colleagues at Wadsworth—Jane Townsend, Senior Production Editor; John Strohmeier, English Editor; Steve Rutter, Editor-in-Chief—and to Evelyn Mercer Ward, copy editor, I owe a great debt. Special thanks go to Kevin Howat, Executive Editor, for encouraging me to embark on this project in the first place.

Finally, I salute my students, whose sensitivity and candor have proven valuable in helping me to choose selections and develop exercises.

Introduction

Science: A Basis for Writing and Learning

Why read about science in a writing class? It is a fair question, and you may be intrigued by the answer.

Many think of science as something that has little to do with writing or with language and communication in general. Indeed, some view science as a remote endeavor having little relevance to their own lives. But the knowledge resulting from scientific inquiry has important implications for all of us, regardless of our interests or background.

Almost all major issues today have a fundamental basis in science: how to protect our atmosphere, land, and water resources; how to combat deadly diseases like AIDS, muscular dystrophy, and cancer; how to explore space cooperatively with other nations; how best to manage the biotechnologies of in vitro fertilization (so-called test-tube babies), organ implantation, and recombinant DNA research; how to regulate nuclear energy and where to dispose of nuclear waste materials. These are the issues all of us must face and struggle with, the issues our candidates for public office discuss—not always with sufficient understanding. They are complicated issues, not easily resolved. In order to make informed, responsible judgments, we must first learn how to approach, evaluate, and convey our own views about these issues.

SCIENCE: A HUMANISTIC CONCERN

Writers and philosophers have emphasized the need to dissolve the rigid boundaries that tend to separate scientific knowledge from ordinary knowledge. Some feel that a deep rift already exists between scientists and the rest of society. In his 1959 "Two Cultures" lecture at Cambridge University, British novelist and physicist C. P. Snow put it this way:

> Literary intellectuals at one pole—and at the other, scientists. Between the two a gulf of mutual incomprehension—sometimes (particularly among the young) hostility and dislike, but most of all lack of understanding. They have a curious distorted image of each other.

Snow refers specifically to literary intellectuals, but his message holds true for all nonscientists. Because science and technology have become so much a part of our lives, we cannot afford to hold ourselves apart from the scientific issues that unite us. Of course, this reconciliation must be a mutual effort. Those directly involved in science must also realize the importance of staying attuned to the important social and ethical issues of our times.

Science and humanism, then, go together—are truly inseparable. But that still does not answer the question, What does reading about science have to do with writing?

COMMON PROCESSES IN SCIENCE AND WRITING

When you read about science, you will learn about the following three techniques of inquiry that are relevant to any field and that underlie good writing:

1. articulating and supporting a hypothesis

2. working out an organizational strategy

3. testing for possible errors or omissions

Let's examine each of these techniques in turn.

1. *Articulating and supporting a hypothesis (thesis).* A writing task is like a scientific investigation: The writer presents a thesis that must be examined closely before it can be accepted or rejected. The writer needs to articulate the thesis as clearly and accurately as possible and then provide a set of reasons for supporting the thesis.

2. *Working out an organizational strategy.* Writers, like scientists, must also organize the argument: introduce the thesis, discuss aspects of the thesis point-by-point, and then draw a conclusion. Writers must work out a plan—a logical framework—that will enable others to follow the train of thought from beginning to end.

3. *Testing for possible errors or omissions.* Just as scientists test hypotheses to demonstrate their validity, good writers search for views that challenge their own and then either reject or accept them. Good writers, like good scientists, strive to weigh contrasting views with equal consideration. Of course, this is more easily said than done. Because some of the problems facing us today call our deepest values into question, it is sometimes tempting to avoid any view that challenges these values. But any value worth keeping should be able to withstand opposing views.

Learning about the techniques of scientific inquiry, then, can help you become a better writer—and a better thinker—regardless of the field of study you plan to pursue. And if you do pursue a career in some field of science or technology, these techniques will be continuously useful.

While many think of science as one general field of study, science branches into innumerable areas of specialization. The realm of scientific knowledge is so vast that it is no longer possible for anyone to be an "all-around scientist." However, while scientists must specialize, they must also work together nearly all the time. When they were developing the famous life-detecting apparatus aboard the *Viking* robot probes that landed on Mars in 1976, astronomers, geologists, biochemists, and engineers alike worked in collaboration for several years. Good writing skills enabled these scientists to effectively exchange ideas, keep track of progress, and record new discoveries. Good writing skills are essential in any collaborative venture, scientific or otherwise.

THE INTENT OF THIS BOOK

The guiding purpose behind *Science and the Human Spirit* is to show how science can be a vast resource for anyone wishing to strengthen and deepen the processes and methods leading to good writing skills. Each of the four sections of the book focuses on a dimension of science to which writing is central.

1. *The Learning Dimension.* Scientific knowledge is essential knowledge about the world and ourselves. In this sense, scientific learning is humanistic learning. Aristotle, Sir Francis Bacon, Alfred North Whitehead, and Jacob Bronowski provide us with rationales for this premise. Each of the other writers included in this section—W. I. B. Beveridge, Vivian Gornick, Martin Gardner, Robert Ornstein, and Richard F. Thompson—focuses on a particular scientific topic to demonstrate the importance of science to education in general.

2. *The Discovery Dimension.* In this section you will encounter some of the most influential scientists of all time addressing in their own words some facet of the revolutionary discovery that made each of them world famous. This section will dramatically demonstrate the important role that conventional language plays in science; the selections are lucid, engaging, and accessible.

3. *The Social and Ethical Dimension.* Science, so often characterized as ethically neutral, is here shown to be highly involved in value-based decision making. Should we devote the enormous amount of time and energy needed to search for intelligent life beyond the earth? Should we permit fetal brain implantations for

treating patients with Alzheimer's disease? Is sex determination before birth ethical or not? How should we control, if at all, the treatment of animals in scientific research? Where should we dump highly toxic nuclear waste? Is creationism truly a science, and is it worthy of equal time in a biology or anthropology course? Careful attention to the readings in this section will provide you with accurate, detailed information. You will learn how to support your own views thoroughly and convincingly when you write.

4. *The Literary Dimension.* One way to test the influence of an idea on society is to observe its manifestations in literature. Scientific ideas have often been introduced in popular literature—in the novels of Jules Verne or Edgar Rice Burroughs, for example; much less common is the use of scientific ideas to explore the depths of human nature. The short stories, poetry, and personal essays included in this section will give you a sense of the way science can illuminate the human condition, as well as carry strong emotional impact.

READING WITH AN ACTIVE MIND

As you read through the selections in this anthology, keep in mind that science is not only a body of knowledge but also a method of inquiry and an attitude toward truth. Science stimulates thinking about ourselves and the world, invites us to interact with the world in ways that call attention to our deepest values. The key word is *invites.* Passive reading will do little to make these new concepts come alive. You must "talk back" to the authors, asking questions, evaluating assertions, comparing your own perceptions to those that you encounter on the page. Not only will this help you understand the ideas better, but it will also prepare you for writing about them.

Another important writing activity is to maintain a notebook. The more frequently you capture your thoughts on paper, the likelier it is that writing will become second nature. Your command of language, your control of syntax, diction, and style will steadily increase—and so will your fluency. When you pick up a pen or sit down at the typewriter or word processor, the words will flow as easily as they do in conversation. Here are a few pointers to keep in mind when you write in your notebook:

1. Record your ideas, observations, meditations, questions, confusions, in rapid freewriting style, with no thought to grammar,

spelling, mechanics, or stylistic polish. Notebook writing is for your eyes only!

2. Have fun trying out wild or offbeat ideas. You can never tell if an idea is brilliant or stupid until you write it down and think about it for a while.

3. Write down your personal reaction to the readings or any of the ideas brought up in class.

4. Follow the suggestions under "For Your Notebook" at the end of each selection, but don't feel confined to these suggestions. Any subject you choose is a valid topic for your notebook.

THE WRITING ASSIGNMENTS

The suggestions for writing that accompany each selection are intended to help you with several objectives: to convey a subjective impression, to explain and analyze, and to argue persuasively for or against a debatable viewpoint. You will sometimes be asked to work in groups—much the way scientists do. But no matter what the writing task, always remember the importance of involving yourself actively with the material and of testing your own assumptions against those of the authors you are reading. In doing so, you are truly reading and writing to learn.

PART ONE

The Learning Dimension

Science as Humanistic Inquiry

A little learning is a dangerous thing;
Drink deep, or touch not the Pierian spring.

Many of us harbor mixed feelings about scientific inquiry and the knowledge that can result from it. We are wary of prying too deeply into the secrets of nature, of making discoveries we are neither emotionally nor intellectually ready to deal with. But as the preceding couplet from Alexander Pope's "Essay on Criticism" suggests, the real danger lies with too little learning, not deep learning. Superficial knowledge makes an ideal breeding ground for half truths. For instance, how can we make judgments about the implications of genetic engineering if we haven't taken the time to read about the latest discoveries in this field—or even to understand the basic principles of genetic engineering (or, as it is more accurately referred to, recombinant DNA technology)? Is it really true that "tinkering" with DNA will produce monstrosities we cannot control? Or are we making that judgment on the basis of the science fiction novels we've been reading? This is not to say, of course, that such technology, misused, could not result in some ecological catastrophe. The point is simply that without sufficient grounding in the science or technology in question, none of us can make well-informed judgments about the crucial issues facing us today.

When the Soviets launched the first artificial satellite in October 1957, they also launched the world into the space age. Virtually overnight, people who once considered rocketships, not to mention space travelers (the word *astronaut* had not yet been coined), as pure gibberish were reading about it on the front page of their newspapers.

A serious deficiency in science education became immediately apparent in the United States. The majority of Americans who read the news about *Sputnik* could not have explained the difference between a real satellite and an artificial one, could not have explained concepts such as orbit or rocket, nor could they have begun to explain the reasons for putting a satellite into orbit in the first place.

Science education has come a long way since the late fifties, but very little has been done to integrate science education with humanistic education. While it is indeed a problem that a great many Americans cannot describe the difference between a real satellite and an artificial one, or the difference between astronomy and astrology, or how our bodies use oxygen to keep us alive, it is an even more serious problem that few understand science's role in human culture. How does science contribute to our understanding of ourselves as human beings? What effect can scientific inquiry have on the way we perceive and understand reality or on our ability to think through any problem, scientific or not, thoroughly and accurately?

8

The selections in this opening section of *Science and the Human Spirit* collectively address these concerns. The selections are concerned with the role of science, or some aspect of science, in education, in the context of humanistic learning. We begin with Aristotle, who places science in the context of other modes of knowledge, then turn to Francis Bacon's brilliant examination—the first of its kind in Western civilization—of the abuses and pitfalls of learning that plagued the education of his day. Bacon laid the groundwork for modern science by distinguishing between knowledge derived from the virtually unquestioned authority of the ancients and the Church and the knowledge gained through rigorous, empirical observation. Whitehead, in the next selection, explicitly ties technical education to literature, making the startling claim that one cannot exist independently of the other. Then, with the selections from Beveridge and Bronowski, we learn, respectively, the importance of precision in observation and of the imagination in forming concrete visual representations of scientific abstractions. Finally, the selections by Gornick, Gardner, and Ornstein and Thompson present us with fascinating glimpses into contemporary science: the influence of women in the sciences, imaginative game playing in mathematics, and the transformations that take place inside the brain itself when engaged in the act of learning.

Together these selections help us understand the many-faceted enterprise we call science and how profoundly science influences and enriches our culture.

The ancient Greeks were the first people to develop true science—that is, the systematic observation of nature as a way of understanding its inner workings. And Aristotle was the first major theorist of science. Even though many of his basic assumptions are no longer valid, Aristotle taught the civilized world to observe nature in all of its manifestations—astronomy, botany, zoology, embryology, meteorology, and so on—and to arrive at logical conclusions based on those observations. In this regard Aristotle differed from his teacher, Plato, who perceived the natural world as a poor imitation of an ideal reality that could be apprehended only through abstract contemplation and rational thought.

For Aristotle, science was one of two virtues, one of which he called "intellectual," the other, moral. We must turn to his great treatise, the *Nicomachean Ethics* (from which the following excerpt is taken), for his definition of science in relation to human intelligence as a whole. Aristotle presents science as one of several modes of thought (art, practical wisdom, and speculative wisdom being some of the others) through which the soul strives for truth.

TERMS TO LEARN

induction: determining a hypothesis (a generalization, or general theory) based on observation of particular things. A physician's diagnosis based on observation of particular symptoms is an example of inductive reasoning.

deduction: working out the principles that make up the generalization, which is the "given," or the general assumption

transcendent value: a value that goes beyond the limits of everyday experience

ARISTOTLE

 ## Science, Art, and Wisdom

What Is Meant by Science?

What is meant by science, in the strict sense of the word and disregarding extensions of it on similar lines, may be rendered clear by this consideration. We all see that scientific knowledge is of things that are never other than they are; for as to things that do admit of variation we cannot, if they are outside the field of our observation, discover whether they exist or not. So anything that science knows scientifically must exist by an unalterable necessity. It must therefore be eternal, because anything which exists by this absolute kind of necessity must be eternal.[1] Again, the view has found acceptance that all scientific knowledge can be imparted by teaching and that what is known in this way can be learned. But, as I say in my treatise on logic, all teaching starts from what we know already, and this is equally true whether the teacher uses the method of induction or deduction. What induction does is to furnish us with a first principle or "universal," while deduction starts from universals. This means that there must be first principles—the first principles from which deduction starts—which cannot be proved by deduction and must therefore be reached by the method of induction. Science, then, may be defined as a habit of mind with an aptitude for demonstration, though to this definition we must add the qualifications made explicit in my logical writings. They may be stated thus. A man has scientific knowledge when (1) he is satisfied in his own mind that he has it as the result of the process described in these writings, and (2) the first principles on which his conviction rests are known to him with certainty. This second condition is necessary because, unless his first principles are more certainly known to him than the conclusion he draws from them, the knowledge he will acquire will not be scientific in the full sense of the word.

What Is Meant by Art?

Among things liable to change we count (1) articles manufactured, (2) actions done. Making and doing are quite different activities. (On this point I am in full agreement with what has been stated

---

[1]What is eternal cannot be brought into or put out of existence.

elsewhere.) Consequently the rational faculty exercised in doing is quite distinct from that which is exercised in making. Moreover, they are mutually exclusive, for doing never takes the form of making, nor making of doing. Take architecture. It is an art, that is, a rational faculty exercised in making something. In fact there is no art which cannot be so described, nor is there any faculty of the kind that is not an art. It follows that an art is nothing more or less than a productive quality exercised in combination with true reason. The business of every art is to bring something into existence, and the practice of an art involves the study of how to bring into existence something which is capable of having such an existence and has its efficient cause in the maker and not in itself. This condition must be present, because the arts are not concerned with things that exist or come into existence from necessity or according to Nature, such things having their efficient cause in themselves. Then, since making is not the same as doing, it follows that art, being a kind of making, cannot be a kind of doing. We may even say that in a manner art and chance work in the same field or—as Agathon puts it: "Art is in love with luck, and luck with art."

We have seen what art is. Its opposite, which can only be called absence of art, is a rational quality exercised in making when associated with *false* reasoning.

What Is Meant by *Phronesis* or Practical Wisdom?

It will help us to comprehend the nature of *phronesis,* if we first consider what sort of persons we call "prudent" or "sagacious." A sagacious man is supposed to be characterized by his ability to reach sound conclusions in his deliberations about what is good for himself and advantageous to him, and this not in one department of life—in what concerns his health, for example, or his physical strength—but what conduces to the good life as a whole. We also speak of a man as sagacious or prudent in a particular way when he calculates well for the attainment of a particular end of a fine sort;[2] and this is good evidence that the man who is sagacious in every department of life will be one who deliberates in general to good purpose. No one, however, deliberates about things which cannot be changed or do not admit of being done by him. Now we saw there can be no science without demonstration, whereas in the case of things whose fundamental assumptions allow of no change or modification there can be no demonstrative proof, since in every respect no change is possible.

---

[2] Of course it must not be an artistic end.

We have also seen that there can be no deliberation about things the existence of which is determined by an absolute necessity. In view of these two facts we must admit that practical wisdom is not the same as science. Nor, we must admit, as art. It is not science, because conduct is variable, and it is not art, because doing and making are different in kind, since the maker of a thing has a different end in view than just making it, whereas in doing something the end can only be the doing of it well. We are left then with our definition: Practical wisdom is a rational faculty exercised for the attainment of truth in things that are humanly good and bad. This accounts for the reputation of Pericles and other men of like practical genius. Such men have the power of seeing what is good for themselves and for humanity; and we assign that character also to men who display an aptitude for governing a household or a state. . . . [3]

We must consider, too, that while there is such a thing as excellence in the quality of a work of art, there cannot be excellence or virtue belonging to practical wisdom, which *is* a virtue. In the arts, again, a deliberate mistake is not so bad as an undesigned one, whereas in matters to which practical wisdom is applicable it is the other way round. Clearly, then, prudence is a virtue and not an art. It must be the virtue of one of the two parts of the soul which have reason, and this must be the calculative or "opining" part. For opinion is concerned with a variable subject matter, and so is prudence. Yet it would not be correct to describe prudence as a purely rational quality. That it is not is shown by the fact that such a quality can be forgotten, whereas to forget prudence or common sense is worse than such an inability to remember.

What Is Meant by Intelligence or Scientific Insight?

Science is the coming to conclusions about universals and necessary truths. Now all science (for science involves a process of reasoning) and all facts scientifically proved depend ultimately upon certain first

---

[3] A note on *sophrosyne* or "temperance." The word comes from *sozein,* "to preserve," and *phronesis,* "prudence," and means "that which preserves prudence." Now it is true that temperance does preserve a belief of this prudential sort. We must not imagine that pleasure and pain destroy or distort every belief—such a belief, for instance, as that the sum of the angles of a triangle is equal to two right angles—but only beliefs about what men do or have done. The first principle of an action is the end to which the action is directed. But a man corrupted by the love of pleasure or the fear of pain cannot see this at all—he cannot see that everything he chooses and does must be chosen and done as a means to this end and for its own sake. For vice produces a kind of moral blindness to the principle to which all our conduct must ultimately be referred.

principles. When we see this we perceive that the first principles upon which all scientific results depend cannot be apprehended by science itself; nor, we may add, by art or common sense. The body of scientific knowledge is the product of logical deduction from premises which are eternally valid; but art and practical wisdom deal with matters susceptible of change. Nor can we say that speculative wisdom is merely a knowledge of first principles. For there are some truths which the philosopher can learn only from demonstration. Now if the qualities by means of which we reach the truth and are never led to what is false in matters variable and invariable are science, prudence, wisdom, and the intelligence which apprehends the truth in reasoning; if, moreover, this mental endowment by means of which we are enabled to grasp first principles cannot be either prudence, science, or wisdom, we are left to conclude that what grasps them is "intelligence."

What Is Meant by Wisdom?

"Wisdom" is a word we use both in a particular and in a general sense. Thus, in the fine arts we attach the epithet of "wise" to the masters—Phidias, for instance, as sculptor and Polyclitus as statuary. Here all that we mean by "wisdom" is excellence in an art. But we also think of some people as wise not in any one of the human aptitudes but in all of them—not "wise in some other things" or (as Homer puts it in his *Margites*):

> Neither a delver nor a ploughman he,
> Nor other wisdom had the gods bestowed.

This makes it evident that of all kinds of knowledge wisdom comes next to perfection. The wise man, you see, must not only know all that can be deduced from his first principles but he must understand their true meaning. So we conclude that wisdom must be a combination of science and reason or intelligence, being in fact the highest form of that knowledge whose objects are of transcendent value. I find it strange that anyone should regard political science or *practical* wisdom as the noblest of studies, for that is to assume that man is what is best in the world. But just as "wholesome" and "good" mean one thing to men and another to fish, whereas "white" and "straight" have always but one meaning, so "wise," as men use the word, would always have the same signification, while "prudent" would not. For every human creature says in effect, "Whoever considers what is to my particular advantage is prudent and to him will I entrust myself."

And this leads people to maintain that some even of the lower animals have prudence, namely, those which evidently possess the ability to foresee what will be needed for their continued existence. Another point that emerges clearly is that wisdom cannot be identified with political science. If men are to give the name of wisdom to the knowledge of what is to their own advantage, there will be more than one form of wisdom as there is more than one species of animal. You cannot have a single wisdom contriving the good of all living beings any more than an art of medicine consulting the health of everybody and everything. It is all very well to say that man is the noblest of the animals. There are creatures far more divine by nature than man, for instance—to take what stares us in the face—those luminaries of which the starry heavens are composed.

Enough has been said to show that wisdom is exact knowledge or science combined with the intelligence that grasps the truth of first principles when this combination is employed upon the grandest subjects of contemplation. The rareness of it leads many to say that men like Thales and Anaxagoras are no doubt wise but lack common sense. They say this when they observe such men at sea about their private interests. They allow that their knowledge is "exceptional," "wonderful," "deep," "superhuman," but they aver that it is useless because it is not the good of humanity that they explore. Common sense or prudence, however, does concern itself with human affairs and such matters as may form the subject of deliberation. To deliberate well—that, people say, is the special business of the practically wise man.[4]

Observe, too, that prudence is something more than a knowledge of general principles. It must acquire familiarity with particulars also, for conduct deals with particular circumstances, and prudence is a matter of conduct. This accounts for the fact that men who know nothing of the theory of their subject sometimes practise it with greater success than others who know it. Let me make my meaning clearer by an illustration. A man is aware that light meats are easily digested and beneficial to health but does not know what meats are light. Such a man is not so likely to make you well as one who only knows that chicken is good for you. It is in fact experience rather than theory that normally gets results. Practical wisdom being concerned with action, we need both kinds of knowledge; nay, we

---

[4]We must not forget that no man deliberates about things that cannot be otherwise than as they are, or about things which, while admitting of variation, are not a means to some end, and that end a good that can be realized in action. Broadly speaking, a man good at deliberations is one who by careful calculation is able to make a good shot at some attainable advantage.

need the knowledge of particular facts more than general principles. But here, too, there must be a faculty—political science—in which the ultimate authority is vested.

Exercises and Projects

CHECKING YOUR COMPREHENSION

1. How does Aristotle distinguish between induction and deduction?

2. According to Aristotle, what conditions must be met before one has scientific knowledge?

3. Explain in your own words the fundamental distinction Aristotle makes between science and art.

4. How does Aristotle justify Agathon's assertion that "Art is in love with luck"?

5. In what way is practical wisdom *(phronesis)* unlike science? Unlike art?

6. Why does Aristotle say that there can be no virtue belonging to practical wisdom?

7. What is the distinction between wisdom and *phronesis*?

FOR DISCUSSION AND DEBATE

1. Is Aristotle's distinction between science and art as convincing as it could be? What would you change or add?

2. Provide specific examples that would illustrate Aristotle's definition of practical wisdom.

3. Is it possible, from a modern perspective, to justify Aristotle's assumption that human beings can reach conclusions based on "premises which are eternally valid"?

4. Do you agree with Aristotle that "wisdom cannot be identified with political science?" Why or why not?

FOR YOUR NOTEBOOK

1. React spontaneously to the word *wisdom*. What associations does it conjure up?

2. Why is art important in our culture? Is art important to you personally? Why or why not?

3. List what you consider to be the principal differences between science and art. Next, list what you consider to be the principal similarities.

FOR WRITING

1. Write an essay on the role of wisdom in science. Can Aristotle's principles be applied to modern scientific pursuits such as space exploration or information technology? Why or why not?

2. Compare the aims of art with those of science, as you understand them. Begin with Aristotle's discussion of these aims.

3. According to *Webster's New World Dictionary,* ethics is defined as 1) "The study of standards of conduct and moral judgment" and 2) "The system or code of morals of a particular person, religion, group, profession, etc." Write an essay persuading your readers that scientific pursuits should or should not be ethical.

4. Reflect for a while on what it means to "know" something. Aristotle's opening sentence in his *Metaphysics* is, "All persons desire to know," but what does this involve? Does knowledge refer only to "hard facts"? Think of the many ways we use the word *know*: "I *know* that song by heart"; "I *know* what it takes to be a successful doctor"; "To *know* me is to love me"; and so on. Study the word's history and usage by consulting the *Oxford English Dictionary* and other, more up-to-date unabridged dictionaries. Also read the entry for *epistemology* (the branch of philosophy that examines the nature of knowledge) in an encyclopedia of philosophy. After you have become thoroughly familiar with this issue, write an essay in which you explore your sense of what it means to know. Be sure to illustrate your generalizations with examples from your own experience.

READING INTRODUCTION

A contemporary of Galileo, Sir Francis Bacon was a key figure in the rise of modern science. In Bacon's day, civilization was thought to be in a state of steady decline, which had begun during the Golden Age of ancient Greece and Rome. The best that contemporary society could do, many believed, was to emulate the ancient Greeks and Romans and accept their authority without question and with reverence.

Bacon objected strongly to this view and devoted himself to abolishing it. Human beings, he insisted, can improve their condition, can advance their learning. Bacon refuted the notion that learning about nature tends to promote disbelief in God, and he wrote in Book 1 of *The Advancement of Learning* (1605):

> It is an assured truth and a conclusion of experience, that a little or superficial knowledge of philosophy [for example, natural philosophy, or science] may incline the mind of man to atheism, but a farther proceeding therein doth bring the mind back again to religion.

The idea that modern thought could replace that of the ancients was considered madness. Not even Galileo's astronomical discovery that Aristotle's model of the universe was wrong did much to change this attitude. Bacon thus applied his talents not to empirical demonstration (which he advocated) but to rhetoric, the art of written or spoken persuasion. Bacon skillfully explained in his *Novum Organum (The New Organon)* the methodology necessary for observing nature and reaching accurate conclusions. In this pioneering work, Bacon isolates four tendencies in traditional thinking (he calls them "idols"), which undermine any accurate understanding of nature: (1) Idols of the Tribe—flaws in human understanding; (2) Idols of the Cave—individual errors of perception or reason; (3) Idols of the Marketplace—distortion caused by overdependence on common language; and (4) Idols of the Theater—interference from traditional beliefs.

Bacon's work greatly influenced the development of what we now call the scientific method, as well as the philosophy of empiricism, which holds that all knowledge comes from experience rather than from spontaneously generated a priori ideas.

TERMS TO LEARN

idol: Bacon's term for a basic tendency in traditional thinking

empiricism: theory that all knowledge comes from experience

instauration: renewal or repair

perturbation: the disturbance of a regular motion (commonly used in an astronomical context, as in the perturbation of a planet's orbit caused by one of its moons)

Heraclitus: one of the earliest Greek philosophers (ca. 500 B.C.), who described the universe as being in a state of continuous flux. The famous saying "You cannot step into the same river twice" is attributed to him.

Democritus: an early Greek philosopher (ca. 450 B.C.) best known for his theory that matter consists of indivisible particles called atoms (from the Greek word *atomos* meaning "indivisible")

sophistic: a descriptive argument based more on clever use of language than on objective reasoning

SIR FRANCIS BACON

 The Four Idols

XXXVIII[1]

The idols and false notions which are now in possession of the human understanding, and have taken deep root therein, not only so beset men's minds that truth can hardly find entrance, but even after entrance obtained, they will again in the very instauration of the sciences meet and trouble us, unless men being forewarned of the danger fortify themselves as far as may be against their assaults.

---

[1]The roman numerals indicate sections of the book. [Ed.]

XXXIX

There are four classes of Idols which beset men's minds. To these for distinction's sake I have assigned names, calling the first class *Idols of the Tribe;* the second, *Idols of the Cave;* the third, *Idols of the Marketplace;* the fourth, *Idols of the Theater.*

XL

The formation of ideas and axioms by true induction is no doubt the proper remedy to be applied for the keeping off and clearing away of idols. To point them out, however, is of great use; for the doctrine of Idols is to the Interpretation of Nature what the doctrine of the refutation of Sophisms is to common Logic.

XLI

The Idols of the Tribe have their foundation in human nature itself, and in the tribe or race of men. For it is a false assertion that the sense of man is the measure of things. On the contrary, all perceptions as well of the sense as of the mind are according to the measure of the individual and not according to the measure of the universe. And the human understanding is like a false mirror, which, receiving rays irregularly, distorts and discolors the nature of things by mingling its own nature with it.

XLII

The Idols of the Cave are the idols of the individual man. For every one (besides the errors common to human nature in general) has a cave or den of his own, which refracts and discolors the light of nature; owing either to his own proper and peculiar nature; or to his education and conversation with others; or to the reading of books, and the authority of those whom he esteems and admires; or to the differences of impressions, accordingly as they take place in a mind preoccupied and predisposed or in a mind indifferent and settled; or the like. So that the spirit of man (according as it is meted out to different individuals) is in fact a thing variable and full of perturbation, and governed as it were by chance. Whence it was well observed by Heraclitus that men look for sciences in their own lesser worlds, and not in the greater or common world.

XLIII

There are also Idols formed by the intercourse and association of men with each other, which I call Idols of the Marketplace, on account of the commerce and consort of men there. For it is by discourse that men associate; and words are imposed according to the apprehension of the vulgar. And therefore the ill and unfit choice of words wonderfully obstructs the understanding. Nor do the definitions or explanations wherewith in some things learned men are wont to guard and defend themselves, by any means set the matter right. But words plainly force and overrule the understanding, and throw all into confusion, and lead men away into numberless empty controversies and idle fancies.

XLIV

Lastly, there are Idols which have immigrated into men's minds from the various dogmas of philosophies, and also from wrong laws of demonstration. These I call Idols of the Theater; because in my judgment all the received systems are but so many stage plays, representing worlds of their own creation after an unreal and scenic fashion. Nor is it only of the systems now in vogue, or only of the ancient sects and philosophies, that I speak; for many more plays of the same kind may yet be composed and in like artificial manner set forth; seeing that errors the most widely different have nevertheless causes for the most part alike. Neither again do I mean this only of entire systems, but also of many principles and axioms in science, which by tradition, credulity, and negligence have come to be received.

But of these several kinds of Idols I must speak more largely and exactly, that the understanding may be duly cautioned.

XLV

The human understanding is of its own nature prone to suppose the existence of more order and regularity in the world than it finds. And though there be many things in nature which are singular and unmatched, yet it devises for them parallels and conjugates and relatives which do not exist. Hence the fiction that all celestial bodies move in perfect circles; spirals and dragons being (except in name) utterly rejected. Hence too the element of Fire with its orb[2] is brought in, to make up the square with the other three which the sense perceives. Hence also the ratio of density of the so-called elements is arbitrarily fixed at ten to one.[3] And so on of other dreams. And these fancies affect not dogmas only, but simple notions also.

XLVI

The human understanding when it has once adopted an opinion (either as being the received opinion or as being agreeable to itself) draws all things else to support and agree with it. And though there be a greater number and weight of instances to be found on the other side, yet these it either neglects and despises, or else by some distinction sets aside and rejects; in order that by this great and pernicious predetermination the authority of its former conclusions may remain inviolate. And therefore it was a good answer that was made by one who when they showed him hanging in a temple a picture of those who had paid their vows as having escaped shipwreck, and would have him say whether he did not now acknowledge the power of the gods—"Aye," asked he again, "but where are they painted that were drowned after their vows?" And such is the way of all superstition, whether in astrology, dreams, omens, divine judgments, or the like; wherein men, having a delight in such vanities, mark the events where they are fulfilled, but where they fail, though this happen much oftener, neglect and pass them by. But with far more subtlety does this mischief insinuate itself into philosophy and the sciences; in which the first conclusion colors and brings into conformity with itself all that come after, though far sounder and better. Besides, independently of that delight and vanity which I have described, it is the peculiar and perpetual error of the human intellect to be more moved and excited by affirmatives than by negatives; whereas it ought properly to hold itself indifferently[4] disposed toward both alike. Indeed in the establishment of any true axiom, the negative instance is the more forcible of the two.

[2]Fire, in Bacon's day, was considered to be one of the four elements (along with Earth, Air, and Water) that lay in spheres ("orbs") around the center of the earth. [Ed.]

[3]In other words, Air was assumed to be ten times heavier than Fire, Water ten times heavier that Air, and Earth ten times heavier than Water. [Ed.]

[4] Nonjudgmentally. [Ed.]

XLVII

The human understanding is moved by those things most which strike and enter the mind simultaneously and suddenly, and so fill the imagination; and then it feigns and supposes all other things to be somehow, though it cannot see how, similar to those few things by which it is surrounded. But for that going to and fro to remote and heterogeneous instances, by which axioms are tried as in the fire, the intellect is altogether slow and unfit, unless it be forced thereto by severe laws and overruling authority.

XLVIII

The human understanding is unquiet; it cannot stop or rest, and still presses onward, but in vain. Therefore it is that we cannot conceive of any end or limit to the world; but always as of necessity it occurs to us that there is something beyond. Neither again can it be conceived how eternity has flowed down to the present day; for that distinction which is commonly received of infinity in time past and in time to come can by no means hold; for it would thence follow that one infinity is greater than another, and that infinity is wasting away and tending to become finite. The like subtlety arises touching the infinite divisibility of lines, from the same inability of thought to stop. But this inability interferes more mischievously in the discovery of causes: for although the most general principles in nature ought to be held merely positive, as they are discovered, and cannot with truth be referred to a cause; nevertheless the human understanding being unable to rest still seeks something prior in the order of nature. And then it is that in struggling toward that which is further off it falls back upon that which is more nigh at hand; namely, on final causes: which have relation clearly to the nature of man rather than to the nature of the universe; and from this source have strangely defiled philosophy. But he is no less an unskilled and shallow philosopher who seeks causes of that which is most general, than he who in things subordinate and subaltern omits to do so.

XLIX

The human understanding is no dry light, but receives an infusion from the will and affections; whence proceed sciences which may be called "sciences as one would." For what a man had rather were true he more readily believes. Therefore he rejects difficult things from impatience of research; sober things, because they narrow hope; the deeper things of nature, from superstition; the light of experience, from arrogance, and pride, lest his mind should seem to be occupied with things mean and transitory; things not commonly believed, out of deference to the opinion of the vulgar. Numberless in short are the ways, and sometimes imperceptible, in which the affections color and inject the understanding.

L

But by far the greatest hindrance and aberration of the human understanding proceeds from the dullness, incompetency, and deceptions of the senses; in that things which strike the sense outweigh things which do not immediately strike it, though they be more important. Hence it is that speculation commonly ceases where sight ceases; insomuch that of things invisible there is little or no observation. Hence all the working of the spirits enclosed in tangible bodies lies hid and unobserved of men. So also all the more subtle changes of form in the parts of coarser substances (which they commonly call alteration, though it is in truth local motion through exceedingly small spaces) is in like manner unobserved. And yet unless these two things just mentioned be searched out and brought to light, nothing great can be achieved in nature, as far as the production of works is concerned. So again the essential nature of our common air, and of all bodies less dense than air (which are very many), is almost unknown. For the sense by itself is a thing infirm and erring; neither can instruments for enlarging or sharpening the senses do much; but all the truer kind of interpretation of nature is effected by instances and experiments fit and apposite; wherein the sense decides touching the experiment only, and the experiment touching the point in nature and the thing itself.

LI

The human understanding is of its own nature prone to abstractions and gives a substance and reality to things which are fleeting. But to resolve nature into abstractions is less to our purpose than to dissect her into parts; as did the school of Democritus, which went further into nature than the rest. Matter rather than forms should be the object of our attention, its configurations and changes of configuration, and simple action, and law of action or motion; for forms are figments of the human mind, unless you will call those laws of action forms.

LII

Such then are the idols which I call *Idols of the Tribe*; and which take their rise either from the homogeneity of the substance of the human spirit, or from its preoccupation, or from its narrowness, or from its restless motion, or from an infusion of the affections, or from the incompetency of the senses, or from the mode of impression.

LIII

The *Idols of the Cave* take their rise in the peculiar constitution, mental or bodily, of each individual; and also in education, habit, and accident. Of this kind there is a great number and variety; but I will instance those the pointing out of which contains the most important caution, and which have most effect in disturbing the clearness of the understanding.

LIV

Men become attached to certain particular sciences and speculations, either because they fancy themselves the authors and inventors thereof, or because they have bestowed the greatest pains upon them and become most habituated to them. But men of this kind, if they betake themselves to philosophy and contemplations of a general character, distort and color them in obedience to their former fancies; a thing especially to be noticed in Aristotle, who made his natural philosophy a mere bond-servant to his logic, thereby rendering it contentious and well nigh useless. The race of chemists again out of a few experiments of the furnace have built up a fantastic philosophy, framed with reference to a few things; and Gilbert also, after he had employed himself most laboriously in the study and observation of the loadstone, proceeded at once to construct an entire system in accordance with his favorite subject.

LV

There is one principal and as it were radical distinction between different minds, in respect of philosophy and the sciences; which is this: that some minds are stronger and apter to mark the differences of things, others to mark their resemblances. The steady and acute mind can fix its contemplations and dwell and fasten on the subtlest distinctions: the lofty and discursive mind recognizes and puts together the finest and most general resemblances. Both kinds however easily err in excess, by catching the one at gradations the other at shadows.

LVI

There are found some minds given to an extreme admiration of antiquity, others to an extreme love and appetite for novelty; but few so duly tempered that they can hold the mean, neither carping at what has been well laid down by the ancients, nor despising what is well introduced by the moderns. This however turns to the great injury of the sciences and philosophy; since these affectations of antiquity and novelty are the humors of partisans rather than judgments; and truth is to be sought for not in the felicity of any age, which is an unstable thing, but in the light of nature and experience, which is eternal. These factions therefore must be abjured, and care must be taken that the intellect be not hurried by them into assent.

LVII

Contemplations of nature and of bodies in their simple form break up and distract the understanding, while contemplations of nature and bodies in their composition and configuration overpower and dissolve the understanding: a distinction well seen in the school of Leucippus and Democritus as compared with the other philosophies. For that school is so busied with the particles that it hardly attends to the structure; while the others are so lost in admiration of the structure that they do not penetrate to the simplicity of nature. These kinds of contemplation should therefore be alternated and taken by turns; that so the understanding may be rendered at once penetrating and comprehensive, and the inconveniences above mentioned, with the idols which proceed from them, may be avoided.

LVIII

Let such then be our provision and contemplative prudence for keeping off and dislodging the *Idols of the Cave,* which grow for the most part either out of the predominance of a favorite subject, or out of an excessive tendency to compare or to distinguish, or out of partiality for particular ages, or out of the largeness or minuteness of the objects contemplated. And generally let every student of nature take this as a rule, that whatever his mind seizes and dwells upon with peculiar satisfaction is to be held in suspicion, and that so much the more care is to be taken in dealing with such questions to keep the understanding even and clear.

LIX

But the *Idols of the Marketplace* are the most troublesome of all: idols which have crept into the understanding through the alliances of words and names. For men believe that their reason governs words; but it is also true that words react on the understanding; and this it is that has rendered philosophy and the sciences sophistical and inactive. Now words, being commonly framed and applied according to the capacity of the vulgar, follow those lines of division which are most obvious to the vulgar understanding. And whenever an understanding of greater acuteness or a more diligent observation would alter those lines to suit the true divisions of nature, words stand in the way and resist the change. Whence it comes to pass that the high and formal discussions of learned men end oftentimes in disputes about words and names; with which (according to the use and wisdom of the mathematicians) it would be more prudent to begin, and so by means of definitions reduce them to order. Yet even definitions cannot cure this evil in dealing with natural and material things; since the definitions themselves consist of words, and those words beget others: so that it is necessary to recur to individual instances, and those in due series and order; as I shall say presently when I come to the method and scheme for the formation of notions and axioms.

LX

The idols imposed by words on the understanding are of two kinds. They are either names of things which do not exist (for as there are things left unnamed through lack of observation, so likewise are there names which result from fantastic suppositions and to which nothing in reality corresponds), or they are names of things which exist, but yet confused and ill-defined, and hastily and irregularly derived from realities. Of the former kind are Fortune, the Prime Mover, Planetary Orbits, Element of Fire, and like fictions which owe their origin to false and idle theories. And this class of idols is more easily expelled, because to get rid of them it is only necessary that all theories should be steadily rejected and dismissed as obsolete.

But the other class, which springs out of a faulty and unskilful abstraction, is intricate and deeply rooted. Let us take for example such as word as *humid;* and see how far the several things which the word is used to signify agree with each other; and we shall find the word *humid* to be nothing else than a mark loosely and confusedly applied to denote a variety of actions which will not bear to be reduced to any constant meaning. For it both signifies that which easily spreads itself round any other body; and that which in itself is indeterminate and cannot solidize; and that which readily yields in every direction; and that which easily divides and scatters itself; and that which easily unites and collects itself; and that which readily flows and is put in motion; and that which readily clings to another body and wets it; and that which is easily reduced to a liquid, or being solid easily melts. Accordingly when you come to apply the word, if you take it in one sense, flame is humid; if in another, air is not humid; if in another, fine dust is humid; if in another, glass is humid. So that it is easy to see that the notion is taken by abstraction only from water and common and ordinary liquids, without any due verification.

There are however in words certain degrees of distortion and error. One of the least faulty kinds is that of names of substances, especially of lowest species and well-deduced (for the notion of *chalk* and of *mud* is good, of *earth* bad); a more faulty kind is that of actions, as *to generate, to corrupt, to alter;* the most faulty is of qualities (except such as are the immediate objects of the sense) as *heavy, light, rare, dense,* and the like. Yet in all these cases some notions are of necessity a little better than others, in proportion to the greater variety of subjects that fall within the range of the human sense.

LXI

But the *Idols of the Theater* are not innate, nor do they steal into the understanding secretly, but are plainly impressed and received into the mind from the play-books of philosophical systems and the perverted rules of demonstration. To attempt refutations in this case would be merely inconsistent with what I have already said: for since we agree neither upon principles nor upon demonstrations there is no place for argument. And this is so far well, inasmuch as it leaves the honor of the ancients untouched. For they are no wise dispar-aged—the question between them and me being only as to the way. For as the saying is, the lame man who keeps the right road outstrips the runner who takes the wrong one. Nay it is obvious that when a man runs the wrong way, the more active and swift he is the further he will go astray.

But the course I propose for the discovery of sciences is such as leaves but little to the acuteness and strength of wits, but places all wits and undertandings nearly on a level. For as in the drawing of a straight line or a perfect circle, much depends on the steadiness and practice of the hand, if it be done by aim of hand only, but if with the aid of rule or compass, little or nothing; so is it exactly with my plan.

But though particular confutations would be of no avail, yet touching the sects and general divisions of such systems I must say something; something also touching the external signs which show that they are unsound; and finally something touching the causes of such great infelicity and of such lasting and general agreement in error; that so the access to truth may be made less difficult, and the human understanding may the more willingly submit to its purgation and dismiss its idols.

LXII

Idols of the Theater, or of Systems, are many, and there can be and perhaps will be yet many more. For were it not that now for many ages men's minds have been busied with religion and theology; and were it not that civil governments, especially monarchies, have been averse to such novelties, even in matters speculative; so that men labor therein to the peril and harming of their fortunes—not only unrewarded, but exposed also to contempt and envy; doubtless there would have arisen many other philosophical sects like to those which in great variety flourished once among the Greeks. For as on the phenomena of the heavens many hypotheses may be constructed, so likewise (and more also) many various dogmas may be set up and established on the phenomena of philosophy. And in the plays of this philosophical theater you may observe the same thing which is found in the theater of the poets, that stories invented for the stage are more compact and elegant, and more as one would wish them to be, than true stories out of history.

In general however there is taken for the material of philosophy either a great deal out of a few things, or a very little out of many things; so that on both sides philosophy is based on too narrow a foundation of experiment and natural history, and decides on the authority of too few cases. For the Rational School of philosophers snatches from experience a variety of common instances, neither duly ascertained nor diligently examined and weighed, and leaves all the rest to meditation and agitation of wit.

Exercises and Projects

CHECKING YOUR COMPREHENSION

1. In Bacon's opinion, what causes a person to become attached to a particular science or speculation?

2. How can thinking about causation "defile" philosophy?

3. What are some of the "numberless" ways that the affections (emotional impulses) "color and infect the understanding"?

4. What does Bacon consider to be the greatest hindrance to human understanding, and why?

5. According to Bacon, how is philosophy like the theater?

FOR DISCUSSION AND DEBATE

1. Illustrate, from your own experience, Bacon's statement that "human understanding is of its own nature prone to suppose the existence of more order and regularity in the world than it finds." Why is this a problem? Can anything useful come of it?

2. Bacon writes that "matter rather than forms should be the object of our attention . . . for forms are figments of the human mind." What does Bacon mean by this? Do you feel his statement should be qualified in any way?

3. Debate the effectiveness versus the ineffectiveness of language to describe scientific concepts.

4. What does Bacon mean when he says, "The human understanding is no dry light, but receives an infusion from the will and affections"? Why is this significant?

FOR YOUR NOTEBOOK

1. What errors in reasoning do you sometimes catch yourself commiting, consciously or otherwise? Are they difficult or easy to avoid? Why?

2. Describe a situation in which you witnessed flawed reasoning being used and going unchallenged.

3. Can science improve the way we think in general? How? Even though your views on the matter may be tentative at this stage, record them anyway. Later in the term you will find it useful to see how your views have developed.

FOR WRITING

1. Write an essay in which you identify, and attempt to explain, the cause of a widespread belief that seems mostly false (for instance, the belief in UFOs or a particular superstition). Here is one possible way to organize your essay: (1) Open with three or four colorful examples of common irrational or superstitious behavior (such as refusing to leave the house before consulting a horoscope or becoming upset over a broken mirror); (2) discuss the probable origin of these irrational ideas or superstitions (after doing some background reading in the library); (3) reflect on the problems a believer in superstitions can encounter in the modern world; (4) conclude with a clear statement of your viewpoint.

2. Does Bacon seem to feel that scientific reason is incompatible with religious belief? Write an essay that draws from "The Four Idols" to support your view.

3. Compare Bacon's attitude toward science with Aristotle's. Point out similarities and differences.

4. In a short essay, relate an experience of yours, or that of someone you know, that illustrates the danger of making a bad judgment about someone or something. Try to pinpoint the probable cause(s): not enough information to make a sound judgment? unwillingness to go against a common assumption, especially if it is held by someone highly regarded? the temptation to make hasty generalizations?

Throughout the nineteenth century, science blossomed. Sir Isaac Newton had shown that the universe was like a great machine whose laws could be accurately determined and mathematically described. Not surprisingly, such achievements gave rise to scientific materialism—the belief that everything in nature, including humanity, is based on physical events that can be observed and measured.

But for Alfred North Whitehead, a distinguished philosopher and mathematician—he coauthored with Bertrand Russell the three-volume *Principia Mathematica* (1910–1913) and laid the foundations of symbolic logic—science could not be separated from philosophy or from humanistic learning in general. In the following selection from *The Aims of Education* (1929), Whitehead states his case with characteristic vigor.

TERMS TO LEARN

Platonic: ideas and values considered ideal in Plato's sense of being part of a higher reality rather than of the material world

disinterested: objective or unbiased; often wrongly used to mean uninterested (lacking interest)

discursive: touching on many related or unrelated ideas

ALFRED NORTH WHITEHEAD

 The Essence of a Liberal Education

In its essence a liberal education is an education for thought and for æsthetic appreciation. It proceeds by imparting a knowledge of the masterpieces of thought, of imaginative literature, and of art. The action which it contemplates is command. It is an aristocratic education implying leisure. This Platonic ideal has rendered imperishable services to European civilization. It has encouraged art, it has fostered that spirit of disinterested curiosity which is the origin of science, it has maintained the dignity of mind in the face of material force, a dignity which claims freedom of thought. Plato did not, like St. Benedict, bother himself to be a fellow-worker with his slaves; but he must rank among the emancipators of mankind. His type of culture is the peculiar inspiration of the liberal aristocrat, the class from which Europe derives what ordered liberty it now possesses. For centuries, from Pope Nicholas V to the school of the Jesuits, and from the Jesuits to the modern headmasters of English public schools, this educational ideal has had the strenuous support of the clergy.

For certain people it is a very good education. It suits their type of mind and the circumstances amid which their life is passed. But more has been claimed for it than this. All education has been judged adequate or defective according to its approximation to this sole type.

The essence of the type is a large discursive knowledge of the best literature. The ideal product of the type is the man who is acquainted with the best that has been written. He will have acquired the chief languages, he will have considered the histories of the rise and fall of nations, the poetic expression of human feeling, and have read the great dramas and novels. He will also be well grounded in the chief philosophies, and have attentively read those philosophic authors who are distinguished for lucidity of style.

It is obvious that, except at the close of a long life, he will not have much time for anything else if any approximation is to be made to the fulfillment of this programme. One is reminded of the calculation in a dialogue of Lucian that, before a man could be justified in practicing any one of the current ethical systems, he should have spent a hundred and fifty years in examining their credentials.

Such ideals are not for human beings. What is meant by a liberal culture is nothing so ambitious as a full acquaintance with the varied literary expression of civilized mankind from Asia to Europe, and from Europe to America. A small selection only is required; but then, as we are told, it is a selection of the very best. I have my doubts of a selection which includes Xenophon and omits Confucius, but then I have read through neither in the original. The ambitious programme of a liberal education really shrinks to a study of some fragments of literature included in a couple of important languagees.

But the expression of the human spirit is not confined to literature. There are the other arts, and there are the sciences. Also education must pass beyond the passive reception of the ideas of others. Powers of initiative must be strengthened. Unfortunately initiative does not mean just one acquirement—there is initiative in thought, initiative in action, and the imaginative initiative of art; and these three categories require many subdivisions.

The field of acquirement is large, and the individual so fleeting and so fragmentary: classical scholars, scientists, headmasters are alike ignoramuses.

There is a curious illusion that a more complete culture was possible when there was less to know. Surely the only gain was that it was more possible to remain unconscious of ignorance. It cannot have been a gain to Plato to have read neither Shakespeare, nor Newton, nor Darwin. The achievements of a liberal education have in recent times not been worsened. The change is that its pretensions have been found out.

My point is, that no course of study can claim any position of ideal completeness. Nor are the omitted factors of subordinate importance. The insistence in the Platonic culture on disinterested intellectual appreciation is a psychological error. Action and our implication in the transition of events amid the inevitable bond of cause to effect are fundamental. An education which strives to divorce intellectual or æsthetic life from these fundamental facts carries with it the decadence of civilization. Essentially culture should be for action, and its effect should be to divest labor from the association of aimless toil. Art exists that we may know the deliverances of our senses as good. It heightens the sense-world.

Disinterested scientific curiosity is a passion for an ordered intellectual vision of the connection of events. But the goal of such curiosity is the marriage of action to thought. This essential intervention of action even in abstract science is often overlooked. No man of science wants merely to know. He acquires knowledge to appease his passion for discovery. He does not discover in order to know, he knows in order to discover. The pleasure which art and science can give to toil is the enjoyment which arises from successfully directed intention. Also it is the same pleasure which is yielded to the scientist and to the artist.

The antithesis between a technical and a liberal education is fallacious. There can be no adequate technical education which is not liberal, and no liberal education which is not technical: that is, no education which does not impart both technique and intellectual vision. In simpler language, education should turn out the pupil with something he knows well and something he can do well. This intimate union of practice and theory aids both. The intellect does not work best in a vacuum. The stimulation of creative impulse requires, especially in the case of a child, the quick transition to practice. Geometry and mechanics, followed by workshop practice, gain that reality without which mathematics is verbiage.

There are three main methods which are required in a national system of education, namely, the literary curriculum, the scientific curriculum, the scientific curriculum, the technical curriculum. But each of these curricula should include the other two. What I mean is, that every form of education should give the pupil a technique, a science, an assortment of general ideas, and æsthetic appreciation, and that each of these sides of his training should be illuminated by the others. Lack of time, even for the most favored pupil, makes it impossible to develop fully each curriculum. Always there must be a dominant emphasis. The most direct æsthetic training naturally falls in the technical curriculum in those cases when the training is that requisite for some art or artistic craft. But it is of high importance in both a literary and a scientific education.

The educational method of the literary curriculum is the study of language, that is, the study of our most habitual method of conveying to others our states of mind. The technique which should be acquired is the technique of verbal expression, the science is the study of the structure of language and the analysis of the relations of language to the states of mind conveyed. Furthermore, the subtle relations of language to feeling, and the high development of the sense organs to which written and spoken words appeal, lead to keen æsthetic appreciations being aroused by the successful employment of language. Finally, the wisdom of the world is preserved in the master-pieces of linguistic composition.

This curriculum has the merit of homogeneity. All its various parts are coordinated and play into each other's hands. We can hardly be surprised that such a curriculum, when once broadly established, should have claimed the position of the sole perfect type of education. Its defect is unduly to emphasize the importance of language. Indeed the varied importance of verbal expression is so overwhelming that its sober estimation is difficult. Recent generations have been witnessing the retreat of literature, and of literary forms of expression, from their position of unique importance in intellectual life. In order truly to become a servant and a minister of nature something more is required than literary aptitudes.

Exercises and Projects

CHECKING YOUR COMPREHENSION

1. What does Whitehead consider to be the essence, or basic nature, of mathematics? Of literature? Of a liberal education?

2. According to Whitehead, a scientific education is primarily a training in what activity? How does this differ from the training obtained in a technical education?

3. Summarize the relationship between mind and body in Whitehead's ideal education.

4. What is the difference between the logic of discovery and the logic of the discovered?

5. What three "cultures" should human beings undertake to get a good balance of intellect and character?

FOR DISCUSSION AND DEBATE

1. Support or challenge Whitehead's statement that "no human being can attain to anything but fragmentary knowledge and a fragmentary training of his capacities."

2. Whitehead tells us that the art of thought—the forming of clear ideas and their application to firsthand experience—should be an integral part of the teaching of science. Suggest concrete situations that would reinforce Whitehead's claim.

3. Notice that Whitehead extends the concept of technical into the realm of the arts. Defend or challenge this premise; include concrete examples.

FOR YOUR NOTEBOOK

1. Write about your own sense of the relationship between body and mind and between brain and mind.

2. What do you see in art that is technical? What do you see in technology that is artistic?

3. Can intellect nurture or impede character? Perhaps you have mixed feelings on the matter. Try to express them in a freewriting session.

1. Write an essay exploring Whitehead's claim that "the antithesis between a technical and a liberal education is fallacious." One possible way to proceed is to (1) summarize those views about technical education and liberal education that insist on hard-and-fast distinctions between the two; (2) carefully analyze these views, paying particular attention to possible logical fallacies and using Whitehead's points to support your views (based, perhaps, on your firsthand experience so far with technical and liberal studies in college) about why such an antithesis is false.

2. Write an essay on the importance of precision in science, in art, or in both. Draw from your own experience, say in a physics or biology lab, or in a drawing or literature class. Does precision in a science class mean the same as precision in an art class? In what ways? How important are these differences?

3. What is your definition of an ideal education? Discuss your views in relation to Whitehead's. Include your own experiences in high school and college.

Jacob Bronowski, who was a senior fellow of the Salk Institute for Biological Studies in San Diego, has demonstrated, perhaps more vividly than anyone, the important links between science and the arts. He is perhaps best remembered for his excellent PBS television series, *The Ascent of Man,* which examined the evolution of culture in light of technological change. Bronowski studied the impact of the nuclear holocaust on Japan in 1945, and this led him to explore the role of values in a scientific age. His resulting work, *Science and Human Values* (1965), is indispensable.

In the following essay, Bronowski presents one of his major concerns—that the creative imagination is as important to scientific pursuits as it is to artistic ones. He first examines the properties of human imagination and then shows how the imagination of one great scientist, Galileo, led to his extraordinary discoveries.

TERMS TO LEARN

primates: animals with binocular vision, hands with fingers and opposable thumbs for grasping, and highly developed brains (includes monkeys, the great apes, and humans)

induction: the mode of formal reasoning typical of scientific investigation. One begins "with an open mind," examines properties and phenomena, and formulates a hypothesis based on those investigations. It is the opposite of deduction, in which one *begins* with a hypothesis and then searches for evidence to support it.

JACOB BRONOWSKI

The Reach of Imagination

For three thousand years, poets have been enchanted and moved and perplexed by the power of their own imagination. In a short and summary essay I can hope at most to lift one small corner of that mystery; and yet it is a critical corner. I shall ask, What goes on in the mind when we imagine? You will hear from me that one answer to this question is fairly specific: which is to say, that we can describe the working of the imagination. And when we describe it as I shall do, it becomes plain that imagination is a specifically *human* gift. To imagine is the characteristic act, not of the poet's mind, or the painter's, or the scientist's, but of the mind of man.

My stress here on the word *human* implies that there is a clear difference in this between the actions of men and those of other animals. Let me then start with a classical experiment with animals and children which Walter Hunter thought out in Chicago about 1910. That was the time when scientists were agog with the success of Ivan Pavlov in forming and changing the reflex actions of dogs, which Pavlov had first announced in 1903. Pavlov had been given a Nobel prize the next year, in 1904; although in fairness I should say that the award did not cite his work on the conditioned reflex, but on the digestive glands.

Hunter duly trained some dogs and other animals on Pavlov's lines. They were taught that when a light came on over one of three tunnels out of their cage, that tunnel would be open; they could escape down it, and were rewarded with food if they did. But once he had fixed that conditioned reflex, Hunter added to it a deeper idea: he gave the mechanical experiment a new dimension, literally— the dimension of time. Now he no longer let the dog go to the lighted tunnel at once; instead, he put out the light, and then kept the dog waiting a little while before he let him go. In this way Hunter timed how long an animal can remember where he has last seen the signal light to his escape route.

The results were and are staggering. A dog or a rat forgets which one of three tunnels has been lit up within a matter of seconds—in Hunter's experiment, ten seconds at most. If you want such an animal to do much better than this, you must make the task much simpler: you must face him with only two tunnels to choose from. Even so, the best that Hunter could do was to have a dog remember for five minutes which one of two tunnels had been lit up.

I am not quoting these times as if they were exact and universal: they surely are not. Hunter's experiment, more than fifty years old now, had many faults of detail. For example, there were too few animals, they were oddly picked, and they did not all behave consistently. It may be unfair to test a dog for what he *saw*, when he commonly follows his nose rather than his eyes. It may be unfair to test any animal in the unnatural setting of a laboratory cage. And there are higher animals, such as chimpanzees and other primates, which certainly have longer memories than the animals that Hunter tried.

Yet when all these provisos have been made (and met, by more modern experiments) the facts are still startling and characteristic. An animal cannot recall a signal from the past for even a short fraction of the time that a man can—for even a short fraction of the time that a child can. Hunter made comparable tests with six-year-old children and found, of course, that they were incomparably better than the best of his animals. There is a striking and basic difference between a man's ability to imagine something that he saw or experienced and an animal's failure.   *Recall?*

Animals make up for this by other and extraordinary gifts. The salmon and the carrier pigeon can find their way home as we cannot; they have, as it were, a practical memory that man cannot match. But their actions always depend on some form of habit: on instinct or on learning, which reproduce by rote a train of known responses. They do not depend, as human memory does, on calling to mind the recollection of absent things.

Where is it that the animal falls short? We get a clue to the answer, I think, when Hunter tells us how the animals in his experiment tried to fix their recollection. They most often pointed themselves at the light before it went out, as some gun dogs point rigidly at the game they scent—and get the name *pointer* from the posture. The animal makes ready to act by building the signal into its action. There is a primitive imagery in its stance, it seems to me; it is as if the animal were trying to fix the light in its mind by fixing it in its body. And indeed, how else can a dog mark and (as it were) name one of three tunnels, when he has no such words as *left* and *right,* and no such numbers as *one, two three?* The directed gesture of attention and readiness is perhaps the only symbolic device that the dog commands to hold on to the past, and thereby to guide himself into the future.

I used the verb *to imagine* a moment ago, and now I have some ground for giving it a meaning. To *imagine* means to make images and to move them about inside one's head in new arrangements. When you and I recall the past, we imagine it in this direct and homely sense. The tool that puts the human mind ahead of the animal is imagery. For us, memory does not demand the preoccupation that it demands in animals, and it lasts immensely longer, because we fix it in images or other substitute symbols. With the same symbolic vocabulary we spell out the future—not one but many futures, which we weigh one against another.

I am using the word *image* in a wide meaning, which does not restrict it to the mind's eye as a visual organ. An image in my usage is what Charles Peirce called a *sign,* without regard for its sensory quality. Peirce distinguished between different forms of signs, but there is no reason to make his distinction here, for the imagination works equally with them all, and that is why we call them all images.

Indeed, the most important images for human beings are simply words, which are abstract symbols. Animals do not have words, in our sense: there is no specific center for language, in the brain of any animal, as there is in the human brain. In this respect at least we know that the human imagination depends on a configuration in the brain that has only evolved in the last one or two million years. In the same period, evolution has greatly enlarged the front lobes in the human brain, which govern the sense of the past and the future; and it is a fair guess that they are probably the seat of our other images. (Part of the evidence for this guess is that damage to the front lobes in primates reduces them to the state of Hunter's animals.) If the guess turns out to be right, we shall know why man has come to look like a highbrow or an egghead: because otherwise there would not be room in his head for his imagination.

The images play out for us events which are not present to our senses, and thereby guard the past and create the future—a future that does not yet exist, and may never come to exist in that form. By contrast, the lack of symbolic ideas, or their rudimentary poverty, cuts off an animal from the past and the future alike, and imprisons him in the present. Of all the distinctions between man and animal, the characteristic gift which makes us human is the power to work with symbolic images: the gift of imagination.

This is really a remarkable finding. When Philip Sidney in 1580 defended poets (and all unconventional thinkers) from the Puritan charge that they were liars, he said that a maker must imagine things that are not. Halfway between Sidney and us, William Blake said, "What is now proved was once only imagin'd." About the same time, in 1796, Samuel Taylor Coleridge for the first time distinguished between the passive fancy and the active imagination, "the living Power and prime Agent of all human Perception." Now we see that they were right, and precisely right: the human gift is the gift of imagination—and that is not just a literary phrase.

Nor is it just a literary gift; it is, I repeat, characteristically human. Almost everything that we do that is worth doing is done in the first place in the mind's eye. The richness of human life is that we have many lives; we live the events that do not happen (and some that cannot) as vividly as those that do; and if thereby we die a thousand deaths, that is the price we pay for living a thousand lives. (A cat, of course, has only nine.) Literature is alive to us because we live its images, but so is any play of the mind—so is chess: the lines of play that we foresee and try in our heads and dismiss are as much a part of the game as the moves that we make. John Keats said that the unheard melodies are sweeter, and all chess players sadly recall that the combinations that they planned and which never came to be played were the best.

I make this point to remind you, insistently, that imagination is the manipulation of images in one's head; and that the rational manipulation belongs to that, as well as the literary and artistic manipulation. When a child begins to play games with things that stand for other things, with chairs or chessmen, he enters the gateway to reason and imagination together. For the human reason discovers new relations between things not by deduction, but by that unpredictable blend of speculation and insight that scientists call induction, which—like other forms of imagination—cannot be formalized. We see it at work when Walter Hunter inquires into a child's memory, as much as when Blake and Coleridge do. Only a restless and original mind would have asked Hunter's questions and could have conceived his experiments, in a science that was dominated by Pavlov's reflex arcs and was heading toward the behaviorism of John Watson.

Let me find a spectacular example for you from history. What is the most famous experiment that you had described to you as a child? I will hazard that it is the experiment that Galileo is said to have made in Sidney's age, in Pisa about 1590, by dropping two unequal balls from the Leaning Tower. There, we say, is a man in the modern mold, a man after our own hearts: he insisted on questioning the authority of Aristotle and St. Thomas Aquinas, and seeing with his own eyes whether (as they said) the heavy ball would reach the ground before the light one. Seeing is believing.

Yet seeing is also imagining. Galileo did challenge the authority of Aristotle, and he did look hard at his mechanics. But the eye that Galileo used was the mind's eye. He did not drop balls from the Leaning Tower of Pisa—and if he had, he would have got a very doubtful answer. Instead, Galileo made an imaginary experiment in his head, which I will describe as he did years later in the book he wrote after the Holy Office silenced him: the *Discorsi . . . intorno à due nuove scienze* (Discourses Concerning Two New Sciences), which was smuggled out to be printed in the Netherlands in 1638.

Suppose, said Galileo, that you drop two unequal balls from the tower at the same time. And suppose that Aristotle is right—suppose that the heavy ball falls faster, so that it steadily gains on the light ball, and hits the ground first. Very well. Now imagine the same experiment done again, with only one difference: this time the two unequal balls are joined by a string between them. The heavy ball will again move ahead, but now the light ball holds it back and acts as a drag or brake. So the light ball will be speeded up and the heavy ball will be slowed down; they must reach the ground together because they are tied together, but they cannot reach the ground as quickly as the heavy ball alone. Yet the string between them has turned the two balls into a single mass which is heavier than either ball—and surely (according to Aristotle) this mass should therefore move faster than either ball? Galileo's imaginary experiment has uncovered a contradiction; he says trenchantly, "You see how, from your assumption that a heavier body falls more rapidly than a lighter one, I infer that a (still) heavier body falls more slowly." There is only one way out of the contradiction: the heavy ball and the light ball must fall at the same rate, so that they go on falling at the same rate when they are tied together.

This argument is not conclusive, for nature might be more subtle (when the two balls are joined) than Galileo has allowed. And yet it is something more important: it is suggestive, it is stimulating, it opens a new view—in a word, it is imaginative. It cannot be settled without an actual experiment, because nothing that we imagine can become knowledge until we have translated it into, and backed it by, real experience. The test of imagination is experience. But then, that is as true of literature and the arts as it is of science. In science, the imaginary experiment is tested by confronting it with physical experience; and in literature, the imaginative conception is tested by confronting it with human experience. The superficial speculation in science is dismissed because it is found to falsify nature; and the shallow work of art is discarded because it is found to be untrue to our own nature. So when Ella Wheeler Wilcox died in 1919, more people were reading her verses than Shakespeare's; yet in a few years her work was dead. It had been buried by its poverty of emotion and its trivialness of thought: which is to say that it had been proved to be as false to the nature of man as, say, Jean Baptiste Lamarck and Trofim Lysenko were false to the nature of inheritance. The strength of the imagination, its enriching power and excitement, lies in its interplay with reality—physical and emotional.

I doubt if there is much to choose here between science and the arts: the imagination is not much more free, and not much less free, in one than in the other. All great scientists have used their imagination freely, and let it ride them to outrageous conclusions without crying "Halt!" Albert Einstein fiddled with imaginary experiments from boyhood, and was wonderfully ignorant of the facts that they were supposed to bear on. When he wrote the first of his beautiful papers on the random movement of atoms, he did not know that the Brownian motion which it predicted could be seen in any laboratory. He was sixteen when he invented the paradox that he resolved ten years later, in 1905, in the theory of relativity, and it bulked much larger in his mind than the experiment of Albert Michelson and Edward Morley which had upset every other physicist since 1881. All h is life Einstein loved to make up teasing puzzles like Galileo's, about falling lifts and the detection of gravity; and they carry the nub of the problems of general relativity on which he was working.

Indeed, it could not be otherwise. The power that man has over nature and himself, and that a dog lacks, lies in his command of imaginary experience. He alone has the symbols which fix the past and play with the future, possible and impossible. In the Renaissance, the symbolism of memory was thought to be mystical, and devices that were invented as mnemonics (by Giordano Bruno, for example, and by Robert Fludd) were interpreted as magic signs. The symbol is the tool which gives man his power, and it is the same tool whether the symbols are images or words, mathematical signs or mesons. And the symbols have a reach and a roundness that goes beyond their literal and practical meaning. They are the rich concepts under which the mind gathers many particulars into one name, and many instances into one general induction. When a man says *left* and *right*, he is outdistancing the dog not only in looking for a light; he is setting in train all the shifts of meaning, the overtones and the ambiguities, between *gauche* and *adroit* and *dexterous,* between *sinister* and the sense of right. When a man counts *one, two, three,* he is not only doing mathematics; he is on the path to the mysticism of numbers in Pythagoras and Vitruvius and Kepler, to the Trinity and the signs of the Zodiac.

I have described imagination as the ability to make images and to move them about inside one's head in new arrangements. This is the faculty that is specifically human, and it is the common root from which science and literature both spring and grow and flourish together. For they do flourish (and languish) together; the great ages of science are the great ages of all the arts, because in them powerful minds have taken fire from one another, breathless and higgledy-piggledy, without asking too nicely whether they ought to tie their imagination to falling balls or a haunted island. Galileo and Shakespeare, who were born in the same year, grew into greatness in the same age; when Galileo was looking through his telescope at the moon, Shakespeare was writing *The Tempest;* and all Europe was in ferment, from Johannes Kepler to Peter Paul Rubens, and from the first table of logarithms by John Napier to the authorized version of the Bible.

Let me end with a last and spirited example of the common inspiration of literature and science, becaust it is as much alive today as it was three hundred years ago. What I have in mind is man's ageless fantasy, to fly to the moon. I do not display this to you as a high scientific enterprise; on the contrary, I think we have more important discoveries to make here on earth than wait for us, beckoning, at the horned surface of the moon. Yet I cannot belittle the fascination which that ice-blue journey has had for the imagination of men, long before it drew us to our television screens to watch the tumbling of astronauts. Plutarch and Lucian, Ariosto and Ben Jonson wrote about it, before the days of Jules Verne and H. G. Wells and science fiction. The seventeenth century was heady with new dreams and fables about voyages to the moon. Kepler wrote one full of deep scientific ideas, which (alas) simply got his mother accused of witchcraft. In England, Francis Godwin wrote a wild and splendid work, *The Man in the Moone,* and the astronomer John Wilkins wrote a wild and learned one, *The Discovery of a New World.* They did not draw a line between science and fancy; for example, they all tried to guess just where in the journey the earth's gravity would stop. Only Kepler understood that gravity has no boundary, and put a law to it— which happened to be the wrong law.

All this was a few years before Isaac Newton was born, and it was all in his head that day in 1666 when he sat in his mother's garden, a young man of twenty-three, and thought about the reach of gravity. This was how he came to conceive his brilliant image, that the moon is like a ball which has been thrown so hard that it falls exactly as fast as the horizon, all the way round the earth. The image will do for any satellite, and Newton modestly calculated how long therefore an astronaut would take to fall round the earth once. He made it ninety minutes, and we have all seen now that he was right; but Newton had no way to check that. Instead he went on to calculate how long in that case the distant moon would take to round the earth, if indeed it behaves like a thrown ball that falls in the earth's gravity, and if gravity obeyed a law of inverse squares. He found that the answer would be twenty-eight days.

In that telling figure, the imagination that day chimed with nature, and made a harmony. We shall hear an echo of that harmony on the day when we land on the moon, because it will be not a technical but an imaginative triumph, that reaches back to the beginning of modern science and literature both. All great acts of imagination are like this, in the arts and in science, and convince us because they fill out reality with a deeper sense of rightness. We start with the simplest vocabulary of images, with *left* and *right* and *one, two, three,* and before we know how it happened the words and the numbers have conspired to make a match with nature: we catch in them the pattern of mind and matter as one.

Exercises and Projects

CHECKING YOUR COMPREHENSION

1. What is the major difference between animal and human recall? How does this difference contribute to the unique quality of human imagination?

2. Summarize the "thought experiment" Galileo used to expose the error in Aristotle's explanation of falling bodies.

3. According to Bronowski, what are our most important images? Why?

4. What is the relationship between the physical human brain and the ability to imagine?

5. Describe the comparison Bronowski makes between the testing of experience in science and the testing of experience in literature.

6. In what way is induction like other forms of imagination?

FOR DISCUSSION AND DEBATE

1. What does Bronowski mean when he says, "The richness of human life is that we have many lives"?

2. Compare the uses of the imagination in the sciences with those in the arts. Do you agree with Bronowski that "the imagination is not much more free, and not much less free, in one than in the other"?

3. Discuss your own sense of the importance of imagination in science; compare it with Bronowski's opinion.

4. Defend or challenge Bronowski's view that "the most important images for human beings are simply words."

FOR YOUR NOTEBOOK

1. Do you consider yourself an imaginative person? If so, list as many characteristics of your imaginativeness as you can. For example, do you like to think about what life will be like one hundred years from now? What, specifically do you envision?

2. How does your imagination assist you, if at all, when you are trying to solve complex abstract problems, such as an algebraic equation?

3. Have a conversation with one or more friends about the uses and abuses of imagination. Record in your notebook the essence of what was discussed.

FOR WRITING

1. Reflect on the differences between logical reasoning and creative imagining. You might find this easier to do if you think of different kinds of courses, such as chemistry or psychology or history. Are imagination and reason contradictory? Can they exist harmoniously under certain circumstances? After jotting down several observations and hunches in your notebook, prepare a well-organized essay in which you compare and contrast the two modes of thought.

2. Investigate the working habits of a scientist and an artist (faculty members or students) in your college community. Write a critical account of the role that imagination plays in their activities.

3. Investigate the working habits of two scientists or two artists (faculty or students) in your college community. Write an account of the similarities and differences in the way each scientist uses imagination (or the way each artist uses logic) in his or her activities.

4. When Bronowski wrote, in the last paragraph, that the landing on the moon "will not be a technical but an imaginative triumph, that reaches back to the beginning of modern science," the first lunar landing was still two years in the future. Do you agree or disagree that Bronowski's prediction held true? Write an essay defending or challenging that prediction.

All too often we cannot see to see, to borrow a line from Emily Dickinson. What we think we see, or want to see, affects what we actually see. One of the great virtues of scientific training is that it teaches one to observe thoroughly and accurately—a skill that is important for all experiences, not just scientific ones.

In a clear and entertaining style that makes *The Art of Scientific Investigation* (1957) a classic, W. I. B. Beveridge, a professor of animal pathology, describes the general principles of observation and then explains how the observational skills necessary for scientific work can be developed.

NAMES TO LEARN

Herodotus (ca. 484–425 B.C.): a Greek historian—the first great historian in Western civilization—whose *History* (from the Greek word *historia,* meaning "inquiry") covered the major cultures of the ancient world

Claude Bernard (1813–1878): a French physiologist, philosopher of science, and author of *An Introduction to the Study of Experimental Medicine* (1865) who is considered the founder of experimental medicine

Michael Faraday (1791–1867): a British chemist and physicist who discovered electromagnetism and the principles of electrolysis

W. I. B. BEVERIDGE

The Powers of Observation

Some General Principles in Observation

In discussing the thoroughly unreliable nature of eyewitness observation of everyday events, W. H. George says,

> What is observed depends on who is looking. To get some agreement between observers they must be paying attention, their lives must not

be consciously in danger, their prime necessities of life must preferably
be satisfied and they must not be taken by surprise. If they are
observing a transient phenomenon, it must be repeated many times
and preferably they must not only look *at* but must look *for* each detail.

As an illustration of the difficulty of making careful observations, he
tells the following story.

At a congress on psychology at Göttingen, during one of the
meetings, a man suddenly rushed into the room chased by another
with a revolver. After a scuffle in the middle of the room a shot was
fired and both men rushed out again about twenty seconds after
having entered. Immediately the chairman asked those present to
write down an account of what they had seen. Although the observers
did not know it at the time, the incident had been previously arranged,
rehearsed and photographed. Of the forty reports presented, only
one had less than 20 percent mistakes about the principal facts, 14
had from 20 to 40 percent mistakes, and 25 had more than 40 percent
mistakes. The most noteworthy feature was that in over half the
accounts, 10 percent or more of the details were pure inventions.
This poor record was obtained in spite of favorable circumstances,
for the whole incident was short and sufficiently striking to arrest
attention, the details were immediately written down by people
accustomed to scientific observation and no one was himself involved.
Experiments of this nature are commonly conducted by psychologists
and nearly always produce results of a similar type.

Perhaps the first thing to realize about observations is that not
only do observers frequently miss seemingly obvious things, but
what is even more important, they often invent quite false observations. False observations may be due to illusions, where the senses
give wrong information to the mind, or the errors may have their
origin in the mind.

Illustrations of optical illusions can be provided from various
geometrical figures . . . and by distortions caused by the refraction of
light when it passes through water, glass or heated air. Remarkable
demonstrations of the unreliability of visual observations are provided by the tricks of "magicians" and conjurers. Another illustration
of false information arising from the sense organs is provided by
placing one hand in hot water and one in cold for a few moments and
then plunging them both into tepid water. A curious fallacy of this
nature was recorded by the ancient Greek historian, Herodotus:

> The water of this stream is lukewarm at early dawn. At the time when
> the market fills it is much cooler; by noon it has grown quite cold; at

this time therefore they water their gardens. As the afternoon advances, the coldness goes off, till, about sunset the water is once more lukewarm.

In all probability the temperature of the water remained constant and the change noticed was due to the *difference* between water and atmospheric temperatures as the latter changed. Fallacious observations of a similar type can be shown to arise from illusions associated with sound.

The second class of error in registering and reporting observation has its origin in the mind itself. Many of these errors can be attributed to the fact that the mind has a trick of unconsciously filling in gaps according to past experience, knowledge and conscious expectations. Goethe has said, "We see only what we know." "We are prone to see what lies behind our eyes rather than what appears before them," an old saying goes. An illustration of this is seen in the cinema film depicting a lion chasing a negro. The camera shows now the lion pursuing, now the man fleeing, and after several repetitions of this we finally see the lion leap on something in the long grass. Even though the lion and the man may have at no time appeared on the screen together, most people in the audience are convinced they actually saw the lion leap on the man, and there have been serious protests that natives were sacrificed to make such a film. Another illustration of the subjective error is provided by the following anecdote. A Manchester physician, while teaching a ward class of students, took a sample of diabetic urine and dipped a finger in it to taste it. He then asked all the students to repeat his action. This they reluctantly did, making grimaces, but agreeing that it tasted sweet. "I did this," said the physician with a smile, "to teach you the importance of observing detail. If you had watched me carefully you would have noticed that I put my first finger in the urine but licked my second finger!"

It is common knowledge that different people viewing the same scene will notice different things according to where their interests lie. In a country scene a botanist will notice the different species of plants, a zoologist the animals, a geologist the geological structures, a farmer the crops, farm animals, and so on. A city dweller with none of these interests may see only a pleasant scene. Most men can pass a day in the company of a woman and afterwards have only the vaguest ideas about what clothes she wore, but most women after meeting another woman for only a few minutes could describe every article the other was wearing.

It is quite possible to see something repeatedly without registering it mentally. For example, a stranger on arrival in London commented to a Londoner on the eyes that are painted on the front of many buses. The Londoner was surprised, as he had never noticed them. But after his attention had been called to them, during the next few weeks he was conscious of these eyes nearly every time he saw a bus.

Changes in a familiar scene are often noticed even though the observer may not have been consciously aware of the details of the scene previously. Indeed sometimes an observer may be aware that something has changed in a familar scene without being able to tell what the change is. Discussing this point, W. H. George says,

> It seems as if the memory preserves something like a photographic negative of a very familiar scene. At the next examination this memory image is unconsciously placed over the visual image present, and, just as with two similar photographic negatives, attention is immediately attracted to the places where the two do not exactly fit, that is, where there is a change in one relative to the other. It is noteworthy that this remembered whole cannot always be recalled to memory so as to enable details to be described.

This analogy should not be taken too literally because the same phenomenon is seen with memory of other things such as stories or music. A child who is familiar with a story will often call attention to slight variations when it is retold even though he does not know it by heart himself. George continues,

> The perception of change seems to be a property of all of the sense organs, for changes of sound, taste, smell and temperature are readily noticed. . . . It might almost be said that a continuous sound is only "heard" when it stops or the sound changes.

If we consider that the comparison of the old and new images takes place in the subconscious, we can draw an analogy with the hypothesis as to how intuitions gain access to the conscious mind. One would expect the person to become aware of the notable facts, that is, the changes, even though he may be unable to bring all the details into consciousness.

It is important to realize that observation is much more than merely seeing something; it also involves a mental process. In all observations there are two elements: (1) the sense-perceptual element (usually visual) and (2) the mental, which, as we have seen, may be partly conscious and partly unconscious. Where the sense-perceptual element is relatively unimportant, it is often difficult to distinguish between an observation and an ordinary intuition. For example, this sort of thing is usually referred to as an observation: "I have noticed that I get hay fever whenever I go near horses." The hay fever and the horses are perfectly obvious, it is the connection between the two that may require astuteness to notice at first, and this is a mental process not distinguishable from an intuition. Sometimes it is possible to draw a line between the noticing and the intuition, for example, Aristotle commented that on *observing* that the bright side of the moon is always toward the sun, it may suddenly *occur* to the observer that the explanation is that the moon shines by the light of the sun. . . .

Scientific Observation

We have seen how unreliable an observer's report of a complex situation often is. Indeed, it is very difficult to observe and describe accurately even simple phenomena. Scientific experiments isolate certain events which are observed by the aid of appropriate techniques and instruments which have been developed because they are relatively free from error and have been found to give reproducible results which are in accord with the general body of scientific knowledge. Claude Bernard distinguished two types of observation: (1) spontaneous or passive observations which are unexpected; and (2) induced or active observations which are deliberately sought, usually on account of a hypothesis. It is the former in which we are chiefly interested here.

Effective spontaneous observation involves firstly noticing some object or event. The thing noticed will only become significant if the mind of the observer either consciously or unconsciously relates it to some relevant knowledge or past experience, or if in pondering on it subsequently he arrives at some hypothesis. In the last section attention was called to the fact that the mind is particularly sensitive to changes or differences. This is of use in scientific observation, but what is more important and more difficult is to observe (in this instance mainly a mental process) resemblances or correlations between things that on the surface appeared quite unrelated. . . . It required the genius of Benjamin Franklin to see the relationship between frictional electricity and lightning. Recently veterinarians have recognized a disease of dogs which is manifest by encephalitis and hardening of the foot pads. Many cases of the disease have probably been seen in the past without anyone having noticed the surprising association of the encephalitis with the hard pads.

One cannot observe everything closely, therefore one must discriminate and try to select the significant. When practicing a branch of science, the "trained" observer deliberately looks for specific things which his training has taught him are significant, but in research he often has to rely on his own discrimination, guided only by his general scientific knowledge, judgment and perhaps a hypothesis which he entertains. As Alan Gregg, the director of Medical Sciences for the Rockefeller Foundation has said:

> Most of the knowledge and much of the genius of the research worker lie behind his selection of what is worth observing. It is a crucial choice, often determining the success or failure of months of work, often differentiating the brilliant discoverer from the . . . plodder.

When Faraday was asked to watch an experiment, it is said that he would always ask what it was he had to look for but that he was still able to watch for other things. He was following the principle enunciated in the quotation from George in the preceding section, that preferably each detail should be looked for. However, this is of little help in making original observations. Claude Bernard considered that one should observe an experiment with an open mind for fear that if we look only for one feature expected in view of a preconceived idea, we will miss other things. This, he said, is one of the greatest stumbling blocks of the experimental method, because, by failing to note what has not been foreseen, a misleading observation may be made. "Put off your imagination," he said, "as you take off your overcoat when you enter the laboratory." Writing of Charles Darwin, his son tells us that

> He wished to learn as much as possible from an experiment so he did not confine himself to observing the single point to which the experiment was directed, and his power of seeing a number of things was wonderful. . . . There was one quality of mind which seemed to be of special and extreme advantage in leading him to make discoveries. It was the power of never letting exceptions pass unnoticed.

If, when we are experimenting, we confine our attention to only those things we expect to see, we shall probably miss the unexpected occurrences and these, even though they may at first be disturbing and troublesome, are the most likely to point the way to important unsuspected facts. It has been said that it is the exceptional phenomenon which is likely to lead to the explanation of the usual. When an irregularity is noticed, look for something with which it might be associated. In order to make original observations the best attitude is not to concentrate exclusively on the main point but to try and keep a look-out for the unexpected, remembering that observation is not passively watching but is an active mental process.

Scientific observation of objects calls for the closest possible scrutiny, if necessary with the aid of a lens. The making of detailed notes and drawings is a valuable means of prompting one to observe accurately. This is the main reason for making students do drawings in practical classes. Sir MacFarlane Burnet has autopsied tens of thousands of mice in the course of his researches on influenza, but he examines the lungs of every mouse with a lens and makes a careful drawing of the lesions. In recording scientific observations one should always be as precise as possible.

Powers of observation can be developed by cultivating the habit of watching things with an active, enquiring mind. It is no exaggeration to say that well-developed habits of observation are more important in research than large accumulations of academic learning. The faculty of observation soon atrophies in modern civilization, whereas with the savage hunter it may be strongly developed. The scientist needs consciously to develop it, and practical work in the laboratory and the clinic should assist in this direction. For example, when observing an animal, one should look over it systematically and consciously note, for instance, breed, age, sex, color markings, points of conformation, eyes, natural orifices, whether the abdomen is full or empty, the mammary glands, condition of the coat, its demeanor and movements, any peculiarities and note is surroundings including any feces or traces of food. This is, of course, apart from, or preliminary to, a clinical examination if the animal is ill.

In carrying out any observation you look deliberately for each characteristic you know may be there, for any unusual feature, and especially for any suggestive associations or relationships among the things you see, or between them and what you know. By this last point I mean such things as noticing that on a plate culture some bacterial colonies inhibit or favor others in their vicinity, or in field observations any association between disease and type of pasture, weather or system of management. Most of the relationships observed are due to chance and have no significance, but occasionally one will lead to a fruitful idea. It is as well to forget statistics when doing this and consider the possibility of some significance behind slender associations in the observed data, even though they would be dismissed at a glance if regarded on a mathematical basis. More discoveries have arisen from intense observation of very limited material than from statistics applied to large groups. The value of the latter lies mainly in testing hypotheses arising from the former. While observing one should cultivate a speculative, contemplative attitude of mind and search for clues to be followed up.

Training in observation follows the same principles as training in any activity. At first one must do things consciously and laboriously, but with practice the activities gradually become automatic and unconscious and a habit is established. Effective scientific observation also requires a good background, for only by being familiar with the usual can we notice something as being unusual or unexplained.

Exercises and Projects

CHECKING YOUR COMPREHENSION

1. Why, according to Beveridge, do people sometimes falsely report what they have seen?

2. How does Beveridge illustrate Goethe's maxim, "We see only what we know"?

3. According to Beveridge, what are the two elements that constitute every act of observation?

4. Name the two kinds of scientific observation distinguished by Claude Bernard.

FOR DISCUSSION AND DEBATE

1. Debate Beveridge's claim that "Most men can pass a day in the company of a woman and afterwards have only the vaguest ideas about what clothes she wore, but most women after meeting another woman for only a few minutes could describe every article the other was wearing."

2. As Beveridge states, Claude Bernard recommended removing one's imagination when entering the laboratory as one removes an overcoat. In light of what Bronowski says about the importance of imagination in science, how valid do you consider Bernard's recommendation?

3. "Powers of observation can be developed by cultivating the habit of watching things with an active, enquiring mind." Discuss.

FOR YOUR NOTEBOOK

1. Write a detailed description of a seemingly simple, everyday object such as a coin, pen, or postage stamp. Are there things about the object you can't include because of insufficient familiarity with its makeup?

2. Take a walk around campus with one or two classmates. Take your notebooks along. When you encounter an object all of you would enjoy describing, observe the object thoroughly, from all sides, and write down everything you see. Compare your observations, and write an additional entry that describes the way your classmates' observations differ from your own.

FOR WRITING

1. Write a personal essay about the difficulty of observing a complex procedure accurately; describe strategies you've used—or should have used—to improve your accuracy.

2. Beveridge advises "not to concentrate exclusively on the main point but to try and keep a look-out for the unexpected." Relate an experience in which keeping an eye out for the unexpected paid off.

3. If you have access to a VCR, rent a film you have never seen before. Immediately after viewing it, describe its contents in as much detail as you can recall, following the chronology of the film. Now view the film once more. What did you miss? More important, what did you distort? Report your findings in a short essay. You may wish to do this experiment with one or two friends. If so, make sure that you do not discuss the film with one another until you have completed your observations of the second viewing. At that time, compare each others' omissions and distortions, and include a summary of them in your essay.

In her introduction to *Women in Science: Portraits from a World in Transition* (1983), from which the following selection is taken, American feminist Vivian Gornick explains that she set out "to document discrimination against women in science." The book is important because it explodes the myth that women by nature are unsuited for scientific work. At the same time, Gornick also argues against the idea that science is a purely mental pursuit: "I discovered how passionate an enterprise science is—how like artists scientists are."

In the following selection, the author demonstrates her thesis by examining the working habits of two genetic researchers, Carol Steiner and Sharlene George.

TERMS TO LEARN

mutation: a sudden change in the "blueprint" of an organism's genetic structure. Mutations occur relatively rarely in nature and cause defects, but mutations are also the basis for evolution. Biologists are able to mutate cells artificially in order to study their genetic behavior

membrane: protective layer of tissue that lines the surface of an organism, organ, or cell

enzyme: type of protein that is able to trigger chemical reactions in plant and animal cells

VIVIAN GORNICK

 ## Two Women of Science: Carol Steiner and Sharlene George

Carol Steiner, a forty-year-old geneticist at a medical school outside of Philadelphia, comes up with a fine metaphor for how to make a working proposition of scientific mystery. "Imagine," she says, "that you have a jigsaw puzzle with no picture printed on it. All you have is pieces you haven't a clue how to make sense of. The pieces are your separate scientific observations. Here's an example of how you might try to get a handle on the puzzle:

"We have a microorganism with a secretory structure on one end. We know this structure is always on the same place in the cell, and that the position of this structure is inherited. The question that we want to answer is: how can inherited information be translated into positional information? Why in that one place, and no place else? Is the genetic code involved, and if so, how? The answer will tell us how the genes work in concert with the rest of the cell to put things where they belong.

"In order to gather pieces of the jigsaw puzzle (that is, pieces of information), we poke at the cell. We change it a little. Now, there are two ways to change the cell. One way is to mutate away the structure and then hope to find out what has changed biochemically inside this cell so that this structure is no longer made. The other way is to make mutations which affect known events occurring in the cell, defining these alterations precisely, both genetically and biochemically, and then ask how these alterations affect the formation of the structure. In my kind of genetics we do the latter.

"A specific mutation that altered the membrane structure of the cell was found to turn off the synthesis of the secretory structure. This was a piece of the jigsaw puzzle. But just one piece. Because we hadn't a clue as to how this *had* happened or *could* happen. Then we got another piece of the jigsaw. It was found that shutting off replication of the chromosome (DNA synthesis) also shut off the formation of the structure. Then we found that mutants which shut off membrane synthesis in fact also shut off DNA synthesis, and two pieces of the puzzle were put together to form a working hypothesis: the structure synthesis of the secretory structure was shut off by mutants in membrane synthesis *because* these mutants in membrane synthesis *first* shut off DNA synthesis. This hypothesis suggests many further questions that will lead to experiments whose results will print pictures on the pieces of the jigsaw puzzle. Not put the puzzle together, mind you. But help us think about what the picture will ultimately look like."

The realized picture on Carol Steiner's jigsaw puzzle is the map of gene expression laid out clearly with all roads, pathways, connecting signal points, and railway junctions marked out so that any tourist can find his or her way in this beautiful country which is confusing only when one is wandering about in ignorance—as we all are now—with a highly incomplete map.

Steiner is a scientist for whom that flash of scientific wholeness—which came to her through genetics—is recalled regularly. When she speaks of the position of the secretory structures on the cell ("The question we want to answer is why in that one place, and no place else") her speech is repeatedly animated by the sentence "This is a question *fundamental* to developmental genetics." The single piece of information about the position of the secretory structure is what Steiner concentrates on in her daily working life, but worrying it, obsessing over it, learning everything there is to know about it, figuring out what it *really* means inevitably puts the glow back in her mind, makes her remember why she does science.

Another scientist with a strong sense of the relation between developmental genetics, moments of discovery, and the daily work in the lab is Sharlene George, a thirty-five-year-old yeast geneticist (colleague and collaborator of Carol Steiner). With Sharlene one begins to see exactly how a scientist lives with a problem for months and years at a time.

Sharlene George works with Tetrahymena because it is an organism whose cells resemble those of humans more than do the cells of bacteria (a Tetrahymena cell, unlike a bacterial cell, has membranes, structures within the cell, lateral chromosomes). George's genetic interest became the regulatory function of the cell's outer membrane. The question she asked as a graduate student was: How does the cell elaborate and control its membrane?

An experimental approach important to biological research—and the one Sharlene George adopted—is the creation and study of mutations. Thousands of mutants are artificially bred in laboratories and studied by scientists who try to see exactly where and how they differ, and deduce what is happening biologically as a result of the departure from the normal. A cell biologist will commonly take a small "known" in the cell, mutate it, and see what can be deduced about the whole from this one specific.

This was Sharlene George's small known: The membrane is composed of an elaborate "sheet" of lipids and proteins that hang together not out of electrical impulses but out of a kind of affinity and an indissolubleness (beads that don't dissolve out). The question: How does the cell make this complex sheet of membranes? That is, how many genes in the organism have the information for telling the cell to make the different components of the membrane? How many genes encode for a particular function? How many genes regulate that function? How is regulation carried out?

It takes years for a scientist to even begin to answer such a question. Hundreds, literally hundreds of experiments are made by first growing large laboratory cultures of cells, then adding to these cells a mutagenic compound that produces hundreds of random mutations, then screening repeatedly for the mutation that will yield up useful results. After which begins the real work: observing keenly, intently, endlessly the results of these mutation experiments to make both large and small sense of them. What's alike here? What's different? How does this square with the last six papers written on this subject? Where does it fit into the theoretical picture? Does this *change* the theoretical picture?

The work is both tedious and imaginative. One must have the patience to perform the experiments meticulously (if the experiments are not absolutely clean and precise they are useless; above all, a scientist's experiments must be such that they can be replicated). Then one must do many, many, many experiments, over and over and over again, so that a legitimate data base is accumulated. Then one must sit down with the data and think hard about it, sifting through one's mind all the literature, all the conversations, all the odd thoughts one has read and had on the subject.

Sharlene George's Ph.D. dissertation established that many genes controlled the structure of the fatty acids of the membranes. This took three years of work, years in which she designed, executed, and analyzed hundreds of cell mutation experiments in the laboratory. Membrane biogenesis remained her subject. Today she is a highly granted principal investigator running a laboratory filled with technicians, graduate students, and postdoctoral fellows. On the shelf above her desk are five dissertation theses by graduate students who have worked in her laboratory, each one advancing the question, adding information to the large picture of how cell regulation of the membrane works.

Slowly, as the years have gone on, an overriding interest developed in this lab. There were four protein components which appeared to be regulated in a common manner. The people in Sharlene George's lab wanted to know: How does the cell control the relative proportions of these four components?

Hundreds of experiments with mutants have been made here over the last few years by changing the DNA which gives altered enzymes to make one or another of these compounds. The genetic structure of each of the mutants was studied and its biochemistry analyzed. A great deal of information was amassed, many speculations filled many notebooks, many conversations went on well into the night. Nothing really jelled.

"I was always thinking about the problem," says Sharlene. "When I was doing something, nothing, anything. Shopping at the supermarket, talking with my friends, cooking dinner. This question of the proportions of the components was always there, waiting for me. It's as though circuits are forged in the brain after years of work. These thoughts become an accompaniment to the day's activity. They're a comfort when I'm down, a goad when I'm lazy, a prod and a friend.

"It came to me on a Friday night in the shower, when I was getting ready to go out. I suddenly realized that a major factor in controlling the proportions of these components was the cell's response to a single precursor. I saw that the response was mediated through the membrane *itself*. The precursor caused an alteration in the activity of an enzyme in the membrane, and this alteration was transmitted to the cytoplasm and turned off the gene responsible for synthesis of the precursor.

"I ran out of the shower dripping wet and immediately put my conclusions on paper. They really *were* synthesizing! Suddenly I could account for so much that had remained puzzling. I was able to make a table of correspondences that explained a dozen different activities in the membrane and accounted better than anything else for the regulation that had been observed. It was a eureka moment.

"I got so excited I began to tell my husband about it. But I really needed to talk to another scientist. I had to call Carol and tell her. Five years of work, and it had come out so beautifully! It was one of those times you think, Jesus, I've put a tiny piece of the creation in place. I was *flying*."

Carol Steiner confirms the memory of that night. "Do you realize what she had done? She had shown that changing the consistency of the membrane affected what happened inside the cell. This revealed that there's a conversation going on between the membrane on the *outside* of the cell and the genetic machinery *inside* the cell. It's a fundamental observation on one of the ways in which the cell controls its own life processes. It was a fine piece of work, the kind of work that reminds you of what it's all about, and keeps you going for *another* five years."

"But you've got to love it all." Sharlene sighs. "The rote work in the lab, the drudgery, the disappointments, the niggling difficulties that can make you jump out of your skin with impatience. Some days you come in, nothing goes right. The petri dishes aren't clean, the water is contaminated, nothing's growing, the equipment isn't working, the results aren't coming up clean. Everything takes forever. Weeks, months. *Forever*. You gotta love it, anyway. Or else you can't get to the moment that makes it all worthwhile."

Exercises and Projects

CHECKING YOUR COMPREHENSION

1. What do geneticists try to learn by causing mutations in cells?

2. Describe in your own words what Steiner discovered about the relationship between DNA synthesis and membrane synthesis.

3. Why has George chosen to work with Tetrahymena cells instead of bacterial cells?

4. What are the major stages of a scientific investigation, as observed by Gornick?

5. Describe George's "eureka moment."

FOR DISCUSSION AND DEBATE

1. What does Gornick mean when she states that scientific work, such as that conducted by Steiner and George, "is both tedious and imaginative"? Do you suppose this is characteristic of all scientific work or only of genetic research?

2. Gornick describes Steiner as "a scientist for whom that flash of scientific wholeness . . . is recalled regularly." What does Gornick mean by this? Why is it important?

3. How will the greater presence of women in science affect science, if at all? Do you agree, with Gornick, that women add "wholeness" to scientific learning? What does wholeness mean in this context?

FOR YOUR NOTEBOOK

1. Describe your earliest experience with science. Do you think your being male or female influenced your attitude toward science?

2. Do feelings interfere with or stimulate scientific work? Or can feelings do both, depending on circumstances? Record your thoughts on the matter, keeping in mind that this can be an "ongoing" entry, subject to modification as you learn more about the way scientists work and think.

FOR WRITING

1. Write an essay on the nature of "eureka moments" and why they are important to science. Before you begin writing, interview one or two science professors on campus and perhaps as many scientists or inventors in the private sector. Quote from these personal testimonies to support your points.

2. Spend a week observing the activities of a professional scientist, then write an objective account of that person's method of "doing science."

3. Argue pro or con: There are "male" and "female" ways of doing science. Report your firsthand observations of male and female scientists at work and compare your observations with those of Vivian Gornick.

 For many, the idea of mathematics being recreational is a contradiction in terms. Math is the epitome of logic, and many find it difficult to reconcile "logic" with "play." Martin Gardner, a mathematician and philosopher of science, has repeatedly shown that logic and play (and thus logic and imagination) are closely interwoven. Much of the playfulness stems from how we approach a problem.

In the fifth century B.C. lived a Greek philosopher named Zeno of Elea, whose fame rests on his mathematical paradoxes. Zeno wished to demonstrate the unreliability of the senses in understanding the nature of the universe. Even an event as seemingly self-evident as motion, according to Zeno, is illusory—a trick of the mind. In his dichotomy paradox, Zeno maintained that it is impossible to move across any given distance. The reason is that half of the distance must first be crossed, but before one can do that, half of *that* distance must be crossed—and so on. Because some infinitesimally small distance is always left over, any motion at all is impossible.

Or consider the nature of a Möbius strip: It is a three-dimensional object with only one side. Impossible? See for yourself. Take a strip of paper about eight inches long and one inch wide, bring the two ends toward each other, then twist the strip so that one end is bottomside up. Now tape the two ends together. Next, take a felt-tip marker and draw a continuous line down the middle of the strip. Watch what happens!

The following brain-teaser is yet another example of the way in which numbers can fire the imagination, showing how math can be fun.

TERMS TO LEARN

irrational number: a number that can only be expressed as a nonrepeating decimal (for example, pi and the square root of two)

isomorphic: the similarity or identity of one element (for instance, in an equation) to another

electron: a negatively charged particle that orbits the nucleus of an atom

integer: any positive or negative whole number (including zero)

MARTIN GARDNER

The Amazing Code

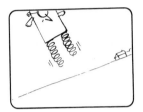

Dr. Zeta is a scientist from Helix, a galaxy in another space-time dimension. One day Dr. Zeta visited the earth to gather information about humans. His host was an American scientist named Herman.

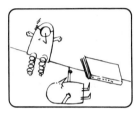

HERMAN: Why don't you take back a set of the *Encyclopaedia Britannica*? It's a great summary of all our knowledge.
DR. ZETA: Splendid idea, Herman. Unfortunately, I can't carry anything with that much mass.

DR. ZETA: However, I can encode the entire encyclopedia on this metal rod. One mark on the rod will do the trick.
HERMAN: Are you joking? How can one little mark carry so much information?

DR. ZETA: Elementary, my dear Herman. There are less than a thousand different letters and symbols in your encyclopedia. I will assign a number from 1 through 999 to each letter or symbol, adding zeros on the left if needed so that each number used will have three digits.

HERMAN: I don't understand. How would you code the word *cat*?
DR. ZETA: It's simple. We use the sort of code I just showed you. *Cat* might be coded 003001020.

Using his powerful pocket computer, Dr. Zeta scanned the encyclopedia quickly, translating its entire content into one gigantic number. By putting a decimal point in front of the number, he made it a decimal fraction.

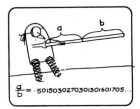

Dr. Zeta then placed a mark on his rod, dividing it accurately into lengths *a* and *b* so that the fraction *a/b* was equivalent to the decimal factions of his code.

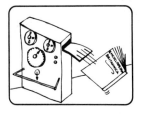

DR. ZETA: When I get back to my planet, one of our computers will measure *a* and *b* exactly, then compute the fraction *a/b*. This decimal fraction will be decoded, and the computer will print your encyclopedia for us!

If you are not already familiar with ciphers, you may enjoy coding and decoding some simple messages in a number code similar to the one used here. Codes illustrate the importance of one-to-one correspondence, and the mapping of one structure onto an isomorphic structure. Such codes are actually used in advanced proof theory. There is a famous proof by Kurt Gödel that every deductive system complicated enough to contain the integers has theorems that cannot be proved true or false within the system. Gödel's proof is based on a number code that translates every theorem of a deductive system into a unique and very large integer.

Coding an entire encyclopedia by placing one mark on a rod works only in theory, not in practice. The difficulty is that the precision needed for marking such a rod is impossible to achieve. The mark would have to be enormously smaller than an electron, and the measurements of the two lengths would have to be precise on the same scale. If we assume that two lengths can be measured accurately enough to yield Dr. Zeta's fraction, then of course his procedure *would* work.

Switching to irrational numbers, mathematicians believe that the decimal expansion of π (pi) is as "unpatterned" as any typical infinite sequence of random digits. If this is true, it means that somewhere in the expansion, any finite sequence of digits is certain to appear. In other words, at some spot in the decimal expansion of π is a sequence that codes the *Encyclopaedia Britannica* as Dr. Zeta did or, indeed, a sequence that codes any other work that has been printed or that *could* be printed!

There are also strongly patterned irrational numbers that contain every finite sequence of digits. An example is the number 123456789101112131415 . . . , formed by writing the counting numbers in counting order.

Exercises and Projects

CHECKING YOUR COMPREHENSION

1. Dr. Zeta's scheme for encoding the encyclopedia is both logical and impossible. Explain.

2. What is the relationship between the kind of number represented by Dr. Zeta's fraction and the kind of number represented by pi?

3. Assuming that Dr. Zeta could mark his measuring rod precisely enough to represent the code for the whole encyclopedia, what other difficult task would he still face?

FOR DISCUSSION AND DEBATE

1. Why does Gardner begin with a discussion of ciphers and codes instead of an explanation of the puzzle itself? In other words, why didn't Gardner begin with paragraph 2?

2. Can puzzles such as "The Amazing Code" help the learning of math fundamentals? Why or why not?

FOR YOUR NOTEBOOK

1. Think about your junior high and high school experiences with math. What did you enjoy the most, or the least, about the way

you were taught math? You may want to profile the math teachers you liked or disliked the most.

2. Choose a mathematical operation you fully understand and introduce it as interestingly as you can to someone who dislikes math.

FOR WRITING

1. Take a mathematical or geometrical principle that you are familiar with (for example, "A straight line is the shortest distance between two points" or "The square root of two is an irrational number") and explain it as clearly as you can to someone who is unfamiliar with the principle. Make sure you define any terms that would cause confusion, such as *irrational* in the second example.

2. Write an essay comparing and contrasting logic with imagination. When are they most alike? Most different?

3. Consider Zeno's paradox of motion. What do you make of it? Do you see a logical flaw in Zeno's argument? Does it give you a new outlook on the reliability of the senses? Write an essay in which you discuss the reliability of the senses in helping you understand "things as they really are." Refer to Zeno's paradox and to any other examples that can demonstrate the apparent unreliability of the senses (such as optical illusions).

Weighing in at about three pounds, somewhat larger than your two fists pressed together, the human brain is the crowning glory of life—vastly more complex than the most complex network of supercomputers we have built (and perhaps will ever be capable of building). From the time of the ancient Greeks, who thought that the brain was some kind of cooling system for the body, to today, we have acquired an enormous amount of knowledge about brain physiology and function, and we are just now beginning to get a glimmering of insight into how the brain controls such tantalizing phenomena as memory (short- and long-term) and learning in all its myriad aspects.

Writing in a clear and engaging manner, Robert Ornstein and Richard Thompson, professors of human biology at Stanford University, here reveal that the brain can actually grow physically as a result of learning.

TERMS TO LEARN

lobe: a major section of the brain's cerebral cortex (convoluted surface). There are four lobes for each hemisphere: temporal (near the temples), specializing in hearing and memory; parietal (near the back), specializing in organizing parts into wholes; occipital (bottom rear), specializing in visual perception; and frontal (behind the forehead), specializing in higher conscious activities like reasoning.

dendrites: long, stringlike message-receptors of a nerve cell. Each of the hundred billion nerve cells in the human brain may have thousands of dendrites as well as thousands of synaptic connectors, which *transmit* messages to other nerve cells.

ROBERT ORNSTEIN
RICHARD F. THOMPSON

 Learning and Brain Growth

It seemed a straightforward job. All one of the authors (Robert Ornstein) was trying to do was to measure the different sizes of the cortex in several brains, to get an idea of the size of the different areas of the brain underneath the skull. He didn't realize how much there was to be discovered by actually looking at real brains. What was most striking was this: like most people, the author's idea of what the brain is came from anatomical drawings, the models he had seen, and the sample brains he had dissected. But as he worked in the laboratory day after day, he began to realize that each brain was distinct. One had characteristic bulges here, one there, one a large occipital lobe, another a small temporal lobe. In fact, people's brains are as different as their faces.

Faces have, of course, some regularity: the eyes are above the nose, the nose is above the mouth, both are above the jaw. But within this regularity there are wide variations: some faces have large noses, some have small eyes. So it is with the brain. The specific features in the brain are different in different individuals. How the brain develops, how it grows and changes within a person's lifetime, and even how it changes within a day is an area just beginning to be explored. We may not think for long of "the brain" as exactly the same in all people. Some of the recent discoveries cited here will make that idea impossible. . . .

Humans are born extraordinarily immature, and the human brain develops largely in the outside world. So environmental conditions play a greater role in the brain development of humans than in that of any other primate.

It is commonly thought that at birth the neurons begin to make connections and that these connections increase as we age and acquire experience. However, the opposite appears to be the case: there may be many *more* connections and nerve cells in the brain of an infant than in an elderly adult. Development seems to be more a matter of "pruning" those original connections than of making any new ones. Consider this about infant babbling: in the first weeks of life, a baby utters almost every sound of every known language. Later on, the infant loses the ability to make sounds that are not in the language he has learned to speak. There may be an enormous potential of sound patterns available to us at birth, but we learn only a few of them. The brain may be "set up" to do many different things, such as to learn the thousands of languages available to humans, only a few of which we actually do learn.

However, the growth of the brain depends on an adequate early environment. Severe malnutrition may cause inadequate brain development, a smaller brain than normal, and severe mental retardation. In a long series of experiments, rats deprived of normal food in infancy show distortions in brain structure, and even shrinkage of certain brain structures. Cells from "deprived" ones look shriveled compared to normal cells. The brain, somewhat like a muscle, then, can grow in response to certain experience—the neurons themselves become larger.

Some of the most revolutionary evidence has come from a series of studies over the last twenty years from work initiated by Mark Rosenzweig and continued by Marion Diamond at the University of California at Berkeley. They study rat brains so that they can control the genetic background. Rats have a fairly short gestation period— twenty-one days—and they have, most beneficially for these purposes, a smooth cerebral cortex. The dog brain is folded, the cat brain is folded, but the rat brain has yet to fold, and that's one of its beauties for making chemical and anatomical measurements—the smooth- surface cerebral cortex allows one to deal with uniform pieces of tissues.

All the animals are in "standard colony" conditions for preliminary measures, which means that there are three rats to a small cage and water and food are provided. Besides standard colonies, the experi- ment involves ones with environments enriched with "toys," or objects to play with, and ones with impoverished conditions, in which there is little stimulation and movement is restricted by cage size. The enriched condition in the postnatal rat consists of twelve rats living together with toys. Every day the experimenters change the objects from a standard pool. If they don't change them, the animals become bored, just as we all do when we've sat too long receiving the same type of stimulus. In the impoverished environment, the rat lives by himself and has no toys; he can see, smell, and hear the other rats but does not play with them.

Typically, Diamond selects three brother rats; one goes into enriched, one into standard colony, and one into impoverished environment. Even in young adults a year old, the enriched environ- ment will cause an increase in the actual *weight* of the brain—about 10 percent in most cases. At first most scientists didn't believe the results, but the evidence has now convinced virtually everyone.

Although their work was revolutionary enough, Diamond and her colleagues were curious to see if they could produce the same result in the brains of very old rats. They put four very old rats in with eight of the young to see whether the stimulating effect of associating young rats with old would result in measurable changes in the brain. It turned out that the old rats enjoyed living with the young more than the young enjoyed living with the old. The brain growth of the rats confirmed this result. *Each* old rat's brain grew by 10 percent while living with the young rats. The young rats' brains did not grow at all while living with the old. Why didn't the young rats' brains grow while the old rats' brains did? A clue may be found in the different responses of the old and young to the experimental situation. Each day when one of the experimenters went to change their toys, the old rats would come to see what toys were available, while the young remained sleeping in the back. So it appears, says Diamond, that there is some sort of hierarchy when the young live with the old; the old dominate. Marion Diamond often jokes that this is why old professors continue to be excited and live to be a hundred—because they are dealing with young people, who are essentially like the young rats. And everybody knows that it is the young students who are sleeping in the back of the lecture hall.

An analysis of the brain growth showed that the specific changes in the brain took place in the dendrites of each nerve cell, which thickened with stimulating experiences. It is as if the forest of nerve cells became literally enriched, and the density of the branches increased; this is what produced a bigger brain.

Not only specific experiences can affect brain growth. Such conditions as increasing negative ionization of the air (the kind of "charged" air found on mountaintops, near waterfalls, or at the sea), when introduced by a negative ion generator to Diamond's rat colonies, produced the same changes in brain growth. So, not only do friends and stimulating experiences get into your head and brain, but so might the fresh air of mountaintops, waterfalls, and other places where the ion concentration (both positive and negative) is greater. The ions can also change the chemical composition of the neurotransmitters, and can elevate or suppress mood, something almost everyone knows who has noted the exhilaration of the mountains, or the depression with a Santa Ana wind.

Exercises and Projects

CHECKING YOUR COMPREHENSION

1. What did Ornstein discover by surprise while he was measuring the cortexes of several brains? What were the implications of that discovery?

2. According to Ornstein and Thompson, how do infants learn to use language? What likely takes place physically in the brain?

3. The theory that environment affects brain development is based on what laboratory evidence?

FOR DISCUSSION AND DEBATE

1. What effect, in your opinion, does environment have on the ability or the desire to learn?

2. In the experiment involving the old rats living with young rats, the old rats' brains developed, whereas the young rats' brains did not. What possible conclusions for human learning communities could you draw, based on this discovery?

3. In your view, how reliable are experiments with rats (or other laboratory animals) in forming hypotheses about human behavior? Can you suggest alternative ways of gaining insight into the relationship between brain development and learning?

FOR YOUR NOTEBOOK

1. Make a list of all the factors that contributed to your desire to learn about the subject you're most interested in.

2. Over the next few weeks, write brief summaries of all the news items you come across that have to do with brain research. Peruse the "Science News" section of your local newspaper, the weekly science newsmagazine, *Science News,* as well as other well-known science magazines such as *Discover, Psychology Today, Scientific American,* and *Omni.*

FOR WRITING

1. Interview two or three faculty members from your college—one from the psychology department and the others from sociology, history, or English—on what an individual can do to increase his or her learning potential. Be sure to present each professor's views accurately and then use these views to develop your own conclusions.

2. Write an essay in which you evaluate the importance of brain research experiments such as those described in this reading. In arguing your case, try to anticipate and refute opposing views; for example, if you agree that brain research experiments are

important, you may wish to argue against the view that the more scientists know about the workings of the brain, the greater the danger of controlling human behavior and resulting loss of individual freedom.

3. Write an essay that focuses on your own learning experiences in or out of school. What stimulated your motivation and ability to learn? What hindered it? Try to be as detailed as you can in supporting your points.

Suggestions for Further Reading

I. SCIENCE AND MATHEMATICS LITERACY

Asimov, Isaac. *Asimov on Numbers*. New York: Doubleday, 1977.

Bogosian, Ted, and WGBH/Boston. *The NOVA National Science Test*. New York: Plume, 1985.
    Includes over 200 questions to test as well as suggest the parameters of basic science literacy.

Davies, Philip J., and Reuben Hersh. *Descartes' Dream: The World According to Mathematics*. New York: Harcourt Brace Jovanovich, 1986.

Gardner, Martin. *Time Travel and Other Mathematical Bewilderments*. New York: W. H. Freeman, 1988.

Kasner, Edward, and James Newman. *Mathematics and the Imagination*. New York: Simon & Schuster, 1940.

Lear, Norman. "Why Johnny Can't Think." *Omni,* 10 (Feb. 1987):30.

Tobias, Sheila. *Overcoming Math Anxiety*. New York: Norton, 1978.

Vergara, William C. *Science in Everyday Life*. New York: Harper & Row, 1980.
    Discusses the importance of written communication in the sciences.

II. NATURE AND EXPERIENCE OF SCIENCE

Bernstein, Jeremy. *Experiencing Science*. New York: Basic Books, 1978.

Beveridge, W.I.B. *Seeds of Discovery*. New York: Norton, 1981.

Brown, Hanbury. *The Wisdom of Science: Its Relevance to Culture and Religion*. Cambridge: Cambridge University Press, 1986.

Florman, Samuel C. *The Existential Pleasures of Engineering*. New York: St. Martin's Press, 1976.

Examines the experience of professional engineering, which involves ethical and aesthetic as well as practical understanding.

Goodfield, June. *An Imagined World: A Story of Scientific Discovery*. New York: Harper & Row, 1981.

Meyer, Leonard B. "Sciences, Arts, and Humanities." *Critical Inquiry* 1 (Sept. 1974): 163–217.

Distinguishes between "propositional" scientific theories and "presentational" works of art.

Reichenbach, Hans. *The Rise of Scientific Philosophy*. Berkeley: University of California Press, 1951.

Explores how scientific philosophy has provided a more effective means of examining the issues of traditional philosophical speculation, such as space, time, and causality.

Sagan, Carl. *Broca's Brain: Reflections on the Romance of Science*. New York: Random House, 1979.

III. HISTORY OF SCIENCE AND TECHNOLOGY

Bronowski, Jacob. *The Ascent of Man*. Boston: Little, Brown, 1974.

Farrington, Benjamin. *Greek Science*. Middlesex: Penguin Books, 1953.

Hodges, Henry. *Technology in the Ancient World*. London: Allan Lane, 1970.

Taylor, F. Sherwood. *A Short History of Science and Scientific Thought*. New York: Norton, 1949.

Presents a concise and readable history, including readings from the major scientists.

Whitehead, Alfred North. *Science in the Modern World.* New York: Macmillan, 1925.

Discusses how Western culture has been influenced from the seventeenth century on by the rise of modern science.

IV. THE LEARNING PROCESS

Bruner, Jerome. *On Knowing: Essays for the Left Hand.* Cambridge: Harvard University Press, 1979.

Explores the role of creative thinking in scientific and artistic discovery.

McMillen, Liz. "Science and Math Professors Are Assigning Writing Drills to Focus Students' Thinking." *Chronicle of Higher Education* (Jan. 22, 1986): 19–21.

Ornstein, Robert. *The Psychology of Consciousness.* New York: Penguin, 1972.

V. SCIENCE AND LANGUAGE

Asimov, Isaac. *Words of Science and the History Behind Them.* Boston: Houghton-Mifflin, 1959.

Presents fascinating mini-essays tracing the evolution of scientific terms.

Harrison, James, ed. *Scientists as Writers.* Cambridge: MIT Press, 1965.

Jones, Roger S. *Physics as Metaphor.* New York: Meridian Books, 1982.

Thomas, Lewis. "A Trip Abroad." *The Medusa and the Snail.* New York: Viking, 1978.

A lighthearted comparison of poets to scientists.

White, Fred D. "Science, Discourse, and Authorial Responsibility." *San Jose Studies* 10 (1984): 25–38.

VI. WOMEN IN SCIENCE

Merchant, Carolyn. *The Death of Nature: Women, Ecology and the Scientific Revolution.* New York: Harper & Row, 1980.

Rossiter, Margaret. *Women Scientists in America: Struggle and Strategies to 1940.* Baltimore, Md.: Johns Hopkins University Press, 1982.

PART TWO

The Discovery Dimension

Scientists Who Have Revolutionized Our Understanding of Nature

Each of the revolutionary thinkers represented in this section has altered our basic understanding of the world, and whenever our basic understanding of the world changes, so does our understanding of ourselves. Moreover—and this is especially important—these great scientists manage to communicate their ideas clearly and in everyday language. They of course understand that everyday language cannot possibly be as precise as mathematical language, but they also understand how vitally important it is for the discoveries of science to become universally understood.

Copernicus became the first of those few scientific thinkers who have fundamentally changed the way we perceive ourselves in relation to nature. It was during the time of Copernicus, in the sixteenth century, when we began to realize that the planet earth, along with its inhabitants, possessed no special privileges—at least spatially speaking—in the cosmic scheme of things. Our planet was but one of several that revolved around an average-sized star.

And when Galileo examined the Milky Way through his telescope, instead of interstellar gases (nebulae), he saw countless stars. "The galaxy," he wrote, "is . . . nothing but a congeries [conglomeration] of innumerable stars grouped together in clusters." The "nothing but" is revealing—truly a keynote in human understanding: the nature of things is ordinary—that is, natural (consisting of observable, measurable phenomena), not metaphysical (beyond logical explanation). Through Galileo's telescope, the moon became an ordinary world, cracked and cratered, no longer the perfect globe, the sphere of angels. The planetary orbits themselves, as Johannes Kepler demonstrated in his *New Astronomy* (1609), were not perfectly circular, as befitted the heavenly realm, but elliptical. Later in the seventeenth century Sir Isaac Newton showed that motion, gravitation, and even light itself were natural phenomena with measurable properties, obeying universal laws that could be precisely—that is, mathematically—described.

As scientists refined their methods of observation and analysis, and created ever more precise tools to carry out incredibly complex tasks, more remarkable discoveries were made—particularly at the atomic level. Henri Becquerel, Lord Rutherford, and the Curies, through their investigations into the properties of radiation, brought us closer to an understanding of the relationship between matter and energy—a relationship that Albert Einstein, in one of the crowning achievements of modern science, was finally to describe with the deceptively simple $E = mc^2$.*

*For an explanation of this famous equation, see the introduction to the Einstein selection, page 106.

Of course, the revolution in scientific knowledge was not limited to the physical sciences. In 1859 Charles Darwin published *On the Origin of Species,* a richly detailed examination of the way all organisms on earth develop and change over time, in relation to their physical environment. Predictably, the work caused a furor because of its apparent contradiction of Biblical pronouncements, such as that all living things are created, full-blown, by God. Human beings, by implication, not only did not occupy a physical center in the universe but they did not occupy a biological one either. The simplest living organisms proved to be incredibly complex, but not beyond the understanding of biologists, although it took nearly another century (1953) before the structure of life's basic building block, the DNA molecule, manufacturer of every gene in every organism on earth, was determined.

Only one area seemed inviolate: the human mind. The work of Sigmund Freud, however, made it clear that even our unarticulated thoughts, our dreams, and our behaviors are describable phenomena that unravel the deepest mysteries of human nature. Of all the explorations of science, from subatomic particles to galaxies, the human mind—the physical brain and all that goes into and out of it—generates the most controversy, the most bafflement. But controversy is inevitable in the pursuit of knowledge, and it would be a mistake to use controversy as a reason for ceasing further scientific investigation.

Good writing "democratizes" knowledge in that it ensures impartiality when it is most needed: when new discoveries or insights are in danger of being rejected because they seem odd or illogical or, most commonly, when they threaten the seemingly inviolable scheme of things. Good writing, because it calls attenton to the details of a new theory, and to what the new theory does to clarify earlier confusions or misconceptions, can often determine the acceptance or rejection of new ideas.

In 1609 Galileo learned about a strange new magnifying device invented in 1608 by the Flemish lensmaker Hans Lippershey. The next year, Galileo built the world's first astronomical telescope (roughly 10 × magnification) and wasted no time turning it toward the heavens.

It was a momentous step in the history of the world. Astronomy, of course, is an ancient science, but until Galileo turned his telescope heavenward, the sun and moon, planets and stars were assumed literally to be made of divine stuff. Imagine, then, everyone's surprise when the also astonished Galileo announced that the moon was pockmarked and cracked, that the sun had "spots" (what we know today to be colossal sunstorms) that moved across its surface (demonstrating the sun's rotation on its axis), and—most amazing of all—that four "stars" were revolving around the planet Jupiter. This was crucial evidence in support of the Copernican theory that the earth revolved around the sun.

One can sympathize somewhat with the public response to Galileo's discovery. The heavens, believed to be divine, were shown to be just ordinary space. Where, then, was God? Unlike most people today, those of Galileo's day found it almost impossible to reconcile scientific findings with their deep religious beliefs. Galileo himself tried to establish a harmony between scientific proof and religious truth in his *Letter to the Grand Duchess Christina* (1615):

> In discussions of physical problems we ought to begin not from the authority of scriptural passages, but from sense-experiences and necessary demonstrations; for the holy Bible and the phenomena of nature proceed alike from the divine Word, and the former as the dictate of the Holy Ghost and the latter as the servant executrix of God's commands. It is necessary for the Bible, in order to be accommodated to the understanding of every man, to speak many things which appear to differ from the absolute truth.... But nature ... is inexorable and immutable; she never transgresses the laws imposed upon her.

Galileo was as much a devoted teacher as he was a scientist; he always managed to instill a love of learning in his pupils; in his writings—and this will become clear in the following selection—he makes every effort to reach a nonscientific audience. Science, he passionately felt, was for everyone, not just for the few.

TERMS TO LEARN

zodiac: an imaginary path across the sky, roughly that of the sun's path, divided into twelve parts, each named for an animal constellation (the word *zodiac* literally means "circle of animals"). The path includes the sun, the moon, and the planets visible to the naked eye.

conjunction: in astronomy, the apparent closeness of two celestial bodies to each other

retrograde movement: in astronomy, the apparent reverse movement of a planet relative to a neighboring planet's movement. This movement occurs when a planet, such as the Earth "catches up with" a slower-orbiting planet, such as Mars.

GALILEO GALILEI

 Observations of the Planet Jupiter

On the seventh day of January in this present year 1610, at the first hour of night, when I was viewing the heavenly bodies with a telescope, Jupiter presented itself to me; and because I had prepared a very excellent instrument for myself, I perceived (as I had not before, on account of the weakness of my previous instrument) that beside the planet there were three starlets, small indeed, but very bright. Though I believed them to be among the host of fixed stars, they aroused my curiosity somewhat by appearing to lie in an exact straight line parallel to the ecliptic, and by their being more splendid than others of their size. Their arrangement with respect to Jupiter and each other was the following:

East   *West*

that is, there were two stars on the eastern side and one to the west. The most easterly star and the western one appeared larger than the other. I paid no attention to the distances between them and Jupiter, for at the outset I thought them to be fixed stars, as I have said.[1] But returning to the same investigation on January eighth—led by what, I do not know—I found a very different arrangement. The three starlets were now all to the west of Jupiter, closer together, and at equal intervals from one another as shown in the following sketch:

East   ⬯ ✳ ✳ ✳   *West*

At this time, though I did not yet turn my attention to the way the stars had come together, I began to concern myself with the question how Jupiter could be east of all these stars when on the previous day it had been west of two of them. I commenced to wonder whether Jupiter was not moving eastward at that time, contrary to the computations of the astronomers, and had got in front of them by that motion.[2] Hence it was with great interest that I awaited the next night. But I was disappointed in my hopes, for the sky was then covered with clouds everywhere.

On the tenth of January, however, the stars appeared in this position with respect to Jupiter:

East   ✳ ✳ ⬯   *West*

that is, there were but two of them, both easterly, the third (as I supposed) being hidden behind Jupiter. As at first, they were in the same straight line with Jupiter and were arranged precisely in the line of the zodiac. Noticing this, and knowing that there was no way in which such alterations could be attributed to Jupiter's motion, yet being certain that these were still the same stars I had observed (in fact no other was to be found along the line of the zodiac for a long way on either side of Jupiter), my perplexity was now transformed into amazement. I was sure that the apparent changes belonged not to Jupiter but to the observed stars, and I resolved to pursue this investigation with greater care and attention.

[1]The reader should remember that the telescope was nightly revealing to Galileo hundreds of fixed stars never previously observed. His unusual gifts for astronomical observation are illustrated by his having noticed and remembered these three merely by reason of their alignment, and recalling them so well that when by chance he happened to see them the following night he was certain that they had changed their positions. No such plausible and candid account of the discovery was given by the rival astronomer Simon Mayr, who four years later claimed priority. [Trans.]

[2]Jupiter was at this time in "retrograde" motion; that is, the earth's motion made the planet appear to be moving westward among the fixed stars. [Trans.]

And thus, on the eleventh of January, I saw the following disposition:

East ✴ ✴ ⭕ *West*

There were two stars, both to the east, the central one being three times as far from Jupiter as from the one farther east. The latter star was nearly double the size of the former, whereas on the night before they had appeared approximately equal.

I had now decided beyond all question that there existed in the heavens three stars wandering about Jupiter as do Venus and Mercury about the sun, and this became plainer than daylight from observations on similar occasions which followed. Nor were there just three such stars; four wanderers complete their revolutions about Jupiter, and of their alterations as observed more precisely later on we shall give a description here. Also I measured the distances between them by means of the telescope, using the method explained before. Moreover I recorded the times of the observations, especially when more than one was made during the same night—for the revolutions of these planets are so speedily completed that it is usually possible to take even their hourly variations.

Thus on the twelfth of January at the first hour of night I saw the stars arranged in this way:

East ✴ ✴⭕ ✴ *West*

The most easterly star was larger than the western one, though both were easily visible and quite bright. Each was about two minutes of arc distant from Jupiter. The third star was invisible at first, but commenced to appear after two hours; it almost touched Jupiter on the east, and was quite small. All were on the same straight line directed along the ecliptic.

On the thirteenth of January four stars were seen by me for the first time, in this situation relative to Jupiter:

East ✴ ⭕✴✴✴ *West*

Three were westerly and one was to the east; they formed a straight line except that the middle western star departed slightly toward the north. The eastern star was two minutes of arc away from Jupiter, and the intervals of the rest from one another and from Jupiter were about one minute. All the stars appeared to be of the same magnitude, and though small were very bright, much brighter than fixed stars of the same size.[3]

. . . .

On the twenty-sixth of February, midway in the first hour of night, there were only two stars:

East   ✳   ◯   ✳   *West*

One was to the east, ten minutes from Jupiter; the other to the west, six minutes away. The eastern one was somewhat smaller than the western. But at the fifth hour three stars were seen:

East   ✳   ◯ ✳   ✳   *West*

In addition to the two already noticed, a third was discovered to the west near Jupiter; it had at first been hidden behind Jupiter and was now one minute away. The eastern one appeared farther away than before, being eleven minutes from Jupiter.

This night for the first time I wanted to observe the progress of Jupiter and its accompanying planets along the line of the zodiac in relation to some fixed star, and such a star was seen to the east, eleven minutes distant from the easterly starlet and a little removed toward the south, in the following manner:

                              ✳   ◯ ✳   ✳   *West*
East

       ✱

On the twenty-seventh of February, four minutes after the first hour, the stars appeared in this configuration:

East   ✳   ✳◯   ✳ ✳   *West*

       ✱

[3]Galileo's day-by-day journal of observations continued in unbroken sequence until ten days before publication of the book, which he remained in Venice to supervise. The observations omitted here contained nothing of a novel character. [Trans.]

The most easterly was ten minutes from Jupiter; the next, thirty seconds; the next to the west was two minutes thirty seconds from Jupiter, and the most westerly was one minute from that. Those nearest Jupiter appeared very small, while the end ones were plainly visible, especially the westernmost. They marked out an exactly straight line along the course of the ecliptic. The progress of these planets toward the east is seen quite clearly by the reference to the fixed star mentioned, since Jupiter and its accompanying and planets were closer to it, as may be seen in the figure above. At the fifth hour, the eastern star closer to Jupiter was one minute away.

At the first hour on February twenty-eighth, two stars only were seen; one easterly, distant nine minutes from Jupiter, and one to the west, two minutes away. They were easily visible and on the same straight line. The fixed star, perpendicular to this line, now fell under the eastern planet as in this figure:

East ✳ ◯ ✳ *West*

✳

At the fifth hour a third star, two minutes east of Jupiter, was seen in this position:

East ✳ ✳◯✳ *West*

On the first of March, forty minutes after sunset, four stars all to the east were seen, of which the nearest to Jupiter was two minutes away, the next was one minute from this, the third two seconds from that and brighter than any of the other; from this in turn the most easterly was four minutes distant, and it was smaller than the rest. They marked out almost a straight line, but the third one counting from Jupiter was a little to the north. The fixed star formed an equilateral triangle with Jupiter and the most easterly star, as in this figure:

East ✳ ✳✳✳ ◯ *West*

 ✳

On March second, half an hour after sunset, there were three planets, two to the east and one to the west, in this configuration:

The most easterly was seven minutes from Jupiter and thirty seconds from its neighbor; the western one was two minutes away from Jupiter. The end stars were very bright and were larger than that in the middle, which appeared very small. The most easterly star appeared a little elevated toward the north from the straight line through the other planets and Jupiter. The fixed star previously mentioned was eight minutes from the western planet along the line drawn from it perpendicularly to the straight line through all the planets, as shown above.

I have reported these relations of Jupiter and its companions with the fixed star so that anyone may comprehend that the progress of those planets, both in longitude and latitude, agrees exactly with the movements derived from planetary tables.

Such are the observations concerning the four Medicean planets recently first discovered by me, and although from these data their periods have not yet been reconstructed in numerical form, it is legitimate at least to put in evidence some facts worthy of note. Above all, since they sometimes follow and sometimes precede Jupiter by the same intervals, and they remain within very limited distances either to east or west of Jupiter, accompanying that planet in both its retrograde and direct movements in a constant manner, no one can doubt that they complete their revolutions about Jupiter and at the same time effect all together a twelve-year period about the center of the universe. That they also revolve in unequal circles is manifestly deduced from the fact that at the greatest elongation[4] from Jupiter it is never possible to see two of these planets in conjunction, whereas in the vicinity of Jupiter they are found united two, three, and sometimes all four together. It is also observed that the revolutions are swifter in those planets which describe smaller circles about Jupiter, since the stars closest to Jupiter are usually seen to the east

---

[4]By this is meant the greatest angular separation from Jupiter attained by any of the satellites. [Trans.]

when on the previous day they appeared to the west, and vice versa, while the planet which traces the largest orbit appears upon accurate observation of its returns to have a semimonthly period.

Here we have a fine and elegant argument for quieting the doubts of those who, while accepting with tranquil mind the revolutions of the planets about the sun in the Copernican system, are mightily disturbed to have the moon alone revolve about the earth and accompany it in an annual rotation about the sun. Some have believed that this structure of the universe should be rejected as impossible. But now we have not just one planet rotating about another while both run through a great orbit around the sun; our own eyes show us four stars which wander around Jupiter as does the moon around the earth, while all together trace out a grand revolution about the sun in the space of twelve years.

Exercises and Projects

CHECKING YOUR COMPREHENSION

1. How many different postions of Jupiter's moons does Galileo report?

2. At what point in his observations of Jupiter does Galileo reach a tentative conclusion about what he discovered?

3. How does Galileo link his observations of Jupiter with Copernicus's theory?

FOR DISCUSSION AND DEBATE

1. Why do you suppose Galileo reported as many different positions of Jupiter's moons as he did?

2. What might Galileo have added to the discussion/conclusions section of his report (paragraphs 15 through 17) to make it more convincing to the skeptics of his day?

3. Galileo does more than just record his observations. What else does he include? What do you find most interesting about his account?

FOR YOUR NOTEBOOK

1. Most professionals use notebooks to record important data as well as to trace their progress in learning a certain task. Over the next few days, devote several notebook entries to a single learning experience, such as your progress in mastering a word processing program or a computer language, or mastering your part in a play.

2. Over the next week or so, record your observations of a single natural phenomenon, such as a weather pattern, a growing puppy or kitten, or the progress of a houseplant. You may wish to combine drawings with your observations.

FOR WRITING

1. Using a star map adjusted for the proper month and latitude, locate the planets Mars, Jupiter, and Saturn; these are easily visible to the naked eye if you know exactly where to look. Then, over the next few nights, sketch their positions relative to a "fixed" star close to each of them. In a report organized similar to Galileo's, describe, with accompanying sketches, each planet's position from night to night. In a concluding section, compare each planet's degree of change.

2. Galileo is notorious for having retracted, before the Inquisition in 1633, his scientific conclusions. After doing the necessary background reading, argue for or against Galileo's decision to recant.

3. Write a personal essay on the nature of God in light of our knowledge of the physical universe. Suggestion: In your writer's notebook, jot down your own sense of God's nature and presence in the universe; next, try to reconcile it with your scientific understanding of the universe. Are there any "loose ends"? As you begin writing the essay, you may wish to open with a discussion of your own struggle to experience God in a scientific age.

The poet James Thomson (1700–1748) in his elegy, "Poem Sacred to the Memory of Sir Isaac Newton" (1727), voiced the sentiment of Western culture when he wrote,

> *The heavens are all his own, from the wide rule*
> *Of whorling vortices and circling spheres*
> *To their first great simplicity restored.*

With startling simplicity and rigorous mathematical and physical demonstration, Newton once and for all shut the door on the medieval view of the cosmos. Newton showed the nature of light and the laws of motion and of universal gravitation to be natural phenomena—objectively and clearly explainable and different from any previously held notions of what the universe should be like. With Newton, modern science had finally arrived.

For example, no longer content to accept on faith the Aristotelian notion that light broke into colors when passed through glass because of the varying thickness of the glass, Newton proved that light broke into colors because it was a combination of light rays of different frequencies. As for the legend about Newton and the falling apple, the beauty of the story lies in Newton's sudden creative realization that the force that drives the moon along its orbit around the earth (or the earth and the other planets around the sun) is the very same force that draws the apple to the ground. The universe may be more far reaching than the ancients ever imagined, but it is more unified and more internally consistent as well.

TERMS TO LEARN

centripetal force: the motion, or potential motion, of an object toward a center of gravity. (Centrifugal force, by contrast, pulls an object *outward* from the center it is spinning rapidly around.)

rectilinear (path): movement in a straight line

excentric (modern spelling: eccentric): referring to circles (or orbits) within each other but not sharing the same center, as do *con*centric circles

SIR ISAAC NEWTON

 The Nature of Planetary Orbits

That by means of centripetal forces, the Planets may be retained in certain orbits, we may easily understand, if we consider the motions of projectiles. For a stone projected is by the pressure of its own weight forced out of the rectilinear path, which by the projection alone it should have pursued, and made to describe a curved line in the air; and through that crooked way is at last brought down to the ground. And the greater the velocity is with which it is projected, the farther it goes before it falls to the Earth. We may therefore suppose the velocity to be so increased, that it would describe an arc of 1, 2, 5, 10, 100, 1000 miles before it arrived at the Earth, till at last exceeding the limits of the Earth, it should pass quite by without touching it.

Let AFB represent the surface of the earth, C its center, VD, VE, VF, the curved lines which a body would describe, if projected in a horizontal direction from the top of a high mountain, successively with more and more velocity. And, because the celestial motions are scarcely retarded by the little or no resistance of the spaces in which they are performed; to keep up the purity of cases, let us suppose either that there is no air about the Earth, or at least that it is endowed with little or no power of resisting. And for the same reason that the body projected with a less velocity, describes the lesser arc VD, and with a greater velocity, the greater arc VE, and augmenting the velocity, it goes farther and farther to F and G; if the velocity was still more and more augmented, it would reach at last quite beyond the circumference of the Earth, and return to the mountain from which it was projected.

And since the areas, which by this motion it describes by a radius drawn to the center of the Earth, are proportional to the times in which they are described; its velocity, when it returns to the mountain, will be no less than it was at first; and retaining the same velocity, it will describe the same curve over and over, by the same law.

But if we now imagine bodies to be projected in the directions of lines parallel to the horizon from greater heights, as of 5, 10, 100, 1000 or more miles, or rather as many semidiameters of the Earth; those bodies, according to their different velocity, and the different force of gravity in different heights, will describe arcs either concentric with the Earth, or variously excentric, and go on revolving through the heavens in those trajectories, just as the Planets do in their orbs.

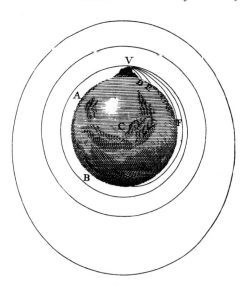

Exercises and Projects

CHECKING YOUR COMPREHENSION

1. What is the relationship between the velocity of a projectile circling the earth and its distance from the earth?

2. How, according to Newton, is a thrown stone forced out of a rectilinear path?

3. Drawing from Newton's description of planetary motion, explain why and how the moon orbits the earth.

FOR DISCUSSION AND DEBATE

1. Describe, specifically, what Newton does to help his readers conceive of planetary motion. How successfully, in your opinion, does this device work?

2. Of what significance is Newton's comment about "the Planets . . . and their orbs" at the end of the selection? How, if at all, might he have elaborated on the significance of this comment?

3. What "givens" in the selection indicate that Newton is addressing readers already familiar with Copernican and Galilean astronomy?

FOR YOUR NOTEBOOK

1. Read a biography of Newton; then use your notebook to record brief descriptions, in your own words, of Newton's contributions to science.

2. Try describing the nature of a planetary orbit to young people of varying age groups—first to tenth graders, then to seventh graders, and finally to fourth graders.

3. Compare the personalities of Galileo and Newton as you encounter them in your reading.

FOR WRITING

1. Write a feature story, addressed to junior high school students, that highlights the main contributions of Galileo and Newton to modern astronomy. You may find it worthwhile to read about two other important astronomers—Johannes Kepler and Edmund Halley—in order to provide useful background information for your readers.

2. Newton invented calculus during 1665 through 1667, yet did not publish his work right away. During the same period, the mathematician-philosopher Gottfried Wilhelm Leibniz (1646–1716) also independently invented calculus, using a different notation. Because Leibniz did publish at once, his notation, not Newton's, became universally adopted. Not surprisingly, a bitter quarrel developed between Newton and Leibniz. Research this quarrel and make it the topic of a short paper.

3. Newton also achieved fame for his pioneer work in optics. He astonished everyone by demonstrating, using a prism, that ordinary sunlight is composed of different rays with different frequencies. Write a short essay in which you compare Newton's theory of color with the predominant theory of color that existed before Newton. Suggestion: Begin by reading articles on color and optics in an encyclopedia of science.

When Charles Darwin was a young man reluctantly studying medicine in Edinburgh (he later dropped out to study for the ministry at Cambridge), the naturalist Alexander von Humboldt published a volume filled with fascinating observations of natural phenomena encountered in his worldwide travels. Humboldt stressed the importance of taking detailed notes, which he kept in a journal; he later used these notes to find new interrelationships among the various phenomena he observed. Darwin, who had already inherited a love of nature through the writings of his poet-naturalist grandfather, Erasmus Darwin, was inspired to become an amateur naturalist himself. His great opportunity came when he was invited by Captain Robert Fitzroy to join him as ship's naturalist aboard the H.M.S. *Beagle* for a trip to South America and the Galápagos Islands.

The result of that five-year voyage led to his *Diary of the Voyage of the Beagle* (1839), which laid the groundwork for his masterwork on evolution, *On the Origin of Species* (1859).

Darwin discovered, as he journeyed along the South American coast and around the islands of the Galápagos, dramatic evidence of a theory first articulated by Jean-Baptiste Lamarck (1744–1829): that species varied in relation to variations in the environment. He noted, for example, that on the Galápagos, 650 miles from the equator, were fourteen different species of finches, none of which were like the finches of the mainland. Could it be that life evolved—and that it evolved in response to changes in the local habitat? Before Darwin, it had generally been assumed that all creatures were created by God and had nothing biologically to do with the forces of nature around them. Darwin eventually came to regard the phenomenon of species variation as "natural selection." This principle holds that those traits of individual members of a species best suited to survival in a particular environment will eventually become the dominant characteristics of that species.

Note, as you read "Understanding Natural Selection," the clear and organized presentation of ideas in Darwin's writing. Darwin was aware of the importance of good writing in communicating scientific ideas, and he avoided anything not directly related to his points.

TERMS TO LEARN

curculio: a type of weevil (a species of beetle) that feeds on fruit and grain *mandible:* the biting jaws of an insect such as a beetle

wattle: the wrinkled skin that hangs from the throats of turkeys and other birds and lizards

CHARLES DARWIN

 # Understanding Natural Selection

It may be said that natural selection is daily and hourly scrutinizing, throughout the world, every variation, even the slightest; rejecting that which is bad, preserving and adding up all that is good; silently and insensibly working, whenever and wherever opportunity offers, at the improvement of each organic being in relation to its organic and inorganic conditions of life. We see nothing of these slow changes in progress, until the hand of time has marked the long lapses of ages, and then so imperfect is our view into long past geological ages, that we only see that the forms of life are now different from what they formerly were.

Although natural selection can act only through and for the good of each being, yet characters and structures, which we are apt to consider as of very trifling importance, may thus be acted on. When we see leaf-eating insects green, and bark-feeders mottled-grey; the alpine ptarmigan white in winter, the red-grouse the color of heather, and the black-grouse that of peaty earth, we must believe that these tints are of service to these birds and insects in preserving them from danger. Grouse, if not destroyed at some period of their lives, would increase in countless numbers; they are known to suffer largely from birds of prey; and hawks are guided by eyesight to their prey— so much so, that on parts of the Continent persons are warned not to keep white pigeons, as being the most liable to destruction. Hence I can see no reason to doubt that natural selection might be most effective in giving the proper color to each kind of grouse, and in keeping that color, when once acquired, true and constant. Nor ought we to think that the occasional destruction of an animal of any particular color would produce little effect: we should remember how essential it is in a flock of white sheep to destroy every lamb with the faintest trace of black. In plants the down on the fruit and the color of the flesh are considered by botanists as characters of the most trifling importance: yet we hear from an excellent horticulturist, Downing, that in the United States smooth-skinned fruits suffer far more from a beetle, a curculio, than those with down; that purple plums suffer far more from a certain disease than yellow plums; whereas another disease attacks yellow-fleshed peaches far more than those with other colored flesh. If, with all the aids of art, these slight differences make a great difference in cultivating the several varieties, assuredly, in a state of nature, where the trees would have to struggle with other trees and with a host of enemies, such differences would effectually settle which variety, whether a smooth or downy, a yellow or purple fleshed fruit, should succeed.

In looking at many small points of difference between species, which, as far as our ignorance permits us to judge, seem to be quite unimportant, we must not forget that climate, food, and so on probably produce some slight and direct effect. It is, however, far more necessary to bear in mind that there are many unknown laws of correlation to growth, which, when one part of the organization is modified through variation, and the modifications are accumulated by natural selection for the good of the being, will cause other modifications, often of the most unexpected nature.

As we see that those variations which under domestication appear at any particular period of life, tend to reappear in the offspring of the same period; for instance, in the seeds of the many varieties of our culinary and agricultural plants; in the caterpillar and cocoon stages of the varieties of the silkworm; in the eggs of poultry, and in the color of the down of their chickens; in the horns of our sheep and cattle when nearly adult; so in a state of nature, natural selection will be enabled to act on and modify organic beings at any age, by the accumulation of profitable variations at that age, and by their inheritance at a corresponding age. If it profit a plant to have its seeds more and more widely disseminated by the wind, I can see no greater difficulty in this being effected through natural selection, than in the cotton-planter increasing and improving by selection the down in the pods on his cotton-trees. Natural selection may modify and adapt the larva of an insect to a score of contingencies, wholly different from those which concern the mature insect. These modifications will no doubt affect, through the laws of correlation, the structure of the adult; and probably in the case of those insects which live only for a few hours, and which never feed, a large part of their structure is merely the correlated result of successive changes in the structure of their larvae. So, conversely, modifications in the adult will probably often affect the structure of the larva; but in all cases natural selection will ensure that modifications consequent on other modifications at a different period of life, shall not be in the least degree injurious: for if they became so, they would cause the extinction of the species.

Natural selection will modify the structure of the young in relation to the parent, and of the parent in relation to the young. In social animals it will adapt the structure of each individual for the benefit of the community; if each in consequence profits by the selected change. What natural selection cannot do, is to modify the structure of one species, without giving it any advantage, for the good of another species; and though statements to this effect may be found in works of natural history, I cannot find one case which will bear investigation. A structure used only once in an animal's whole life, if of high importance to it, might be modified to any extent by natural selection; for instance, the great jaws possessed by certain insects, and used exclusively for opening the cocoon—or the hard tip to the beak of nestling birds, used for breaking the egg. It has been asserted, that of the best short-beaked tumbler-pigeons more perish in the egg than are able to get out of it; so that fanciers assist in the act of hatching. Now, if nature had to make the beak of a full-grown pigeon very short for the bird's own advantage, the process of modification would be very slow, and there would be simultaneously the most rigorous selection of the young birds within the egg, which had the most powerful and hardest beaks, for all with weak beaks would inevitably perish: or, more delicate and more easily broken shells might be selected, the thickness of the shell being known to vary like every other structure.

Sexual Selection

Inasmuch as peculiarities often appear under domestication in one sex and become hereditarily attached to that sex, the same fact probably occurs under nature, and if so, natural selection will be able to modify one sex in its functional relations to the other sex, or in relation to wholly different habits of life in the two sexes, as is sometimes the case with insects. And this leads me to say a few words on what I call sexual selection. This depends, not on a struggle for existence, but on a struggle between the males for possession of the females; the result is not death to the unsuccessful competitor, but few or no offspring. Sexual selection is, therefore, less rigorous than natural selection. Generally, the most vigorous males, those which are best fitted for their places in nature, will leave most progeny. But in many cases, victory will depend not on general vigor, but on having special weapons, confined to the male sex. A hornless stag or spurless cock would have a poor chance of leaving offspring. Sexual selection by always allowing the victor to breed might surely give indomitable courage, length to the spur, and strength to the wing to strike in the spurred leg, as well as the brutal cock-fighter, who knows well that he can improve his breed by careful selection of the best cocks. How low in the scale of nature this law of battle descends, I know not; male alligators have been described as fighting, bellowing, and whirling round, like Indians in a war dance, for the possession of the females; male salmons have been seen fighting all day long; male stag-beetles often bear wounds from the huge mandibles of other males. The war is, perhaps, severest between the males of polygamous animals, and these seem oftenest provided with special weapons. The males of carnivorous animals are already well armed; though to them and to others, special means of defence may be given through means of sexual selection, as the mane to the lion, the shoulder-pad to the boar, and the hooked jaw to the male salmon; for the shield may be as important for victory, as the sword or spear.

Amongst birds, the contest is often of a more peaceful character. All those who have attended to the subject, believe that there is the severest rivalry between the males of many species to attract by singing the females. The rock-thrush of Guiana, birds of Paradise, and some others, congregate; and successive males display their gorgeous plumage and perform strange antics before the females, which standing by as spectators, as last choose the most attractive partner. Those who have closely attended to birds in confinement well know that they often take individual preferences and dislikes: thus Sir R. Heron has described how one pied peacock was eminently attractive to all his hen birds. It may appear childish to attribute any effect to such apparently weak means: I cannot here enter on the details necessary to support this view; but if man can in a short time give elegant carriage and beauty to his bantams, according to his standard of beauty, I can see no good reason to doubt that female birds, by selecting, during thousands of generations, the most melodious or beautiful males, according to their standard of beauty, might produce a marked effect. I strongly suspect that some well-known laws with respect to the plumage of male and female birds, in comparison with the plumage of the young, can be explained on the view of plumage having been chiefly modified by sexual selection, acting when the birds have come to the breeding age or during the breeding season; the modifications thus produced being inherited at corresponding ages or seasons, either by the males alone, or by the males and females; but I have not space here to enter on this subject.

Thus it is, as I believe, that when the males and females of any animal have the same general habits of life, but differ in structure, color, or ornament, such differences have been mainly caused by sexual selection; that is, individual males have had, in successive generations, some slight advantage over other males, in their weapons, means of defence, or charms; and have transmitted these advantages to their male offspring. Yet, I would not wish to attribute all such sexual differences to this agency: for we see peculiarities arising and becoming attached to the male sex in our domestic animals (as the wattle in male carriers, horn-like protuberances in the cocks of certain fowls, and so on), which we cannot believe to be either useful to the males in battle, or attractive to the females. We see analogous cases under nature, for instance, the tuft of hair on the breast of the turkey-cock, which can hardly be either useful or ornamental to this bird; indeed, had the tuft appeared under domestication, it would have been called a monstrosity.

Illustration of the Action of Natural Selection

. . . Let us take the case of a wolf, which preys on various animals, securing some by craft, some by strength, and some by fleetness; and let us suppose that the fleetest prey, a deer for instance, had from any change in the country increased in numbers, or that other prey had decreased in numbers, during that season of the year when the wolf is hardest pressed for food. I can under such circumstances see no reason to doubt that the swiftest and slimmest wolves would have the best chance of surviving, and so be preserved or selected—provided always that they retained strength to master their prey at this or at some other period of the year, when they might be compelled to prey on other animals. I can see no more reason to doubt this, than that man can improve the fleetness of his greyhounds by careful and methodical selection, or by that unconscious selection which results from each man trying to keep the best dogs without any thought of modifying the breed.

Even without any change in the proportional numbers of the animals on which our wolf preyed, a cub might be born with an innate tendency to pursue certain kinds of prey. Nor can this be thought very improbable; for we often observe great differences in the natural tendencies of our domestic animals; one cat, for instance, taking to catch rats, another mice; one cat . . . bringing home winged game, another hares or rabbits, and another hunting on marshy ground and almost nightly catching woodcocks or snipes. The tendency to catch rats rather than mice is known to be inherited.

Now, if any slight innate change of habit or of structure benefited an individual wolf, it would have the best chance of surviving and of leaving offspring. Some of its young would probably inherit the same habits or structure, and by the repetition of this process, a new variety might be formed which would either supplant or coexist with the parent-form of wolf. Or, again, the wolves inhabiting a mountainous district, and those frequenting the lowlands, would naturally be forced to hunt different prey; and from the continued preservation of the individuals best fitted for the two sites, two varieties might slowly be formed. These varieties would cross and blend where they met; but to this subject of intercrossing we shall soon have to return. I may add, that . . . there are two varieties of the wolf inhabiting the Catskill Mountains in the United States, one with a light greyhound-like form, which pursues deer, and the other more bulky, with shorter legs, which more frequently attacks the shepherd's flocks.

Exercises and Projects

CHECKING YOUR COMPREHENSION

1. According to Darwin, what is the one thing that natural selection cannot do?

2. How does Darwin distinguish between natural selection and sexual selection?

3. What species of animal does Darwin consider to be in need of the assistance of natural selection? Why?

4. What is the significance of the size and hardness of tumbler-pigeon beaks in terms of these birds' survival?

FOR DISCUSSION AND DEBATE

1. In the opening sentence, Darwin refers to natural selection as "daily and hourly scrutinizing . . . every [species'] variation, even in the slightest." Why do you suppose Darwin chose to introduce the concept in this manner?

2. What do you consider to be most logical about natural selection? Does any part of it seem illogical?

3. In illustrating the action of natural selection, Darwin uses an imaginary rather than an actual example. What may have been his reason for this?

4. Darwin is regarded as an excellent writer as well as a first-rate scientist. What do you find particularly effective about Darwin's writing in this selection?

FOR YOUR NOTEBOOK

1. To what degree have your ideas and your personality been influenced by external environmental factors?

2. Think back to when you first heard about "evolution." Describe the context in which it was introduced to you.

3. Over the next several days, observe your pet's behavior closely, and record your observations. Speculate on the reasons behind a particular behavioral characteristic.

FOR WRITING

1. How true is the assumption that natural selection operates, in the human community, on a behavioral level—that certain behavioral traits (competitiveness, manners, protectiveness) are more successful than others in ensuring the success of a given social structure. In a short essay take a stand on this issue and decide which behavioral traits are most advantageous and why.

2. Write an essay in which you explain, as clearly as possible to an audience of high school students, the role that environment plays in the evolution of species. You may wish to restrict your focus to one species or to one biological family, such as the dinosaurs. Another possible focus might be human beings as an environmental influence. In this case you might discuss the effects of unrestricted hunting of endangered species.

3. Argue pro or con in a two-page essay: Hunting deer is commendable because, like natural selection, it keeps deer populations from growing too large for the environment to handle.

In an age when women were discouraged from entering just about any profession, particularly physics and chemistry, Marie Curie (born Manya Sklodowska) was nevertheless admitted into the Sorbonne in 1891, received her doctorate in 1903, and in that very year shared the Nobel Prize (her first of two!) with her husband, Pierre Curie, and Henri Becquerel. In 1906 she became the first woman professor at the Sorbonne, but because of her sex, she failed to be elected to membership in the French Academy of Sciences. Mme Curie was awarded a second Nobel Prize in 1911 for her discovery of radium and polonium. She spent her last years researching the applications of radioactivity to medicine.

Not only did Mme Curie discover radium but she also worked out a technique for extracting it from pitchblende (a major ore of uranium). Out of one ton of pitchblende, she was able to extract but a fraction of a gram of radium chloride. She finally succeeded in isolating the pure radium—a highly luminous, whitish metal—several years later.

Mme Curie examined the properties of radiation, and her research, like that of Becquerel's, revealed that there were three kinds of radiation, which she termed (using Ernest Rutherford's notation) alpha, beta, and gamma. Through her work, the perplexing secrets of the atom began to reveal themselves—a revelation that is still continuing.

TERMS TO LEARN

fluorescence: the generation of radiant energy (light) as a result of being exposed to ultraviolet rays or X-rays

cathode ray: an electron stream generated from a cathode (the negative electrode of an electrolyte battery)

Crookes tube: a tube for discharging gasses; invented by Sir William Crookes (1832–1919), a British chemist and physicist, in his study of electrical discharges

ionization: a means of electrically charging a substance, such as a gas, by exposing it to radiation

MARIE CURIE

 The Energy and Nature of Radiation

Energy of Radiation

Whatever be the method of research employed, the energy of radiation of the new radioactive substances is always found to be considerably greater than that of uranium and thorium. Thus it is that, at a short distance, they act instantaneously upon a photographic plate, whereas an exposure of twenty-four hours is necessary when operating with uranium and thorium. A fluorescent screen is vividly illuminated by contact with the new radioactive bodies, whilst no trace of luminosity is visible with uranium and thorium. Finally, the ionizing action upon air is considerably stronger in the ratio of 10^6 approximately. But it is, strictly speaking, not possible to estimate the *total intensity of the radiation,* as in the case of uranium, by the electrical method described at the beginning. . . . With uranium, for example, the radiation is almost completely absorbed by the layer of air between the plates, and the limiting current is reached at a tension of 100 volts. But the case is different for strongly radioactive bodies. One portion of the radiation of radium consists of very penetrating rays, which penetrate the condenser and the metallic plates, and are not utilized in ionizing the air between the plates. Further, the limiting current cannot always be obtained for the tensions supplied; for example, with very active polonium the current remains proportional to the tension between 100 and 500 volts. Therefore the experimental conditions which give a simple interpretation are not realized, and, consequently, the numbers obtained cannot be taken as representing the measurement of the total radiation; they merely point to a rough approximation.

Complex Nature of the Radiation

The researches of various physicists (M.M. Becquerel, Meyer and von Schweidler, Giesel, Villard, Rutherford, M. and Mme Curie) have proved the complex nature of the radiation of radioactive bodies. It will be convenient to specify three kinds of rays, which I shall denote, according to the notation adopted by Mr. Rutherford, by the letters α, β, γ.

I.   The α are very slightly penetrating, and appear to constitute the principal part of the radiation. These rays are characterized by the laws by which they are absorbed by matter. The magnetic field acts very slightly upon them, and they were formerly thought to be quite unaffected by the action of this field. However, in a strong magnetic field, the α-rays are slightly deflected; the deflection is caused in the same manner as with cathode rays, but the direction of the deflection is reversed; it is the same as for the canal rays of the Crookes tubes.

II.   The β-rays are less absorbable as a whole than the preceding ones. They are deflected by a magnetic field in the same manner and direction as cathode rays.

III.   The γ-rays are penetrating rays, unaffected by the magnetic field, and comparable to Röntgen rays.

Consider the following imaginary experiment: Some radium, R, is placed at the bottom of a small deep cavity, hollowed in a block of lead, P [see Figure]. A sheaf of rays, rectilinear and slightly expanded, streams from the receptacle. Let us suppose that a strong uniform magnetic field is established in the neighborhood of the receptacle, normal to the plane of the figure and directed toward the back. The three groups of rays, α, β, γ, will now be separated. Then rather faint γ-rays continue in their straight path without a trace of deviation. The β-rays are deflected in the manner of cathode rays, and describe circular paths in the plane of the figure. If the receptacle is placed on a photographic plate, A C, the portion, B C, of the plate which receives the β-rays is acted upon. Lastly, the α-rays form a very intense shaft which is slightly deflected, and which is soon absorbed by the air. These rays describe in the plane of the figure a path of great curvature, the direction of the deflection being the reverse of that with the β-rays.

If the receptacle is covered with a thin sheet of aluminum (0.1 mm. thick), the α-rays are suppressed almost entirely, the β-rays are lessened, and the γ-rays do not appear to be absorbed to any great extent.

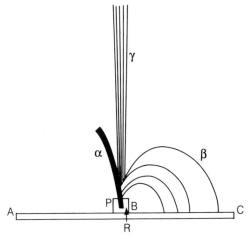

Exercises and Projects

CHECKING YOUR COMPREHENSION

1. What criteria does Curie use to determine the level of intensity of a radioactive substance?

2. How does radium radiation differ from uranium radiation?

3. What are the essential differences among alpha, beta, and gamma radiation?

FOR DISCUSSION AND DEBATE

1. Who is likely to be Curie's audience for this piece? Why?

2. As with most formal scientific writing, Curie's treatise on radio-activity is impersonal in the sense that the author does not refer to herself in the first person, nor does she attempt to be lively or to add color to the facts. Discuss the possible reasons for this. Do you think that the impersonal voice makes for more or less interesting reading?

FOR YOUR NOTEBOOK

1. Observe a chemistry experiment and jot down details of the procedure. Ask the experimenter to explain the reason behind each step if you do not understand it.

2. Marie Curie and her husband, Pierre, were one of the most successful collaborative teams in the history of science. Read Marie Curie's biography to determine what may have contributed to their ability to work productively together. Record your assumptions in your notebook.

FOR WRITING

1. Science is very largely a collaborative effort. Even scientists working alone must be continually aware of what others in the field are doing. Marie Curie worked very closely with her husband and several other physicists and chemists (especially

Rutherford and Becquerel). Write a critical essay on the details of this collaborative research into the properties of radiation. For example, did those involved work together on each task, or did they work separately, meeting frequently to discuss the results with each other?

2. Writing, too, is frequently collaborative, especially when writers are learning their craft. You have probably experienced this already in your writing classes: You and your classmates exchange drafts of essays-in-progress and respond to the draft's clarity, organization, development, and so on. Receiving such reader response is enormously helpful when preparing a revision.

   Collaboration also means working together on a single project (this is the common meaning of the term) or assisting one another with separate projects. Using one of these two modes of collaboration (check your choice with your instructor), write a biographical essay on one of the pioneers of radioactivity other than Marie and Pierre Curie. Becquerel, Wilhelm Röntgen, Rutherford, and the second generation of Curies—Irène and Frédéric Joliot-Curie—are possible choices.

3. Prepare a report entitled "The Nature of _____." Limit your scope to analyzing one substance or energy source encountered in a science lab or through your own research. Possible topics: infrared or ultraviolet radiation, static electricity, dry ice, heavy water (deuterium). Use the following format in preparing your report:

   I. Introduction
      A. Purpose
      B. Description of the procedure (overview)
      C. Equipment and materials needed
   II. Step-by-step procedure (including measurements and calculations)
   III. Conclusion (discussion of results, implications for further research)

Einstein has done more to revolutionize our understanding of nature than any other scientist. $E = mc^2$, perhaps the most famous formula of all time, reveals the astonishing fact that mass *is equivalent to* energy when multiplied by the square of the speed of light. It explains why the sun (and every star in the universe) "shines" (that is, radiates energy in a sustained thermonuclear reaction) as well as why atomic bombs work so devastatingly well.

Mass-energy equivalence is just one aspect of a theory of dynamics (the physics of movement) known as relativity—a term that is in nearly everyone's vocabulary but is often imperfectly understood outside of physics. One frequently overhears, for example, the statement that "everything is relative"—all too often an excuse for selfishly pursuing one's own wishes. But as Bertrand Russell points out in one of the most popular presentations of relativity theory, *The ABC of Relativity* (1925), such an assertion "is of course, nonsense, because if *everything* were relative, there would be nothing for it to be relative to."

Einstein's Theory of Relativity is actually two theories: the Special Theory (1905) and the General Theory (1916). The Special Theory focuses on the relationship between matter and motion, showing that a body's mass and temporal duration are *relative* to that body's velocity and are not absolute constants as assumed by Newtonian mechanics. At first, this seems to shatter common sense. According to the Special Theory, if one of two bodies possessing identical mass at rest begins to move, its mass and its duration will increase (in others words, it will get heavier and its time will go slower) *relative to the body remaining at rest.* Relative to itself, the moving body will not detect any change whatsoever. The limit to such an increase is set by the velocity of light (186,200 miles per second—which happens to be the absolute speed limit in our universe).

Special Relativity, then, demonstrates that there can be no single absolute system of time-based or space-based measurement for *all* moving bodies in the universe, as Newton supposed. In an Einsteinian universe, any description of a given body's dynamics must be relative to an external frame of reference. As you read this you are motionless in your chair, but *motionless* is a relative term. You are motionless relative to the chair and the floor on which the chair rests. But relative to the earth's axis, around which you and the ground are rotating, your speed is about 1000 miles per hour. Relative to the sun, around which you and the earth are revolving, you are moving at nearly 10,000 miles an hour. And so it goes: The entire solar system is moving through the galaxy, the galaxy is rotating on its axis and moving through space.

The General Theory of Relativity, by contrast, shifts focus from the dynamics of moving bodies to the perplexing phenomenon of gravitational attraction in the universe. For centuries, scientists could not understand how a body such as the earth could exert a force "at a distance." For Einstein, such a description of gravity seemed wrong. He reasoned that a body's inertia, its resistance to motion when it is accelerating, feels no different from gravitational attraction. The earth moving through space, just like a rocket through the atmosphere, generates inertia; the larger the body, the greater the inertia. But to say that gravity and inertia are two aspects of the same force still does not explain how the earth can exert an influence on the moon (or the moon on the earth by way of tides). Einstein's answer is mind boggling: Gravity is not a force but a field; it affects and "warps" the very space it inhabits. Think of a large sheet of rubber, stretched taut, on which are placed iron balls of different sizes. The larger the ball, the deeper the warp it will make in the rubber sheet. The sheet is analogous to space. Of course it is necessary to adjust our usual concept of space. As Einstein explains in his Note to the fifteenth edition of *Relativity: The Special and the General Theory* (1952), "Physical objects are not *in space,* but *spatially extended.* In this way the concept 'empty space' loses its meaning."

In the following selection, Einstein discusses the relationship between gravity and acceleration.

TERMS TO LEARN

magnetic field: the region of space in which magnetic force exerts its influence

inertia: the tendency of an object to remain at rest until it is overcome by an external force. Inertia can also be described as an object's resistance to motion.

mass: in physics, the total amount of matter in an object, which is measured in terms of its relation to inertia

ALBERT EINSTEIN

 The General Theory of Relativity

The Gravitational Field

"If we pick up a stone and then let it go, why does it fall to the ground?" The usual answer to this question is: "Because it is attracted by the earth." Modern physics formulates the answer rather differently for the following reason. As a result of the more careful study of electromagnetic phenomena, we have come to regard action at a distance as a process impossible without the intervention of some intermediary medium. If, for instance, a magnet attracts a piece of iron, we cannot be content to regard this as meaning that the magnet acts directly on the iron through the intermediate empty space, but we are constrained to imagine—after the manner of Faraday—that the magnet always calls into being something physically real in the space around it, that something being what we call a "magnetic field." In its turn this magnetic field operates on the piece of iron, so that the latter strives to move towards the magnet. We shall not discuss here the justification for this incidental conception, which is indeed a somewhat arbitrary one. We shall only mention that with its aid electromagnetic phenomena can be theoretically represented much more satisfactorily than without it, and this applies particularly to the transmission of electromagnetic waves. The effects of gravitation also are regarded in an analogous manner.

The action of the earth on the stone takes place indirectly. The earth produces in its surroundings a gravitational field, which acts on the stone and produces its motion of fall. As we know from experience, the intensity of the action on a body diminishes according to a quite definite law, as we proceed farther and farther away from the earth. From our point of view this means: The law governing the properties of the gravitational field in space must be a perfectly definite one, in order correctly to represent the diminution of gravitational action with the distance from operative bodies. It is something like this: The body (for example, the earth) produces a field in its immediate neighborhood directly; the intensity and direction of the field at points farther removed from the body are thence determined by the law which governs the properties in space of the gravitational fields themselves.

In contrast to electric and magnetic fields, the gravitational field exhibits a most remarkable property, which is of fundamental importance for what follows. Bodies which are moving under the sole influence of a gravitational field receive an acceleration, *which does not in the least depend either on the material or on the physical state of the body.* For instance, a piece of lead and a piece of wood fall in exactly the same manner in a gravitational field (*in vacuo*[1]), when they start off from rest or with the same initial velocity. This law, which holds most accurately, can be expressed in a different form in the light of the following consideration.

According to Newton's law of motion, we have

$$(\text{Force}) = (\text{inertial mass}) \times (\text{acceleration})$$

where the "inertial mass" is a characteristic constant of the accelerated body. If now gravitation is the cause of the acceleration, we then have

$$(\text{Force}) = (\text{gravitational mass}) \times (\text{intensity of the gravitational field})$$

where the "gravitational mass" is likewise a characteristic constant for the body. From these two relations follows:

$$(\text{acceleration}) = \frac{(\text{gravitational mass})}{(\text{inertia mass})} \times (\text{intensity of the gravitational field})$$

If now, as we find from experience, the acceleration is to be independent of the nature and the condition of the body and always the same for a given gravitational field, then the ratio of the gravitational to the inertial mass must likewise be the same for all bodies. By a suitable choice of units we can thus make this ratio equal to unity. We then have the following law: The *gravitational* mass of a body is equal to its *inertial* mass.

It is true that this important law had hitherto been recorded in mechanics, but it had not been *interpreted.* A satisfactory interpretation can be obtained only if we recognize the following fact: *The same* quality of a body manifests itself according to circumstances as "inertia" or as "weight" (literally, "heaviness"). In the following section we shall show to what extent this is actually the case, and how this question is connected with the general postulate of relativity.

The Equality of Inertial and Gravitational Mass as an Argument for the General Postulate of Relativity

We imagine a large portion of empty space, so far removed from stars and other appreciable masses, that we have before us approxi-

[1]In a vacuum. [Ed.]

mately the conditions required by the fundamental law of Galilei. It is then possible to choose a Galilean reference-body for this part of space (world), relative to which points at rest remain at rest and points in motion continue permanently in uniform rectilinear motion. As reference-body let us imagine a spacious chest resembling a room with an observer inside who is equipped with apparatus. Gravitation naturally does not exist for this observer. He must fasten himself with strings to the floor, otherwise the slightest impact against the floor will cause him to rise slowly towards the ceiling of the room.

To the middle of the lid of the chest is fixed externally a hook with rope attached, and now a "being" (what kind of a being is immaterial to us) begins pulling at this with a constant force. The chest together with the observer then begin to move "upward" with a uniformly accelerated motion. In course of time their velocity will reach unheard-of values—provided that we are viewing all this from another reference-body which is not being pulled with a rope.

But how does the man in the chest regard the the process? The acceleration of the chest will be transmitted to him by the reaction of the floor of the chest. He must therefore take up this pressure by means of his legs if he does not wish to be laid out full length on the floor. He is then standing in the chest in exactly the same way as anyone stands in a room of a house on our earth. If he releases a body which he previously had in his hand, the acceleration of the chest will no longer be transmitted to this body, and for this reason the body will approach the floor of the chest with an accelerated relative motion. The observer will further convince himself *that the acceleration of the body toward the floor of the chest is always of the same magnitude, whatever kind of body he may happen to use for the experiment.*

Relying on his knowledge of the gravitational field (as it was discussed in the preceding section), the man in the chest will thus come to the conclusion that he and the chest are in a gravitational field which is constant with regard to time. Of course he will be puzzled for a moment as to why the chest does not fall in this gravitational field. Just then, however, he discovers the hook in the middle of the lid of the chest and the rope which is attached to it, and he consequently comes to the conclusion that the chest is suspended at rest in the gravitational field.

Ought we to smile at the man and say that he errs in his conclusion? I do not believe we ought to if we wish to remain consistent; we must rather admit that his mode of grasping the situation violates neither reason nor known mechanical laws. Even though it is being accelerated with respect to the "Galilean space" first considered, we can nevertheless regard the chest as being at rest. We have thus good grounds for extending the principle of relativity to include bodies of reference which are accelerated with respect to each other, and as a result we have gained a powerful argument for a generalized postulate of relativity.

We must note carefully that the possibility of this mode of interpretation rests on the fundamental property of the gravitational field of giving all bodies the same acceleration, or, what comes to the same thing, on the law of the equality of inertial and gravitational mass. If this natural law did not exist, the man in the accelerated chest would not be able to interpret the behavior of the bodies around him on the supposition of a gravitational field, and he would not be justified on the grounds of experience in supposing his reference-body to be "at rest."

Suppose that the man in the chest fixes a rope to the inner side of the lid, and that he attaches a body to the free end of the rope. The result of this will be to stretch the rope so that it will hang "vertically" downwards. If we ask for an opinion of the cause of tension in the rope, the man in the chest will say: "The suspended body experiences a downward force in the gravitational field, and this is neutralized by the tension of the rope; what determines the magnitude of the tension of the rope is the *gravitational mass* of the suspended body." On the other hand, an observer who is poised freely in space will interpret the condition of things thus: "The rope must perforce take part in the accelerated motion of the chest, and it transmits this motion to the body attached to it. The tension of the rope is just large enough to effect the acceleration of the body. That which determines the magnitude of the tension of the rope is the *inertial mass* of the body." Guided by this example, we see that our extension of the principle of relativity implies the *necessity* of the law of the equality of inertial and gravitational mass. Thus we have obtained a physical interpretation of this law.

Exercises and Projects

CHECKING YOUR COMPREHENSION

1. Summarize the relationship Einstein established between a gravitational field and a magnetic field.

2. Why is it possible to equate gravity with inertia?

3. What is the usual clue we get that tells us we are experiencing acceleration rather than gravity? In what way can this clue mislead us in our understanding of the nature of acceleration?

FOR DISCUSSION AND DEBATE

1. Einstein often uses analogy to illustrate his points. Describe the major analogies used in this selection and discuss how they make the concepts more understandable.

2. Why is it an error to think of gravity as a force—as action at a distance?

3. In what way are Michael Faraday's experiments with electromagnetism important to Einstein's General Theory of Relativity?

4. What are the key differences between the Special and the General Theories of Relativity? How do the two theories interrelate?

FOR YOUR NOTEBOOK

1. Einstein is the most celebrated scientist of the twentieth century. What may have been the factors that led to this universal adulation?

2. *Relativity* is a common and often misused word these days. Record the different uses of the word as you encounter them. After a while, look over these different uses and decide which ones seriously distort the original scientific meaning.

3. What other scientific words have had a fate similar to *relativity*? Keep a running list of them, along with their various meanings, in your notebook.

FOR WRITING

1. Some of the tenets in both the Special and the General Theories of Relativity have been verified by experiments. For example, according to the General Theory, a beam of light would be bent ever so slightly by an intense gravitational field. During an

eclipse of the sun one year, scientists observed that light from a star that became visible during the eclipse was indeed influenced by the sun's gravity and to the degree predicted by Einstein. In a short report, describe one or two of these experiments in detail.

2. Write an essay on the impact that relativity physics has had on some aspect of modern culture, such as modern art, literature, religion, law, or psychology. To what extent has the scientific concept been distorted in this area (if at all)?

3. In developing his theories of relativity, Einstein made use of the work of several other scientists and mathematicians, including Hendrik Lorentz, Henri Poincaré, and Hermann Minkowski. For a term project, research the contributions of these other scientists and present your findings in a well-documented six- to eight-page paper. Suggestion: Begin by reading introductory articles on relativity in general scientific reference works such as *The Dictionary of the History of Science.*

Freud may well be the most misunderstood of all revolutionary scientific thinkers, as a recent study by the famous child psychologist Bruno Bettelheim, *Freud and Man's Soul* (1982), makes clear. The common assumption that Freudian psychology ties all human endeavor to a sex drive or that it portrays the mind as a mere mechanism is false and injurious. Freud instead strove to help people understand enough of the workings of their unconscious drives to be able to control them. But this in no way suggested that the nature of those drives was simple or fully understandable. As a case in point, Freud used the term *erotic* specifically to invoke the mythic god of love, Eros. Bettelheim explains:

> For most readers who, like Freud, were steeped in the classic tradition, words such as *Eros* and *erotic* called up Eros's charm and cunning and—perhaps more important—his deep love for Psyche, the soul, to whom Eros is wedded in everlasting love and devotion.... To view Eros ... as grossly sexual or monstrous is an error that, according to the myth, can lead to catastrophe. In order for sexual love to be an experience of true erotic pleasure, it must be imbued with beauty (symbolized by Eros) and express the longings of the soul (symbolized by Psyche).

No facet of psychoanalysis is more fascinating to the public than the nature of dreams, and understandably so. Dreams are beautifully complex symbolic dramas that our mind constructs out of the raw material of daily life, much of which calls into play subconscious drives that our rational mind has difficulty acknowledging. It was Freud's aim to guide his patients in interpreting their dreams so that they could understand and control their own impulses better.

In the following selection, originally one of twenty-eight lectures delivered at the University of Vienna between 1915 and 1917, Freud explains the nature of dream "censorship"—that is, how a dream disguises a subconscious desire or fear through ordinary symbols.

TERMS TO LEARN

libido: a fundamental source of psychic energy, manifested as sexual desire

ego: popular usage has all but buried Freud's original psychoanalytic meaning, which is: that facet of the human psyche that experiences the external world by way of the senses and shapes rational thought. The ego also resolves tensions between the id (the source of raw impulses) and the superego (that part of the psyche that demands restraint, moral rectitude, and order).

SIGMUND FREUD

 The Dream-Censorship

Ladies and gentlemen, the study of the dreams of children has taught us the origin, the essential nature and the function of dreams. *Dreams are things which get rid of (psychical) stimuli disturbing to sleep, by the method of hallucinatory satisfaction.* We have, however, only been able to explain one group of the dreams of adults—those which we have described as dreams of an infantile type. What the facts are about the others we cannot yet say, but we do not understand them. We have arrived at a provisional finding, however, whose importance we must not underestimate. Whenever a dream has been completely intelligible to us, it has turned out to be the hallucinated fulfillment of a wish. This coincidence cannot be a chance one nor a matter of indifference.

We have assumed of dreams of another sort, on the basis of various considerations and on the analogy of our views on parapraxes, that they are a distorted substitute for an unknown content, and that the first thing is to trace them back to it. Our immediate task, then, is an enquiry which will lead to an understanding of this *distortion in dreams.*

Dream-distortion is what makes a dream seem strange and unintelligible to us. We want to know a number of things about it: firstly, where it comes from—its dynamics—, secondly, what it does and, lastly, how it does it. We can also say that dream-distortion is carried out by the dream-work; and we want to describe the dream-work and trace it back to the forces operating in it.

And now listen to this dream. It was recorded by a lady belonging to our group,[1] and, as she tells us, was derived from a highly-esteemed and cultivated elderly lady. No analysis was made of the dream; our informant remarks that for a psychoanalyst it needs no interpreting. Nor did the dreamer herself interpret it, but she judged

[1]Frau Dr. von Hug-Hellmuth.

it and condemned it as though she understood how to interpret it;
for she said of it: "And disgusting, stupid stuff like this was dreamt
by a woman of fifty, who has no other thoughts day and night but
worry about her child!"

Here then, is the dream—which deals with "love services" in
wartime.[2]

> *She went to Garrison Hospital No. I and informed the sentry at the
> gate that she must speak to the Chief Medical Officer (mentioning a
> name that was unknown to her) as she wanted to volunteer for service
> at the hospital. She pronounced the word service in such a way that the
> N.C.O. at once understood that she meant "love service." Since she was
> an elderly lady, after some hesitation he allowed her to pass. Instead of
> finding the Chief Medical Officer, however, she reached a large and
> gloomy apartment in which a number of officers and army doctors
> were standing and sitting round a long table. She approached a staff
> surgeon with her request, and he understand her meaning after she
> had said only a few words. The actual wording of her speech in the
> dream was: "I and many other women and girls in Vienna are ready
> to. . . " at this point in the dream her words turned into a mumble ". . .
> for the troops—officers and other ranks without distinction." She could
> tell from the expressions on the officers' faces, partly embarrassed and
> partly sly, that everyone had understood her meaning correctly. The
> lady went on: "I'm aware that our decision must sound surprising, but
> we mean it in bitter earnest. No one asks a soldier in the field whether
> he wishes to die or not." There followed an awkward silence of some
> minutes. The staff surgeon then put his arm round her waist and said:
> "Suppose, madam, it actually came to . . . (mumble)." She drew away
> from him, thinking to herself: "He's like all the rest of them," and
> replied: "Good gracious, I'm an old woman and I might never come
> to that. Besides, there's one condition that must be observed: age must
> be respected. It must never happen that an elderly woman . . . (mum-
> ble) . . . a mere boy. That would be terrible." "I understand perfectly,"
> replied the staff surgeon. Some of the officers, and among them one
> who had been a suitor of hers in her youth, laughed out loud. The lady
> then asked to be taken to the Chief Medical Officer, with whom she was
> acquainted, so that the whole matter could be thrashed out; but she
> found, to her consternation, that she could not recall his name.
> Nevertheless, the staff surgeon, most politely and respectfully, showed
> her the way up to the second floor by a very narrow, iron, spiral
> staircase, which led directly from the room to the upper storeys of the
> building. As she went up she heard an officer say: "That's a tremendous
> decision to make—no matter whether a woman's young or old!
> Splendid of her!" Feeling simply that she was doing her duty, she
> walked up an interminable staircase.*

[2]*Liebesdienste* means in the first instance "services performed for love," i.e., "unre-
munerated services"; but it could bear another, less respectable, meaning. [Ed.]

The dream was repeated twice in the course of a few weeks, with, as the lady remarked, some quite unimportant and meaningless modifications.

From its continuous nature, the dream resembles a daytime fantasy: there are few breaks in it, and some of the details of its content could have been explained if they had been enquired into, but that, as you know, was not done. But what is remarkable and interesting from our point of view is that the dream shows several gaps—gaps not in the dreamer's memory of the dream but in the content of the dream itself. At three points the content was, as it were, extinguished; the speeches in which these gaps occurred were interrupted by a mumble. As no analysis was carried out, we have, strictly speaking, no right to say anything about the sense of the dream. Nevertheless there are hints on which conclusions can be based (for instance, in the phrase "love services"); but above all, the portions of the speeches immediately preceding the mumbles call for the gaps to be filled in, and in an unambiguous manner. If we make the insertions, the content of the fantasy turns out to be that the dreamer is prepared, by way of fulfilling a patriotic duty, to put herself at the disposal of the troops, both officers and other ranks, for the satisfaction of their erotic needs. This is, or course, highly objectionable, the model of a shameless libidinal fantasy—but it does not appear in the dream at all. Precisely at the points at which the context would call for this admission, the manifest dream contains an indistinct mumble: something has been lost or suppressed.

You will, I hope, think it plausible to suppose that it was precisely the objectionable nature of these passages that was the motive for their suppression. Where shall we find a parallel to such an event? You need not look far in these days. Take up any political newspaper and you will find that here and there the text is absent and in its place nothing except the white paper is to be seen. This, as you know, is the work of the press censorship. In these empty places there was something that displeased the higher censorship authorities and for that reason it was removed—a pity, you feel, since no doubt it was the most interesting thing in the paper—the "best bit."

On other occasions the censorship has not gone to work on a passage *after* it has already been completed. The author has seen in advance which passages might expect to give rise to objections from the censorship and has on that account toned them down in advance, modified them slightly, or has contented himself with approximations and allusions to what would genuinely have come from his pen. In that case there are no blank places in the paper, but circumlocutions and obscurities of expression appearing at certain points will enable you to guess where regard has been paid to the censorship in advance.

Well, we can keep close to this parallel. It is our view that the omitted pieces of the speeches in the dream which were concealed by a mumble have likewise been sacrificed to a censorship. We speak in so many words of *"dream-censorship,"* to which some share in dream-distortion is to be attributed. Wherever there are gaps in the manifest dream the dream-censorship is responsible for them. We should go further, and regard it as a manifestation of the censorship wherever a dream-element is remembered especially faintly, indefinitely and doubtfully among other elements that are more clearly constructed. But it is only rarely that this censorship manifests itself so undisguisedly—no naively, one might say—as in this example of the dream of "love services." The censorship takes effect much more frequently according to the second method, by producing softenings, approximations and allusions instead of the genuine thing.

I know of no parallel in the operations of the press-censorship to a third manner of working by the dream-censorship; but I am able to demonstrate it from precisely the one example of a dream which we have analysed so far. You will recall the dream of the "three bad theater tickets for one florin and a half." In the latent thoughts of that dream the element "over-hurriedly, too early" stood in the foreground. Thus: it was absurd to marry so *early*—it was also absurd to take the theater tickets so *early*—it was ridiculous of the sister-in-law to part with her money in such a *hurry* to buy jewelry with it. Nothing of this central element of the dream-thoughts passed over into the manifest dream; in it the central position is taken by the "going to the theater" and "taking the tickets." As a result of this displacement of accent, this fresh grouping of the elements of the content, the manifest dream has become so unlike the latent dream-thoughts that no-one would suspect the presence of the latter behind the former. This displacement of accent is one of the chief instruments of dream-distortion and it is what gives the dream the strangeness on account of which the dreamer himself is not inclined to recognize it as his own production.

Omission, modification, fresh grouping of the material—these, then, are the activities of the dream-censorship and the instruments of dream-distortion. The dream-censorship itself is the originator, or one of the originators, of the dream-distortion which we are now engaged in examining. We are in the habit of combining the concepts of modification and rearrangement under the term "displacement."

After these remarks on the activities of the dream-censorship, we will now turn to its dynamics. I hope you do not take the term too anthropomorphically, and do not picture the "censor of dreams" as a severe little manikin or a spirit living in a closet in the brain and there discharging his office; but I hope too that you do not take the term in too "localizing" a sense, and do not think of a "brain center," from which a censoring influence of this kind issues, an influence which would be brought to an end if the "center" were damaged or removed. For the time being it is nothing more than a serviceable term for describing a dynamic relation. The word does not prevent our asking by what purposes this influence is exercised and against what purposes it is directed. And we shall not be surprised to learn that we have come up against the dream-censorship once already, though perhaps without recognizing it.

For that is in fact the case. You will recall that when we began to make use of our technique of free association we made a surprising discovery. We became aware that our efforts at proceeding from the dream-element to the unconscious element for which it is a substitute were being met by a *resistance.* This resistance, we said, could be of different magnitudes, sometimes enormous and sometimes quite insignificant. In the latter case we need to pass through only a small number of intermediate links in our work of interpretation; but when the resistance is large we have to traverse long chains of associations from the dream-element, we are led far away from it and on our path we have to overcome all the difficulties which represent themselves as critical objections to the ideas that occur. What we met with as resistance in our work of interpretation must now be introduced into the dream-work in the form of the dream-censorship. The resistance to interpretation is only a putting into effect of the dream-censorship. It also proves to us that the force of the censorship is not exhausted in bringing about the distortion of dreams and thereafter extinguished, but that the censorshp persists as a permanent institution which has as its aim the maintenance of the distortion. Moreover, just as the strength of the resistance varies in the interpretation of each element in a dream, so too the magnitude of the distortion introduced by the censorship varies for each element in the same dream. If we compare the manifest and the latent dream, we shall find that some particular latent elements have been completely eliminated, others modified to a greater or less extent, while yet others have been carried over into the manifest content of the dream unaltered or even perhaps strengthened.

But we wanted to enquire what are the purposes which exercise the censorship and against what purposes it is directed. Now this question, which is fundamental for the understanding of dreams and perhaps, indeed, of human life, is easy to answer if we look through the series of dreams which have been interpreted. The purposes which exercise the censorship are those which are acknowledged by the dreamer's waking judgment, those with which he feels himself at one. You may be sure that if you reject an interpretation of one of your own dreams which has been correctly carried out, you are doing so for the same motives for which the dream-censorship has been exercised, the dream-distortion brought about and the interpretation made necessary. Take the dream of our fifty-year-old lady. She thought her dream disgusting without having analyzed it, and she would have been still more indignant if Dr. von Hug-Hellmuth had told her anything of its inevitable interpretation; it was precisely because of this condemnation by the dreamer that the objectionable passages in her dream were replaced by a mumble.

The purposes *against* which the dream-censorship is directed must be described in the first instance from the point of view of that agency itself. If so, one can only say that they are invariably of a reprehensible nature, repulsive from the ethical, aesthetic and social point of view—matters of which one does not venture to think at all or thinks only with disgust. These wishes, which are censored and given a distorted expression in dreams, are first and foremost manifestations of an unbridled and ruthless egoism. And, to be sure, the dreamer's own ego appears in every dream and plays the chief part in it, even if it knows quite well how to hide itself so far as the manifest content goes. This *sacro egoismo* of dreams is certainly not unrelated to the attitude we adopt when we sleep, which consists in our withdrawing our interest from the whole external world.

The ego, freed from all ethical bonds, also finds itself at one with all the demands of sexual desire, even those which have long been condemned by our aesthetic upbringing and those which contradict all the requirements of moral restraint. The desire for pleasure—the libido, as we call it—chooses its objects without inhibition, and by preference, indeed, the forbidden ones: not only other men's wives, but above all incestuous objects, objects sanctified by the common agreement of mankind, a man's mother and sister, a woman's father and brother. (The dream of our fifty-year-old lady, too, was incestuous; her libido was unmistakably directed to her son.) Lusts which we think of as remote from human nature show themselves strong enough to provoke dreams. Hatred, too, rages without restraint. Wishes for revenge and death directed against those who are nearest and dearest in waking life, against the dreamer's parents, brothers and sisters, husband or wife, and his own children are nothing unusual. These censored wishes appear to rise up out of a positive

Hell; after they have been interpreted when we are awake, no censorship of them seems to us too severe.

But you must not blame the dream itself on account of its evil content. Do not forget that it performs the innocent and indeed useful function of preserving sleep from disturbance. This wickedness is not part of the essential nature of dreams. Indeed you know too that there are dreams which can be recognized as the satisfaction of justified wishes and of pressing bodily needs. These, it is true, have no dream-distortion; but they have no need of it, for they can fulfil their function without insulting the ethical and aesthetic purposes of the ego. Bear in mind, too, that dream-distortion is proportionate to two factors. On the one hand it becomes greater the worse the wish that has to be censored; but on the other hand it also becomes greater the more severe the demands of the censorship at the moment. Thus a strictly brought-up and prudish young girl, with a relentless censorship, will distort dream-impulses which we doctors, for instance, would have to regard as permissible, harmless, libidinal wishes, and on which in ten years' time the dreamer herself will make the same judgement.

Furthermore, we have not got nearly far enough yet to be able to feel indignant at this result of our work of interpretation. We do not yet, I think, understand it properly; but our first duty is to defend it against certain aspersions. There is no difficulty in finding a weak point in it. Our dream-interpretations are made on the basis of the premises which we have already accepted—that dreams in general have a sense, that it is legitimate to carry across from hypnotic to normal sleep the fact of the existence of mental processes which are at the time unconscious, and that everything that occurs to the mind is determined. If on the basis of these premises we had arrived at plausible findings from dream-interpretation, we should have been justified in concluding that the premises were valid. But how about it if these findings seem to be as I have pictured them? We should then be tempted to say: "These are impossible, senseless or at the least most improbable findings; so there was something wrong about the premises. Either dreams are not physical phenomena, or there is nothing unconscious in the normal state, or our technique has a flaw in it. Is it not simpler and more satisfactory to suppose this rather than accept all the abominations which we are supposed to have discovered on the basis of our premises?"

Yes, indeed! Both simpler and more satisfactory—but not necessarily on that account more correct. Let us give ourselves time: the matter is not yet ripe for judgment. And first, we can further strengthen the criticism of our dream-interpretations. The fact that the findings from them are so disagreeable and repellent need not, perhaps, carry very great weight. A stronger argument is that the dreamers to whom we are led to attribute such wishful purposes by the interpretation of their dreams reject them most emphatically and for good reasons. "What?" says one of them, "you want to convince me from this dream that I regret the money I have spent on my sister's dowry and my brother's education? But that cannot be so. I work entirely for my brothers and sisters; I have no other interest in life but to fulfill my duties to them, which, as the eldest of the family, I promised our departed mother I would do." Or a woman dreamer would say: "You think I wish my husband was dead? That is a shocking piece of nonsense! It is not only that we are most happily married—you would probably not believe me if I said that—but his death would rob me of everything I possess in the world." Or another man would answer us: "You say that I have sensual desires for my sister? That is ridiculous! She means nothing at all to me. We are on bad terms with each other and I have not exchanged a word with her for years." We might still take it lightly, perhaps, if these dreamers neither confirmed nor denied the purposes we attribute to them; we might say that these were just things they did not know about themselves. But when they feel in themselves the precise contrary of the wish we have interpreted to them and when they are able to prove to us by the lives they lead that they are dominated by this contrary wish, it must surely take us aback. Has not the time come to throw aside the whole work we have done on dream-interpretation as something which its findings have reduced *ad absurdum*?[3]

No, not even now. Even this stronger argument collapses if we examine it critically. Granted that there are unconscious purposes in mental life, nothing is proved by showing that purposes opposed to these are dominant in conscious life. Perhaps there is room in the mind for contrary purposes, for contradictions, to exist side by side. Possibly, indeed, the dominance of one impulse is precisely a necessary condition of its contrary being unconscious. We are after all left, then, with the first objections that were raised: the findings of dream-interpretation are not simple and they are very disagreeable. We may reply to the first that all your passion for what is simple will not be able to solve a single one of the problems of dreams. You must get accustomed here to assuming a complicated state of affairs. And we may reply to the second that you are plainly wrong to use a liking

---

[3]Disproof of a theorem by showing its absurdity when taken to its logical conclusion. [Ed.]

or disliking that you may feel as the ground for a scientific judgment. What difference does it make if the findings of dream-interpretation seem disagreeable to you or, indeed, embarrassing and repulsive? *Ça n'empêche pas d'exister,*[4] as I heard my teacher Charcot say in a similar case when I was a young doctor. One must be humble and hold back one's sympathies and antipathies if one wants to discover what is real in this world. If a physicist were able to prove to you that in a short period organic life on this earth would be brought to an end by freezing, would you venture to make the same reply to him: "That cannot be so, the prospect is too disagreeable?" You would, I think, be silent, until another physicist came and pointed out to the first one an error in his premises or calculations. When you reject something that is disagreeable to you, what you are doing is *repeating* the mechanism of constructing dreams rather than understanding it and surmounting it.

You will promise now, perhaps, to disregard the repellent character of the censored dream-wishes and will withdraw upon the argument that after all it is unlikely that such a large space should be given to the evil in the constitution of human beings. But do your own experiences justify your saying this? I will not discuss how you may appear to yourselves; but have you found so much benevolence among your superiors and competitors, so much chivalry among your enemies and so little envy in your social surroundings that you feel it your duty to protest against egoistic evil having a share in human nature? Are you not aware of how uncontrolled and untrustworthy the average person is in everything to do with sexual life? Or do you not know that all the transgressions and excesses of which we dream at night are daily committed in real life by waking men? What does psychoanalysis do here but confirm Plato's old saying that the good are those who are content to dream of what the others, the bad, really do?

And now turn your eyes away from individuals and consider the Great War which is still laying Europe waste. Think of the vast amount of brutality, cruelty and lies which are able to spread over the civilized world. Do you really believe that a handful of ambitious and deluding men without conscience could have succeeded in unleashing all these evil spirits if their millions of followers did not share their guilt? Do you venture, in such circumstances, to break a lance on behalf of the exclusion of evil from the mental constitution of mankind?

[4]French for "that doesn't keep it from existing." [Ed.]

You will represent to me that I am giving a one-sided judgment on the War: that it has also brought to light what is finest and noblest in men, their heroism, their self-sacrifice, their social sense. No doubt; but are you not now showing yourselves as accessories to the injustice that has so often been done to psychoanalysis in reproaching it with denying one thing because it has asserted another? It is not our intention to dispute the noble endeavors of human nature, nor have we ever done anything to detract from their value. On the contrary; I am exhibiting to you not only the evil dream-wishes which are censored but also the censorship, which suppresses them and makes them unrecognizable. We lay a stronger emphasis on what is evil in men only because other people disavow it and thereby make the human mind, not better, but incomprehensible. If now we give up this one-sided ethical valuation, we shall undoubtedly find a more correct formula for the relation between good and evil in human nature.

There it is, then. We need not give up the findings of our work on the interpretation of dreams even though we cannot but regard them as strange. Perhaps we shall be able to approach an understanding of them later from another direction. For the time being let us hold fast to this: dream-distortion is a result of the censorship which is exercised by recognized purposes of the ego against wishful impulses in any way objectionable that stir within us at night-time during our sleep. Why this should happen particularly at night-time and where these reprehensible wishes come from—these are matters on which, no doubt, much still remains for questioning and research.

But it would be unfair if we neglected at this point to emphasize sufficiently another outcome of our investigations. The dream-wishes which seek to disturb us in our sleep are unknown to us and indeed we only learnt of them through dream-interpretation. They are thus to be described, in the sense we have discussed, as unconscious for the time being. But we must reflect that they are unconscious too for more than the time being. The dreamer also disavows them, as we have seen in so many instances, after he has come to know them through the interpretation of his dream. We are then faced once again with the position we first came across in the "hiccoughing" slip of the tongue, where the proposer of the toast protested indignantly that neither then nor at any earlier time had he become conscious of any disrespectful impulse towards his Chief. Already at the time we felt some doubts about the weight of an assurance of this kind, and suggested instead the hypothesis that the speaker was permanently unaware of the presence of this impulse in him. This situation is repeated now with every interpretation of a strongly distorted dream and consequently gains an increased importance in its bearing on the view we have taken. We are now prepared to assume that there are in the mind processes and purposes of which one knows nothing at all, has known nothing for a long time, and has even perhaps never known anything. With this the unconscious acquires a new sense for us; the characteristic of "for the time being" or "temporary" disappears from its essential nature. It can mean *permanently* unconscious and not merely "latent at the time." We shall of course have to hear more about this on some other occasion.

Exercises and Projects

CHECKING YOUR COMPREHENSION

1. What does Freud mean by "distortion" in dreams, and how does it relate to dream censorship?

2. Freud describes three modes of dream censorship. Briefly describe each mode.

3. At one point Freud cautions his readers not to compare dream censorship too closely with literal, public censorship. Why not?

FOR DISCUSSION AND DEBATE

1. How effectively, in your opinion, does Freud answer opposing views to his theory of dream interpretation?

2. Freudian psychology has sometimes been criticized as undermining human dignity. Freud maintains (paragraph 24), "It is not our intention to dispute the noble endeavors of human nature." Debate this issue.

3. Do you agree or disagree with Freud when he says that "When you reject something that is disagreeable to you, what you are doing is *repeating* the mechanism of constructing dreams rather than understanding and surmounting it" (paragraph 21)?

FOR YOUR NOTEBOOK

1. Choose a particularly pleasant or unpleasant dream of yours and try to interpret it. Don't try to be conclusive; merely speculate on the possible links between the dream content and actual experience.

2. Ask your friends and relatives to tell you their dreams, and record them in your notebook, along with possible interpretations.

FOR WRITING

1. Discuss, in a short essay, the possible psychological benefits of dream interpretation. Why would one supposedly have better mental health by understanding what it is the dream mechanism distorts? Support your claims by referring to the reading.

2. Over the next few days, keep a dream journal. Immediately on awakening, record as much of your dreams as you remember. Important: Do not edit or censor anything. Write down everything that comes to mind.

   In a short essay, analyze your dreams, following Freud's approach as closely as possible. You may wish to read the additional chapters on dreams in *A General Introduction to Psychoanalysis* (1924) as well as *The Interpretation of Dreams* (1900; 8th ed., 1932; English revised ed., 1932) particularly Chapter 2, "The Method of Interpreting Dreams."

3. One of Freud's famous disciples—who later became a rival—is Carl Gustav Jung (1875–1961). The two psychologists differed in their interpretation of the nature of the unconscious, particularly in the interpretation of dreams. In several studies, later collected as *Dreams* (see Suggestions for Further Reading at the end of this section), Jung relates dream symbolism to the universal symbolism of myths and folklore. For a term project, examine the similarities and differences between Freud's and Jung's interpretation of dream symbolism.

To understand the magnitude of Heisenberg's contribution to modern physics, we need to imagine what the unbelievably small world of the atom is like. From the time of Democritus in the fifth century B.C., an "atom" was considered a fundamental unit of matter that could not be further divided (the word *atom* comes from the Greek *atomos,* meaning "undivided"). In 1911, Ernest Rutherford presented a more complex model: The atom consisted of even more minute particles—a positively charged nucleus and negatively charged orbiting electrons.

Even after the nucleus was further found to have protons and chargeless neutrons, the model of the atom was still fundamentally wrong. The problem was that on the atomic level, the laws of classical physics did not apply: electron orbits, unlike planets' orbits, did not decay. Physicists had to come up with a new theory of matter.

As it turned out, the electron, rather than being a charged, solid entity, was a cross between pure energy and matter—a matter-wave, or quantum of radiation. According to Max Planck, the physicist who formulated this new conception of radiation, energy is radiated *only* as quanta—in other words, as matter-wave particles. Mathematically, radiation can be treated as both a wave and as a particle; that is, as individual particlelike units of energy rather than as the pure wave radiation of classical mechanics.

Werner Heisenberg, who won the Nobel Prize for physics in 1932, made his great contribution of quantum mechanics in 1927 when he realized that the position and the velocity of a given electron—which in classical physics would constitute two entirely independent variables—could not be simultaneously predicted. The very act of determining an electron's velocity would affect its position and vice versa. The best that anyone could do would be to establish a probability figure for one variable or another. Heisenberg called this his *uncertainty principle,* and its implications were staggering: Indeterminacy was not merely the result of human limitations but existed in the very nature of matter.

In the following selection, Heisenberg gives lay readers a deeper insight into the uncertainty principle by placing it in a philosophical context.

TERMS TO LEARN

a priori: Immanuel Kant (1724–1804) stated that all of our knowledge is derived from the senses—that is, *a posteriori* ("that which comes later"). He also stated that the sources of this sense-derived knowledge are preestablished categories in the mind and are prior to all other forms of knowing—that is, cannot be derived empirically (from experience). These are what Kant calls *a priori* categories, and they include space, time, and causality (every effect is caused).

α [alpha] particle: a particle of radiation emitted by radioactive substances such as radium. It consists of two protons and will become an atom of helium if it encounters two electrons.

quantum theory: a theory that describes the action of subatomic particles, the properties of light, and the effect of radiation on matter. Max Planck laid the groundwork by discovering in 1900 that energy is absorbed into matter only in discrete units, which Planck called quanta.

WERNER HEISENBERG

 The Uncertainty Principle

Kant says that whenever we observe an event we assume that there is a foregoing event from which the other event must follow according to some rule. This is, as Kant states, the basis of all scientific work. In this discussion it is not important whether or not we can always find the foregoing event from which the other one followed. Actually we can find it in many cases. But even if we cannot, nothing can prevent us from asking what this foregoing event might have been and to look for it. Therefore, the law of causality is reduced to the method of scientific research; it is the condition which makes science possible. Since we actually apply this method, the law of causality is "a priori" and is not derived from experience.

Is this true in atomic physics? Let us consider a radium atom, which can emit an α-particle. The time for the emission of the α-particle cannot be predicted. We can only say that in the average the emission will take place in about two thousand years. Therefore, when we observe the emission we do not actually look for a foregoing event from which the emission must according to a rule follow. Logically it would be quite possible to look for such a foregoing event, and we need not be discouraged by the fact that hitherto none has been found. But why has the scientific method actually changed in this very fundamental question since Kant?

Two possible answers can be given to that question. The one is: We have been convinced by experience that the laws of quantum theory are correct and, if they are, we know that a foregoing event as cause for the emission at a given time cannot be found. The other answer is: We know the foregoing event, but not quite accurately. We know the forces in the atomic nucleus that are responsible for the emission of the α-particle. But this knowledge contains the uncertainty which is brought about by the interaction between the nucleus and the rest of the world. If we wanted to know why the α-particle was emitted at that particular time we would have to know the microscopic structure of the whole world including ourselves, and that is impossible. Therefore, Kant's arguments for the a priori character of the law of causality no longer apply.

A similar discussion could be given on the a priori character of space and time as forms of intuition. The result would be the same. The a priori concepts which Kant considered an undisputable truth are no longer contained in the scientific system of modern physics.

Still they form an essential part of this system in a somewhat different sense. In the discussion of the Copenhagen interpretation of quantum theory it has been emphasized that we use the classical concepts in describing our experimental equipment and more generally in describing that part of the world which does not belong to the object of the experiment. The use of these concepts, including space, time and causality, is in fact the condition for observing atomic events and is, in this sense of the word *a priori*. What Kant had not foreseen was that these a priori concepts can be the conditions for science and at the some time can have only a limited range of applicability. When we make an experiment we have to assume a causal chain of events that leads from the atomic event through the apparatus finally to the eye of the observer; if this causal chain was not assumed, nothing could be known about the atomic event. Still we must keep in mind that classical physics and causality have only a limited range of applicability. It was the fundamental paradox of quantum theory that could not be foreseen by Kant. Modern physics has changed Kant's statement about the possibility of synthetic judgments a priori from a metaphysical one into a practical one. The synthetic judgments a priori thereby have the character of a relative truth.

Exercises and Projects

CHECKING YOUR COMPREHENSION

1. Why is it necessary for Heisenberg to refer to Kant's notion of a priori in explaining the basis of the uncertainty principle?

2. According to Heisenberg, the finding of a cause to explain an observed effect is no longer the fundamental concern of science. Why not?

3. Why is it impossible ever to describe precisely the forces that cause the emission of an alpha particle?

4. In what way is Kant's notion of causality still applicable in science?

FOR DISCUSSION AND DEBATE

1. Not everyone was convinced of the ultimate indeterminacy of matter, Einstein included. "God," Einstein said, "does not play dice with the universe." Drawing from your understanding of the uncertainty principle, how valid is Einstein's comment?

2. Why do you suppose the a priori concepts that Kant considered beyond dispute no longer were within the boundaries of modern physics?

FOR YOUR NOTEBOOK

1. Try to articulate your own feelings about ultimate certainty or uncertainty. Since these are only notebook jottings, don't worry about organization, precision, or even consistency at this point. Your goal is to discover a point of view that seems to fit into your own sense of reality.

2. Quantum mechanics is still an evolving science. Look up non-specialized articles on new discoveries or on current research being conducted in the field; summarize the articles in your notebook.

FOR WRITING

1. Write an essay on the philosophical implications of the uncertainty principle, as you perceive them. Possible points to consider: Does the indeterminacy we encounter at the atomic level (microcosm) inevitably suggest that indeterminacy must exist in the larger world (macrocosm)? Is it even possible for human beings to make any conclusions about the ultimate nature of reality, since the very act of observation influences what is observed?

2. After reading an introduction to quantum theory, write an essay that profiles the contributions of one of the physicists, other than Heisenberg, associated with the theory. Possibilities include Max Planck, Neils Bohr, Erwin Schrödinger, and Louis de Broglie.

3. Create an imaginary dialogue between Heisenberg and, say, Einstein, who rejected indeterminacy ("God does not play dice with the universe," he once told Niels Bohr). You may begin with the following opening lines, or invent your own opening.

   EINSTEIN: I'll say it again, Werner, if we physicists find it impossible to predict when an atom is going to emit an alpha particle, that is our fault, not God's.

   HEISENBERG: Who said it was God's fault? I'm saying that *God's* laws are indeterminate.

   EINSTEIN: But that is absurd!

   HEISENBERG: Why should it be?

Before James Watson and Francis Crick revealed to the world in 1953 the structure, properties, and function of the DNA molecule, biologists did not understand how parents' genes were transmitted to offspring. Ever since Gregor Mendel's famous experiments with peas in 1865, the characteristics of trait distribution were understood. However, it wasn't until the 1940s when biologists realized that DNA (deoxyribonucleic acid), long known to be present in the nuclei of living cells, was what genes were built from. Other biologists attempted to determine molecular structure through a process known as X-ray crystallography. In 1951 Linus Pauling determined the helical (spiral) structure of a protein molecule; and finally in 1953 Watson and Crick—drawing from the work of Pauling and crystallographers W. L. Bragg, J. D. Bernal, and Rosalind Franklin—worked out the double-helical structure of the DNA molecule.

In the following excerpt from Watson's colorful memoir, *The Double Helix* (1968), we get a sense of the creative energy that researchers use to solve perplexing scientific puzzles. In this case, Watson is struggling to figure out how the base pairs of the four different nucleic acids in DNA fit together.

TERMS TO LEARN

hydrogen bond: hydrogen atoms that hold other elements together in a compound

adenine, thymine, guanine, cytosine: the four nucleic-acid bases that make up DNA

purine, pyrimidine: two contrasting types of DNA bases. Adenine and guanine are purines; cytosine and thymine are pyrimidines.

stereochemistry: the study of the three-dimensional structure of molecules, which often requires the construction of models

Jerry Donohue: an American crystallographer

Erwin Chargaff: the Austrian-American biochemist whose pioneering study of DNA in 1952 helped lay the groundwork for Watson and Crick's discovery

JAMES D. WATSON

 The DNA Puzzle: Finding How the Pieces Fit

I quickly cleared away the papers from my desktop so that I would have a large, flat surface on which to form pairs of bases held together by hydrogen bonds. Though I initially went back to my like-with-like prejudices, I saw all too well that they led nowhere. When Jerry came in I looked up, saw that it was not Francis, and began shifting the bases in and out of various other pairing possibilities. Suddenly I became aware that an adenine-thymine pair held together by two hydrogen bonds was identical in shape to a guanine-cytosine pair held together by at least two hydrogen bonds. All the hydrogen bonds seemed to form naturally; no fudging was required to make the two types of base pairs identical in shape. Quickly I called Jerry over to ask him whether this time he had any objection to my new base pairs.

When he said no, my morale skyrocketed, for I suspected that we now had the answer to the riddle of why the number of purine residues exactly equaled the number of pyrimidine residues. Two irregular sequences of bases could be regularly packed in the center of a helix if a purine always hydrogen-bonded to a pyrimidine. Furthermore, the hydrogen-bonding requirement meant that adenine would always pair with thymine, while guanine could pair only with cytosine. Chargaff's rules then suddenly stood out as a consequence of a double-helical structure for DNA. Even more exciting, this type of double helix suggested a replication scheme much more satisfactory than my briefly considered like-with-like pairing. Always pairing adenine with thymine and guanine with cytosine meant that the base sequences of the two intertwined chains were complementary to each other. Given the base sequence of one chain, that of its partner was automatically determined. Conceptually, it was thus very easy to visualize how a single chain could be the template for the synthesis of a chain with the complementary sequence.

Upon his arrival Francis did not get more than halfway through the door before I let loose that the answer to everything was in our hands. Though as a matter of principle he maintained skepticism for a few moments, the similarly shaped A-T and G-C pairs had their expected impact. His quickly pushing the bases together in a number of different ways did not reveal any other way to satisfy Chargaff's rules. A few minutes later he spotted the fact that the two glycosidic bonds (joining base and sugar) of each base pair were systematically related by a diad axis perpendicular to the helical axis. Thus, both pairs could be flipflopped over and still have their glycosidic bonds facing in the same direction. This had the important consequence that a given chain could contain both purines and pyrimidines. At the same time, it strongly suggested that the backbones of the two chains must run in opposite directions.

The question then became whether the A-T and G-C base pairs would easily fit the backbone configuration devised during the previous two weeks. At first glance this looked like a good bet, since I had left free in the center a large vacant area for the bases. However, we both knew that we would not be home until a complete model was built in which all the stereochemical contacts were satisfactory. There was also the obvious fact that the implications of its existence were far too important to risk crying wolf. Thus I felt slightly queasy when at lunch Francis winged into the Eagle to tell everyone within hearing distance that we had found the secret of life.

Exercises and Projects

CHECKING YOUR COMPREHENSION

1. How did Watson determine the way the four DNA bases link together?

2. Why did Watson find that his newly discovered base-pairing scheme made more sense than his older, incorrect scheme?

3. How did Crick react to Watson's new configuration?

FOR DISCUSSION AND DEBATE

1. What do you find noteworthy about Watson's personality as it is revealed in this reading?

2. Discuss Watson's approach to his subject matter. Were you able to easily understand the selection? Why or why not? What might Watson have done differently?

FOR YOUR NOTEBOOK

1. Keep a list of possible benefits that DNA technology can have for humanity Also keep a list of possible dangers.

2. DNA-related topics frequently make the news. Scan the daily newspaper for such topics and record your reactions to each one in your notebook.

FOR WRITING

1. No scientist ever works in isolation. Even the most original of scientists must list the contributions to their work of many predecessors and colleagues. Watson and Crick are no exception and have in their professional papers (as well as in Watson's memoir) acknowledged many scientists who contributed to the important discovery. Here are some of them: Linus Pauling, Jerry Donohue, Maurice Wilkins, Rosalind Franklin, R. B. Corey, and Erwin Chargraff.

   In a six-page term paper, report on the particular way in which at least two of the above scientists contributed to Watson and Crick's discovery.

2. Read Watson's *The Double Helix* in its entirety and then write a term paper on one of the following topics:
   a. the importance of "imaging" in molecular biology (contributions of stereochemistry and X-ray crystallography)
   b. the role of serendipity in Watson and Crick's discovery
   c. the element of subjectivity in scientific research (using the testimonies of both James Watson and Vivian Gornick (see Part 1).

3. Write an essay in response to Watson's claim, at the end of the selection, that "we had found the secret of life." You might wish to take as your premise that the secret of life goes beyond any biochemical explanation of it. Or you might adopt the contrasting approach that the better we understand the biochemistry of life, the better we will understand its secrets and, as a result, be better able to appreciate life. No matter what premise you choose, suggest a way of interpreting what is meant by the "secret" of life.

Suggestions for Further Reading

I. GENERAL WORKS

Biographical Encyclopedia of Scientists, 2 vols. New York: Facts on File, 1981.

Comprehensively summarizes the lives and achievements of scientists from ancient times to the present.

Bynum, W. F., E. J. Browne, and Roy Porter, eds. *Dictionary of the History of Science.* London: Macmillan, 1981.

Harre, Rom. *Great Scientific Experiments.* London: Phaidon Press, 1981.

Includes detailed accounts of twenty significant experiments and the scientists who designed them.

Kuhn, Thomas S. *The Copernican Revolution: Planetary Astronomy in the Development of Western Thought.* Cambridge: Harvard University Press, 1957.

Kuhn, Thomas S. *The Structure of Scientific Revolutions.* 2d ed. Chicago: University of Chicago Press, 1970.

Makes a definitive statement on the paradigmatic nature of normal science and how discovery proceeds from a perception of anomaly in the paradigm.

Parkinson, Claire L. *Breakthroughs: A Chronology of Great Achievements in Science and Mathematics, 1200–1930.* Boston: G. K. Hall, 1985.

II. GALILEO

Brecht, Bertolt. *Galileo.* Translated by Charles Laughton. New York: Grove Press, 1966.

This play by the major German dramatist of the twentieth century gives a contemporary coloring to Galileo's ideas, social interactions, and recantation.

Drake, Stillman. *Galileo at Work.* Chicago: University of Chicago Press, 1978.

III. NEWTON

Christensen, Gale E. *In the Presence of the Creator: Isaac Newton and His Times.* New York: Free Press, 1985.

More, Louis Trenchard. *Isaac Newton: A Biography.* New York: Scribner's, 1934.

Newton, Sir Isaac. *Newton's Philosophy of Nature: Selections from His Writings.* Edited by H. S. Thayer. New York: Hafner, 1953.

IV. DARWIN

Appleman, Philip, ed. *Darwin: A Norton Critical Edition.* New York: Norton, 1970.

Includes annotated selections from *On the Origin of Species, The Descent of Man,* and Darwin's notebooks and also contains numerous critical essays and a bibliography.

Darwin, Charles. *Charles Darwin's Diary of the Voyage of H.M.S. "Beagle."* Edited by Nora Barlow. Cambridge: Cambridge University Press, 1933.

Darwin, Charles. *Life and Letters of Charles Darwin.* 3 vols. Edited by Francis Darwin. London: John Murray, 1933.

Eiseley, Loren. *Darwin's Century.* New York: Doubleday, 1958.

This absorbing account is winner of the 1959 Phi Beta Kappa Science Award and chronicles Darwin's contributions to evolutionary biology.

V. CURIE

Curie, Eve. *Madame Curie.* Translated by Vincent Sheean. New York: Doubleday, 1937.

This definitive biography of Marie Curie is by her daughter.

Reid, Robert. *Marie Curie.* New York: Saturday Review Press, 1974.

VI. EINSTEIN

Barnett, Lincoln. *The Universe and Dr. Einstein.* Rev. ed. New York: Harper & Row, 1959.

One of the most lucid of the innumerable discussions of Einstein's work, this account was sanctioned by Einstein himself in his Foreward to the book.

Einstein, Albert. *Ideas and Opinions.* New York: Crown Publishers, 1954.

Provides selected essays on scientific and political topics.

Gardner, Martin. *The Relativity Explosion* [revised and updated version of *Relativity for the Millions*]. New York: Vintage Books, 1976.

Hoffman, Banesh. *Albert Einstein: Creator and Rebel.* New York: Viking Press, 1972.

This excellent biography is by one of Einstein's Princeton friends and collaborators.

Pais, Abraham. *Subtle Is the Lord: The Science and the Life of Albert Einstein.* New York: Oxford University Press, 1983.

VII. FREUD

Bettleheim, Bruno. *Freud and Man's Soul.* New York: Vintage Books, 1982.

A valuable reassessment of Freud's ideas and treatises.

Freud, Sigmund. *The Interpretation of Dreams* (1900). Translated by James Strachey. London: The Hogarth Press, 1953.

Jones, Ernest. *The Life and Work of Sigmund Freud.* Rev. ed. 3 vols. New York: Basic Books, 1961.

A definitive biography by one of Freud's associates.

Jung, Carl Gustav. *Dreams.* Translated by R. F. C. Hull. Princeton: Princeton University Press, 1974.

Jung's collected papers on dreams are divided into Dreams and Psychoanalysis, Dreams and Psychic Energy, the Practical Use of Dream Analysis, and Individual Dream Symbolism in Relation to Alchemy.

VIII. WATSON AND CRICK

Crick, Francis. *Life Itself: Its Origin and Nature.* New York: Simon & Schuster, 1981.

Judson, Horace Freeland. *The Eighth Day of Creation: Makers of the Revolution in Biology.* New York: Simon & Schuster, 1979.

Sayre, Ann. *Rosalind Franklin and DNA.* New York: Norton, 1975.
A full-fledged account of Franklin's important role in the discovery of the structure of the DNA molecule.

IX. HEISENBERG

Heisenberg, Werner. *Across the Frontiers.* New York: Harper & Row, 1978.

Pagels, Heinz R. *The Cosmic Code: Quantum Physics as the Language of Nature.* New York: Simon & Schuster, 1982.

Shimony, Abner. "The Reality of the Quantum World." *Scientific American* 258 (Jan. 1988): 46–53.

Trefil, James S. *From Atoms to Quarks: An Introduction to the Strange World of Particle Physics.* New York: Scribner's, 1980.

PART THREE

The Social and Ethical Dimension

Issues in Science and Technology

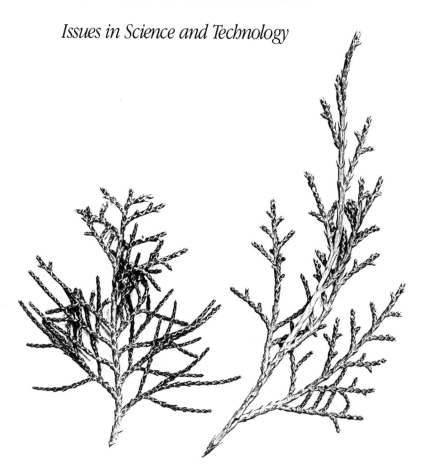

Science, like other bodies of knowledge and inquiry, is communicated widely through writing and discussion—not just to other scientists but to the public at large. Scientists know that even the most seemingly insignificant discovery can trigger insights into larger problems. For example, the archaeologist who reconstructs a portion of the ancient past enhances our understanding of civilization. This helps us realize that our very understanding of the past—our cultural roots—is largely due to the investigations of scientists working within their specialties. Take another example: Experiments with animal learning are beginning to suggest that some animals have greater intelligence and perception than previously realized; this in turn can influence the way we treat animals—and can give new meaning to the concept of animal rights.

Because the discoveries of science can affect the way we think of and act toward other creatures and the environment, it becomes clear that science cannot truly be separated from values. The pursuit of knowledge is itself a value; the decision to test a hypothesis rather than rely on hearsay or on venerable authority is a value-based decision. Of course, traditional values that have been highly esteemed for ages may be usurped (for better or worse), but value itself is never usurped in the search for truth. "Science is not a mechanism," Jacob Bronowski writes in *Science and Human Values* (1965), "but a human progress, and not a set of findings but a search for them. Those who think that science is ethically neutral confuse the findings of science, which are, with the activity of science, which is not." Moreover, the findings of science—in other words, facts in themselves—are not only ethically neutral but meaningless in the sense that they have not been placed into a larger framework. It may be a "fact" that $E = mc^2$, but the creative reasoning that led Einstein to his discovery of mass-energy equivalence stemmed from his sense of values involving independent, unrestrained inquiry into the mysteries of nature. At the other end of the spectrum, the building of an atomic-powered generator, or an atomic bomb—impossible without Einstein's discovery—is as much an ethical pursuit as a scientific and technical one.

Each of the scientific topics presented in this part—the possibility of life on other planets, nuclear waste disposal, animal rights, genetic engineering, evolution, and computer technology—is truly an issue, a problem or cluster of interrelated problems complex enough to require the breadth and depth of inquiry we refer to as scientific but far reaching enough to encompass matters we generally think of as the good life—matters that promote happiness and well-being, such as justice, spirituality, morality, welfare, and compassion. All of us, not just scientists, must accept the responsibility for understanding those scientific and technological issues that have a bearing on the good life. We are a human community, a global village, in which the deeds of one person can affect the many. If we choose to pass on the responsibilities of scientific understanding to the experts, then we are abdicating not only our responsibility but also our freedom.

The Possibility of Extraterrestrial Life

One of the most common themes in science fiction is "human meets alien," but just how likely is such an encounter? Given the rather slim possibility of any sort of extraterrestrial life in our own solar system—let alone intelligent life as we understand it—and given the unimaginably vast distances to even the nearest stars, the idea of making physical contact with beings from other planets seems little more than a fantasy.

But what about radio contact? Radio waves travel at the speed of light (186,200 miles per second), which is about 200,000 times faster than any spaceship we could build given our current technology. Whereas humans would need centuries to make a "short" interstellar voyage (assuming their ship could travel at 10 percent of the speed of light), a radio signal would take only a dozen or so years to cover the same distance. Assuming that we knew where to look, on what frequency to transmit, and those at the receiving end could decipher our message, it might be possible to exchange greetings within a human lifetime.

Is it worth the effort and expense?

Over the past quarter century, many astronomers have felt strongly that it is. Using giant radio-telescope dishes, they have searched the sky for nearby stars similar to our sun and have transmitted signals to these stars—with absolutely no assurance that there are even planets there. To some, such as William Oldendorf, the effort is futile and somewhat ridiculous; to others, such as Carl Sagan, the effort is immensely important. For Stephen Jay Gould, the likelihood of encountering intelligent beings like ourselves seems nil, but the possibility of discovering some kind of intelligence out there may be real. At any rate, Gould feels it is worth the effort to find out.

Carl Sagan is David Duncan Professor of Astronomy at Cornell, creator of the twelve-part PBS series "Cosmos" (and author of the book by that name), and winner of the Pulitzer Prize for his book *The Dragons of Eden* (1977). William Oldendorf is a neurology professor at UCLA Medical School. Stephen Jay Gould teaches anthropology at Harvard and is the author of several collections of essays on natural science and evolutionary biology.

TERMS TO LEARN

light-year: the distance light, traveling at more than 186,000 miles per second, covers in one year, or roughly 6 trillion miles

cryptography: the science of decoding messages written in an unknown language or code

exobiology: the branch of biology that speculates on the nature and origin of life beyond the earth

Extraterrestrial Life: An Idea Whose Time Has Come

We now have, for the first time, the tools to make contact with civilizations on planets of other stars. It is an astonishing fact that the great one-thousand-foot-diameter radio telescope of the National Astronomy and Ionosphere Center, run by Cornell University in Arecibo, Puerto Rico, would be able to communicate with an identical copy of itself anywhere in the Milky Way Galaxy. We have at our command the means to communicate not merely over distances of hundreds or thousands of light-years; we can communicate over tens of thousands of light-years, into a volume containing hundreds of billions of stars. The hypothesis that advanced technical civilizations exist on planets of other stars is amenable to experimental testing. It has been removed from the arena of pure speculation. It is now in the arena of experiment.

Our first attempt to listen to broadcasts from extraterrestrial societies was Project Ozma. Organized by Frank Drake in 1960 at the National Radio Astronomy Observatory (NRAO), it looked at two stars at one frequency for two weeks. The results were negative. Slightly more ambitious projects are, at the time of writing, being performed at the Gorky Radiophysical Institute in the Soviet Union and at NRAO in the United States. All in all, perhaps a few hundred nearby stars will be examined at one or two frequencies. But even the most optimistic calculations on the distances to the nearest stars suggest that hundreds of thousands to millions of stars must be examined before an intelligible signal from one of them will be received. This requires a large effort covering a sizable period of time. But it is well within our resources, our abilities, and our interests.

The change in the climate of opinion about extraterrestrial life was reflected in 1971 by a scientific conference held in Byurakan, Soviet Armenia, and sponsored jointly by the Soviet Academy of Sciences of the U. S. S. R. and the National Academy of Sciences of the United States. I had the privilege of chairing the U. S. delegation to this meeting. The participants represented astronomy, physics, mathematics, biology, chemistry, archaeology, anthropology, history, electronics, computer technology, and cryptography. The group, which included two skeptical Nobel laureates, was marked for its crossing of national as well as disciplinary boundaries. The conference concluded that the chances of there being extraterrestrial communicative societies and our present technological ability to contact them were both sufficiently high that a serious search was warranted Some of the specific conclusions that were reached were these:

1. The striking discoveries of recent years in the fields of astronomy, biology, computer science and radiophysics have transferred some of the problems of extraterrestrial civilizations and their detection from the realm of speculation to a new realm of experiment and observation. For the first time in human history, it has become possible to make serious and detailed experimental investigations of this fundamental and important problem.

2. This problem may prove to be of profound significance for the future development of Mankind. If extraterrestrial civilizations are ever discovered, the effect on human scientific and technological capabilities will be immense, and the discovery can positively influence the whole future of Man. The practical and philosophical significance of a successful contact with an extraterrestrial civilization would be so enormous as to justify the expenditure of substantial efforts. The consequences of such a discovery would greatly add to the total of human knowledge.

3. The technological and scientific resources of our planet are already large enough to permit us to begin investigations directed toward the search for extraterrestrial intelligence. As a rule, such studies should provide important scientific results even when specific searches for extraterrestrial intelligence do not succeed. At present, these investigations can be carried out effectively in the various countries by their own scientific institutions. Even at this early stage, however, it would be useful to discuss and coordinate specific programs of research and to exchange scientific information. In the future, it would be desirable to combine the efforts of investigators in various countries to achieve the experimental and observational objectives. It seems to us appropriate that the search for extraterrestrial intelligence should be made by representatives of the whole of mankind.

4. Various modes of search for extraterrestrial intelligence were discussed in detail at the Conference. The realization of the most elaborate of these proposals would require considerable time and effort and an expenditure of funds comparable to the funds devoted to space and nuclear research. Useful searches can, however, also be initiated at a very modest scale.

5. The Conference participants consider highly valuable present and forthcoming space-vehicle experiments directed toward searching for life on the other planets of our solar system. They recommend the continuation and strengthening of work in such areas as prebiological organic chemistry, searches for extrasolar planetary systems, and evolutionary biology, which bear sharply on the problem.

6. The Conference recommends the initiation of specific new investigations directed toward modes of search for signals. . . .

Another sign of the increasing acceptability of the search for extraterrestrial intelligence is the recommendations of the Astronomy Survey Committee of the U. S. National Academy of Sciences, which has been asked to summarize the needs of astronomy in the decade of the 1970s. The Committee's report was the first such national report on the future of astronomy to lay stress on the search for extraterrestrial intelligence—as a possibly important by-product of astronomical research in the near future and as a justification for the construction of large radio telescopes.

Nearer to home, there is an accelerating set of laboratory studies of the origin of life on Earth. If the origin of life on Earth turns out to have been exceedingly "easy," the chances of life elsewhere are correspondingly high.

There is also a concerted effort in the United States—Project Viking—to land instrumented payloads on the surface of Mars to search for indigenous life forms.[1]

The idea of extraterrestrial life is an idea whose time has come.

[1]This goal was accomplished in 1976. No signs of life were detected. [Ed.]

WILLIAM OLDENDORF

 # Should We Seek Out Alien Life?

The prospect of intelligent beings on other worlds fires the imagination as never before. Daily, the media reassure us that they are out there. Many proposals, some of them alarmingly expensive, offer schemes to communicate with these other life-forms. But it seems to me, with all the human misery on Earth, great expenditures for seeking intelligence elsewhere are clearly unwarranted.

When I was a boy in the 1930s, everyone I knew was sure there was life on Mars; that is why Orson Welles's 1938 radio drama describing a landing by Martians caused a general panic. But as the space probes of the past decade gave us first-hand knowledge of the moon and most of the planets, it became clear that even the most inhospitable place on Earth was a Garden of Eden compared with the next-best place elsewhere in the solar system. Most people gave up the idea of life on Mars. Yet today's extraterrestrial enthusiasts are convinced that there are other cultures in our galaxy or beyond, ready to lead us to utopia with their advanced technologies.

The advocates argue that we cannot be unique. The fact that very specific conditions are required for humanlike life—a planet with the correct gravity, distance from a star, chemical composition and atmosphere—is usually dismissed by citing the phenomenal number of stars in our own galaxy (about 100 billion). Undoubtedly many billions of planets circle the stars of our galaxy alone, and the observable universe probably contains 100 billion other galaxies. Surely, the argument goes, somewhere in this vast universe there must be another planet so closely resembling Earth that its history is similar to ours; a planet on which life has appeared and evolved into creatures enough like us that we can identify with them.

But the search-for-extraterrestrial-life movement has tended to sweep under the rug several important factors. First of all, most stars are incomprehensibly far away. Only about a thousand fall within 50 light-years of Earth. This means that if we were to send a message traveling at the speed of light, it would spread out and pass these thousand stars within 50 years. If there were some creature able to receive, recognize, interpret and reply to it, the return message could take another 50 years to reach Earth. So to sample these thousand stars could require a century, and no one reading this would be alive to see the response.

There may be a few hundred or few thousand planets around these nearby thousand stars. But we are not likely to find the very specific requirements for even remotely humanoid life on any. To support water-based life-forms such as ourselves, a planet must possess great bodies of water, be at a very precise distance from its sun and rotate once on its axis in less than a few Earth days. Why? Our oceans and clouds act as buffers to solar radiation. As the planet rotates, water heats up, evaporates, condenses and freezes, evening out the enormous fluctuations in radiant energy occurring at any one point on the Earth's surface. Thus, we experience only a few degrees of temperature change between night and day. But if the Earth were 5 percent closer to the sun or 5 percent farther away, the solar energy it received would be either too strong or too weak for the water to cycle between solid, liquid and gas. Life as we know it would not exist.

A hypothetical twin Earth must also have an appreciable atmosphere; thus, it must have a mass nearly as great as Earth's to prevent the gradual escape of its atmospheric gas molecules into space. Without a substantial atmosphere for a shield, evolving life would be destroyed by radiation from outer space. Our atmosphere places the equivalent of about a one-meter-thick layer of lead between us and extraterrestrial radiation.

Say a planet capable of supporting recognizable life *did* exist in our galactic neighborhood. Would its life be of interest to us? There are millions of species of life-forms on Earth, yet most people pay attention only to those few that pose a threat, can be eaten or are amusing. If somewhere there were another Earth identical with ours, but without humans, we would find it of only academic interest.

A Millionth of a Planet's Past

And consider this: On Earth, our recorded history of a few thousand years represents only about one-millionth of the planet's past. If we arrived on a planet identical with Earth but only 10,000 years younger or older, we would find little there of interest to ordinary people. If indeed we did find a planet capable of evolving humanlike creatures, the overwhelming likelihood is that our contact would have come too early or too late. The inhabitants might not yet have appeared or might already be extinct, leaving us to the archeological analysis of their artifacts.

The favorite fantasy of the believer in extraterrestrial life is that there is somewhere a humanlike culture, technically at least a few centuries beyond ours; that its members would generously share their technology, allowing us to vault over tedious years of research. But if this advanced culture possessed wisdom on a par with its technology, it would no doubt hesitate to give its knowledge to an Earth that still uses its most advanced technology to make war. An advanced civilization might simply incinerate Earth, deeming it a potential threat.

I may be totally in error. Perhaps some benevolent culture actually will deliver some very advanced technology. But if so, we probably won't know what to do with it. Only a very small percentage of the world's population is able to benefit from what we already know. Imagine if nuclear fission had been one such technical gift bestowed upon us from the benevolent stars! After almost half a century we are still bickering about how it should be managed, and much of the world believes it to be a fundamental evil that should be abandoned completely.

But the most compelling argument against a search for life in space is our narrow view of what life is. We base our ideas on what we are familiar with. If there were another type of life far different from our own, how would we know what to look for or how to communicate with it? On our own planet we unknowingly coexisted for untold ages with an unseen life-form—the virus. A case could be made that viruses represent extraterrestrial life that came to Earth and invaded the cells of all life-forms. In most instances, the invaders did not make their presence known. They might have gone forever undetected had some of them not caused detectable disease. Once man recognized the invaders, war was declared, and at least one of the enemy, smallpox, has been slain.

If science someday overcomes the limitation of the speed of light, then presumably the entire universe will become accessible. We may well find evidence that there is or (more likely) was humanlike life elsewhere in the universe. But the vanishingly small likelihood of finding recognizable extraterrestrial life within our lifetime, the great expense of the search and the pressing needs of humans here on Earth should give us pause.

As a physician, I am daily confronted with human misery. Starvation, cancer and drug addiction are everywhere. We cannot contain population growth, poverty or the arms race. Denying these realities while squandering precious research dollars to pursue extraterrestrial life falls, in my view, somewhere between irrational and immoral.

STEPHEN JAY GOULD

 ## SETI and the Wisdom of Casey Stengel

Since the study of extraterrestrial life lacks any proven subject, opinions about the form and frequency of nonearthly beings record the hopes and fears of speculating scientists more than the constraints of evidence. Alfred Russel Wallace, for example, Darwin's partner in the discovery of natural selection and the first great evolutionist to consider exobiology in any detail, held firmly that man must be alone in the entire cosmos—for he could not bear the thought that human intelligence had not been the uniquely special gift of God, conferred upon an ideally suited planet. He wrote in 1903 that the existence of abundant and brainy extraterrestrials "would imply that man is an animal and nothing more, is of no importance in the universe, needed no great preparations for his advent, only, perhaps, a second-rate demon, and a third- or fourth-rate earth." . . .

The endless debate about extraterrestrial life has focused upon the calculation of probabilities—how many stars, how many suitable planets, the chance that life will originate on appropriate earths, the probability that life will eventually generate intelligence. I must confess that I have always viewed this literature as dreary and inconclusive, too mixed up with hope and uncertainty to reach any respectable conclusion.

Recently, several astronomers and astrophysicists have advocated a different approach—a direct search for the technological by-products of intelligence by scanning the skies systematically with radio telescopes, probing for signals emitted by other civilizations. This so-called SETI program (search for extraterrestrial intelligence) has been vigorously debated. Proponents claim that it would require but a minute fraction of the annual NASA budget and, whatever its chances of success, would at least move the subject from fruitless debate about probabilities to an experimental probe by the only means now available. Opponents counter that the scheme is a boondoggle, still costing millions and so virtually assured of failure that it merits not a penny of sparse public funds for science.

As an evolutionary biologist, I have no expert knowledge in most areas motivating this debate. I am moved to comment only because opponents of SETI have featured an argument from my field as one of their most powerful weapons. They state that all leading evolution-ary biologists have proclaimed the existence of extraterrestrial life as nearly inconceivable. The optimism of some physical scientists therefore resides in their failure to understand the distinctive character of evolutionary reasoning. But opponents of SETI have misstated the biological argument, and I would like to explain why at least one evolutionary biologist thinks that SETI is a long shot well worth trying.

Frank J. Tipler, a mathematical physicist from Tulane University, has been the most indefatigable critic of SETI. In a long series of strongly worded articles for both technical and popular journals (*New Scientist, Mercury, Physics Today, Quarterly Journal of the Royal Astronomical Society*, for example), he gives "two basic reasons for my disbelief in the existence of extraterrestrial intelligent beings." . . .

The second reason lies outside my field and I shall not dwell on it, though it must be mentioned. Tipler argues that "if 'they' existed, they would already be here. . . . Because they are not here, no such beings exist." In short, Tipler claims that any truly intelligent creatures would search or colonize the cosmos with a device that he calls a von Neumann machine—"a computer with intelligence close to the human level, capable of self-replication and capable, indeed, of constructing anything for which it has plans, using the raw materials available in the solar system it is aimed at." Intelligent life could therefore explore an entire galaxy "for the price of one von Neumann machine"—for this computer would mine astroids and comets for material to build replicas of itself and its enclosing probe. These replicas would then scurry off to other suitable stars and replicate again. In a mere 300 million years, a whole galaxy could be saturated with the duplicated products of one von Neumann machine.

Such a machine could even fabricate the flesh and blood of extraterrestrials by mining the needed chemicals and then running the genetic program of its creator from stored memory:

> This information could in principle be stored in the memory of a von Neumann machine, which could be instructed to synthesize an egg and place the "fertilized cell" in an artificial womb. . . . In nine months there would be a human baby in the stellar system, and this could be raised to adulthood by surrogate parents, constructed by the von Neumann machine.

I don't mean to be a philistine, but I must confess that I simply don't know how to react to such arguments. I have enough trouble predicting the plans and reactions of people closest to me. I am usually baffled by the thoughts and accomplishments of humans in different cultures. I'll be damned if I can state with certainty what some extraterrestrial source of intelligence might do. Thus, Tipler's second argument follows the speculative tradition that SETI, with its experimental approach, is designed to transcend.

As his first argument, however, Tipler features a different kind of claim based on the methods and data of my field. He writes: 10

> First, all the great contemporary experts in the theory of evolu-
> tion—Francisco Ayala, Theodosius Dobzhansky, Ernst Mayr, and
> George Simpson—are unanimous in claiming that the evolution of an
> intelligent species from simple one-celled organisms is so improbable
> that we are likely to be the only intelligent species ever to exist.

On the most mundane level, if I may play the irrelevant "expert game" for just one sentence, Tipler's statement is empirically false. I count at least four quite respectable evolutionists in the international pro-SETI petition recently released by Carl Sagan (Tom Eisner of Cornell, Dave Raup of the University of Chicago, Ed Wilson of Harvard, and with apologies for arrogance, yours truly). Evolutionary biologists, in their usual consistency with nature's primary theme, maintain a *diversity* of views on this subject.

More importantly, I think that Tipler has misunderstood what evolutionary biologists dismiss with such forcefulness by conflating two very different issues. All evolutionists who have discussed exobiology at length have clearly delineated two separate concerns— a specific claim and a general argument.

The *specific* issue considers *detailed repeatability* of any particular evolutionary sequence—in this case the evolution of creatures looking pretty much like us: bilaterally symmetrical with sense organs up front, two eyes, a nose in the middle, a mouth, and a brain. If we could start the earth's tape anew, would intelligent creatures evolve again in this form? If other worlds share our basic chemistry and conditions, would such "humanoids" evolve on them?

The *general* question asks whether attributes that we would identify as intelligence might arise in creatures of any conformation— blobs, films, spheres of pulsating energy, or diffuse and unimagined forms far beyond the limited visions of most science fiction writers.

All evolutionists have vociferously denied the specific claim, and I join them in all their vigor. Many evolutionists have also gone a step further to doubt the general argument as well, but never with such certainty—and always as a personal opinion, not as a proclamation bearing the indelible imprimatur of "evolutionary theory." I stand among those evolutionists who deny the specific claim but feel that no strong opinion can be entertained about the general argument. SETI only needs the general argument to bolster its case for support.

Gregory Bateson, the recently deceased guru of sciences that deal with complex objects and interacting systems, often emphasized that confusion of hierarchical categories may be the most common and serious fallacy of human reasoning (see his book *Mind and Nature,* for example). As a primary example of "category confusions," Bateson identified the substitution of individuals for classes (or vice versa).

Casey Stengel, one of the greatest general gurus of our time, consciously committed Bateson's fallacy of categories to avoid the heat of scrutiny in a tough moment. He was roundly criticized for blowing the Mets' first pick in the expansion draft on a *particular* catcher of quite modest ability (one Hobie Landrith by name). Casey answered by invoking the *class* of catchers in general—"You have to have a catcher, because if you don't, you're likely to have a lot of passed balls." Now Ol' Case, as usual, knew exactly what he was saying (never let the patter known as "Stengelese" fool you). He used humor to blunt criticism because he knew that we would all recognize the fallacy of reasoning and laugh at the conflation. But we commit the same error in subtler circumstances and fail to identify our confusion.

When we use "evolutionary theory" to deny categorically the possibility of extraterrestrial intelligence, we commit the classic fallacy of substituting specifics (*individual* repeatability of humanoids) for classes (the probability that evolution elsewhere might produce a creature in the *general* class of intelligent beings). I can present a good argument from "evolutionary theory" against the repetition of anything like a human body elsewhere; I cannot extend it to the general proposition that intelligence in some form might pervade the universe.

Physical scientists following the stereotype of science as a predictable, deterministic enterprise, have often reasoned that if humans arose on earth, then we must infer (since cause leads inexorably to effect) that intelligent creatures of roughly human form would arise on any planet beginning with physical and chemical conditions similar to those that prevailed on the early earth. Perhaps this deterministic outlook is responsible for the paltry imagination of film makers and science fiction writers, with their endless creatures, all designed on a human model with two eyes, a nose, a mouth, two arms, and two legs (*Close Encounters, ET,* and even the more imaginative *Star Wars*). This tendency could be forgiven when human actors had to play the roles in our movies, but now that pieces of plastic can evoke our deepest emotions and move so subtly that ET becomes a national hero, this excuse no longer holds.

But styles of science are as diverse as their subject matter. Classical determinism and complete predictability may prevail for simple macroscopic objects subject to a few basic laws of motion (balls rolling down inclined planes in high school physics experiments), but complex historical objects do not lend themselves to such easy treatment. In the history of life, all results are products of long series of events, each so intricately dependent upon particular environments and previous histories that we cannot predict their future course with any certainty. The historical sciences try to explain unique situations—immensely complex historical accidents. Evolutionary biologists, as historical scientists, do not expect detailed repetition and cannot use the actual results of history to establish probabilities for recurrence (would a Caesar again die brutally in Rome if we could go back to *Australopithecus* in Africa and start anew?). Evolutionists view the origin of humans (or any particular butterfly, roach, or starfish) as a historical event of such complexity and improbability that we would never expect to see anything exactly like it again (or elsewhere)—hence our strong opposition to the *specific* argument about humanoids on other worlds. Consider just two of the many reasons for uniqueness of complex events in the history of life.

1. *Mass extinction as a key influence upon the history of life on earth.* . . . Dinosaurs died some 65 million years ago in the great worldwide Cretaceous extinction that also snuffed out about half the species of shallow water marine invertebrates. They had ruled terrestrial environments for 100 million years and would probably reign today if they had survived the debacle. Mammals arose at about the same time and spent their first 100 million years as small creatures inhabiting the nooks and crannies of a dinosaur's world. If the death of dinosaurs had not provided their great opportunity, mammals would still be small and insignificant creatures. We would not be here, and no consciously intelligent life would grace our earth. Evidence gathered since 1980 . . . indicates that the impact of an extraterrestrial body triggered this extinction. What could be more unpredictable and unexpected than comets or asteroids striking the earth literally out of the blue. Yet without such impact, our earth would lack consciously intelligent life. Many great extinctions (several larger than the Cretaceous event) have set basic patterns in the history of life, imparting an essential randomness to our evolutionary pageant.

2. *Each species as a concatenation of improbabilities.* Any animal species—human, squid, or coral—is the latest link of an evolutionary chain stretching through thousands of species back to the inception of life. If any of these species had become extinct

or evolved in another direction, final results would be markedly different. Each chain of improbable events includes adaptations developed for a local environment and only fortuitously suited to support later changes. Our ancestors among fishes evolved a peculiar fin with a sturdy, central bony axis. Without a structure of this kind, landbound descendants could not have supported themselves in a nonbuoyant terrestrial environment. (Most lineages of fishes did not and could not evolve terrestrial descendants because they lacked fins of this form.) Yet these fins did not evolve in anticipation of future terrestrial needs. They developed as adaptations to a local environment in water, and were luckily suited to permit a new terrestrial direction later on. All evolutionary sequences include such a large set of *sine quibus non,* a fortuitous series of accidents with respect to future evolutionary success. Human brains and bodies did not evolve along a direct and inevitable ladder, but by a circuitous and tortuous route carved by adaptations evolved for different reasons, and fortunately suited to later needs.

The improbabilities of history proclaim that all species are unique and unrepeatable in detail. Evolutionary theory, as a science of history, does deny the specific argument for humanoids on other worlds. All leading evolutionists, in their writings on exobiology, have said so with gusto, and I agree. Wallace began the theme in 1903:

> The ultimate development of man has, therefore roughly speaking, depended on something like a million distinct modifications, each of a special type and dependent on some precedent changes in the organic and inorganic environments, or in both. The chances against such an enormously long series of definite modifications having occurred twice over... are almost infinite.

Simpson has expressed the theme most eloquently in recent years, in his famous essay on "the nonprevalence of humanoids" ... :

> This essential nonrepeatability of evolution on earth obviously has a decisive bearing on the chances that it has been repeated or closely paralleled on any other planet. The assumption, so freely made by astronomers, physicists, and some biochemists, that once life gets started anywhere, humanoids will eventually and inevitably appear is plainly false.... Let us grant the unsubstantiated claim of millions or billions of possible planetary abodes of life; the chances of such historical duplication are still vanishingly small.

But all these evolutionists have also clearly distinguished this specific proposition about humanoids from the general argument that intelligence in some other form might arise elsewhere. On the general proposition, they have maintained a diversity of opinions—leading to the empirical conclusion that "evolutionary theory" has no clear pronouncement to make. Both Wallace and Simpson extended their argument to doubt the general claim as well, but ever so much more gently, and as a personal opinion only. Simpson, for example, wrote:

> Even in planetary histories different from ours might not some quite different and yet comparably intelligent beings . . . have evolved? Obviously these are questions that cannot be answered categorically. I can only express an opinion . . . I think it extremely unlikely that anything enough like us for real communication of thought exists anywhere in our accessible universe.

Other evolutionists, however, including two cited by Tipler as denying any possibility for SETI's success, also distinguish the specific from the general argument, but express far more optimism for the generality. Dobzhansky and Ayala, in a leading textbook (coauthored with G. L. Stebbins and J. W. Valentine), write . . . :

> Granting that the possibility of obtaining a man-like creature is vanishingly small even given an astronomical number of attempts . . . there is still some small possibility that another intelligent species has arisen, one that is capable of achieving a technological civilization.

I am not convinced that the possibility is so small.

Does evolutionary theory offer any insight about the general argument? We gain some sense of probabilities for repetition of a basic theme (but not of specific details) from the phenomenon known as "convergence." Flight has evolved separately in insects, birds, pterosaurs (flying reptiles), and bats. Aerodynamic principles do not change, but morphologies differ widely (birds use feathers; bats and pterosaurs employ a membrane, but bats stretch it between several fingers, pterosaurs only from one). Marsupial "moles" and "wolves" evolved on Australia, a continent isolated from placental mammals elsewhere. Since adaptive themes are limited and animals so diverse, convergence of different evolutionary lineages to the same general solution (but not to detailed repetition) are common. Highly adaptive forms that are easy to evolve arise again and again. More complex morphologies without such adaptive necessity offer little or no prospect for repetition. Conscious intelligence has evolved only once on earth, and presents no real prospect for reemergence should we choose to use our gift for destruction. But does intelligence lie within the class of phenomena too complex and historically conditioned for repetition? I do not think that its uniqueness on earth specifies such a conclusion. Perhaps, in another form on another world, intelligence would be as easy to evolve as flight on ours.

Tipler dismisses the issue of convergence by stating that biologist Leonard Ornstein (in an article supporting Tipler...) has refuted the most famous of all convergences—the "camera eye" of vertebrates and cephalopods (squids and their allies)—by suggesting that this structure arose in both groups from a common ancestor, and not separately in each. Even if Ornstein were right the dismissal of a specific case does not deny the importance of convergence as a general phenomenon. But Ornstein's arguments are seriously flawed. He never mentions the strongest, "classical" argument for convergence—that the eyes, although so similar in design and operation, develop embryologically in fundamentally different ways (squid eyes form from skin precursors, while vertebrate eyes, the lens excepted, develop from the brain). Moreover, Ornstein's main argument for evolution from a common ancestor relies upon a biological principle disproved more than fifty years ago. He invokes Haeckel's discredited law that "ontogeny recapitulates phylogeny"—that an organism's embryological development repeats the sequence of ancestral adults in its evolutionary lineage. Since the eye develops so early in embryology, Ornstein argues that it may have already existed in a very remote ancestor—early enough to predate the evolutionary split of vertebrate and squid lineages. Not only has Haeckel's law been disproved (embryos do not repeat ancestral stages), but even Haeckel himself, in the heyday of his principle, rarely used time of appearance in embryology to specify moment of evolutionary origin—for he himself had identified and named a large class of exceptions to such a facile generality.

Even if we follow Tipler in arguing that von Neumann machines are the only proper way to go, he admits that we won't have the technology to build one for a century. I'm an impatient and mortal fellow. As I think it cruel to ask disadvantaged minorities to "go slow" in demands for political change—thus guaranteeing that any practical benefits will fall only upon their children's children—so too do I selfishly wish to see some exobiological results (positive or negative) in my lifetime. SETI is all we have for now. It is relatively cheap, and (in my view) entirely sensible from those perspectives that evolutionary theory can enlighten. Frankly, I think the chances of its success are a good deal lower than the probabilities envisioned by its more enthusiastic supporters among physical scientists. But we can't know until we try. Ultimately, however, I must justify the attempt at such a long shot simply by stating that a positive result would be the most cataclysmic event in our entire intellectual history. Curiosity impels, and makes us human. Might it impel others as well?

Exercises and Projects

CHECKING YOUR COMPREHENSION

1. How distant are the nearest stars from us? Why does Oldendorf raise the issue of distance in arguing against the reasonableness of searching for extraterrestrial life?

2. What does Oldendorf consider to be the strongest argument against the search for life beyond earth?

3. Explain the connection Oldendorf makes between his livelihood (as a physician) and his attitude toward the search for life in space. What similar connection does Gould make between his profession as an evolutionary biologist and the search for life in space?

4. What reason does Sagan give to support the likelihood that life exists beyond earth?

5. Restate in your own words the six conclusions reached by the scientists participating in the 1971 conference on the chances of extraterrestrial life.

6. What distinction does Gould make between the specific claim and the general claim regarding extraterrestrial intelligence?

7. What is "category confusion," and why, according to Gould, is it a serious fallacy in human reasoning?

8. Summarize the two reasons Gould gives for the uniqueness of complex events in the history of life on earth.

FOR DISCUSSION AND DEBATE

1. Summarize the most persuasive point each author makes in defense of his respective point of view. Next, which of these two contrary points do you feel is most persuasive? Debate the matter with other students in class.

2. Examine these statements from each essay for possible flaws in reasoning:

   SAGAN: "There is an accelerating set of laboratory studies of the origin of life on Earth. If the origin of life on Earth turns out to have been exceedingly 'easy,' the chances of life elsewhere are correspondingly high."

   OLDENDORF: "If [an] advanced culture possessed wisdom on a par with its technology, it would no doubt hesitate to give its knowledge to an Earth that still uses its most advanced technology to make war."

   GOULD: "Does intelligence lie within the class of phenomena too complex and historically conditioned for repetition? I do not think that its uniqueness on earth specifies such a conclusion."

3. Discuss the effectiveness or ineffectiveness of each author's use of facts and statistics to support his respective point of view.

FOR YOUR NOTEBOOK

1. Describe your own imaginary extraterrestrials. First, think up a particular planetary environment, then record the anatomical requirements of creatures inhabiting that environment.

2. After reading the three selections, list your own reasons for, and reasons against, searching for extraterrestrial intelligence.

FOR WRITING

1. Write an essay on the impact that contact with extraterrestrials might have on humans—for better or worse. Would the primary reaction be one of fear? Of curiosity? Would our main collective ambition be to learn from them? If so, to what ends? Or would we use them to help us solve our problems? In any case, what possible dangers might arise?

2. Prepare a progress report on current searches for extraterrestrial life. Include a description of the kinds of transmitting equipment used. Useful periodicals to consult would be *Astronomy, The Planetary Report* (published by The Planetary Society, Pasadena, CA), and *Sky & Telescope*. For earlier work in the search for extraterrestrial life, see the first section of the Suggestions for Further Reading on page 235.

3. Write a critical review of a science fiction film in which human-alien contact is the major theme. Possible choices: *The Day the Earth Stood Still, War of the Worlds, The Thing, Close Encounters, E. T., 2001: A Space Odyssey*. Points to consider: Are the films mere fantasies, or are they based to some extent on known (or probable) scientific principles? How much psychological realism is reflected in the human-alien encounters? How realistically have the anatomical differences been treated?

Nuclear Waste Disposal

In most areas of high technology, practical necessity must be weighed against hazards to ourselves and the environment. The *Challenger* tragedy in January 1986 led officials to reassess not only safety standards and decision-making procedures in the space program but also the need to use astronauts at all in conducting experiments in space. Similarly, the Three Mile Island and Chernobyl nuclear reactor accidents of 1978 and 1986 reminded us of the potential for nuclear catastrophe. Should we improve safety standards and quality control, or should we abandon atomic energy use altogether?

Barry Commoner and Victor Gilinsky each suggest different ways of approaching the enormously complex issue of coping with atomic waste. Are all methods of disposal too dangerous to consider? Or is there at least one reasonably safe method? Even the experts disagree. Commoner, who directs the Center for the Biology of Natural Systems at Queens College, is the author of *Science and Survival* (1966), the Phi Beta Kappa Award-winning *The Closing Circle* (1971), and *The Poverty of Power* (1976), from which the reading is taken. Gilinsky is a former commissioner of the Nuclear Regulatory Commission.

TERMS TO LEARN

thermal pollution: contamination of a natural resource, such as a lake or river, by substances that cause the water temperature to rise to levels toxic to plant and animal life

enrichment (of uranium): a process of increasing the amount of fissionable uranium in uranium ore

isotope: a form of an element that differs in atomic number (for example, has one or more additional electrons) while the atomic weight remains the same

BARRY COMMONER

 # The Dangers of Nuclear-Waste Disposal

As it exists today, the U. S. nuclear-power system is a one-way process: Uranium ore goes in and electricity, highly radioactive waste, and the waste heat inevitably emitted by any power plant come out. Nuclear power plants produce more waste heat than most conventional plants of equal size and therefore cause more serious thermal-pollution problems.

The problem of permanently "disposing" of the radioactive waste—somehow keeping the damaging radiation away from people and environmental situations—has been studied for a number of years, but the problem has not yet been solved. The difficulties involved in finding some final resting place for this hideously dangerous material can be judged from the following: The waste produced by a billion-watt nuclear power plant (the typical size of recent ones) is equivalent in radioactivity to about 2500 tons of radium. In contrast, the total amount of radium used thus far in the world for medical and scientific purposes—all of it handled in very small amounts and elaborately contained and shielded—probably amounts to a few pounds. Another sobering comparison is that the radiation from the wastes produced by a city's nuclear power plant—if it were released into the environment—would be sufficient to kill 100 times the city's population.

In bulk, this radioactive waste does not amount to much—a fact that can readily lead to a highly deceiving conclusion. Thus, the head of the Federal Energy Administration, Frank G. Zarb, in a recent speech in support of his conviction, relative to the nuclear-waste problem, that "the facts are reassuring," offered the following evidence:

> A single aspirin tablet has the same volume as the waste produced in generating 7,000 kilowatt-hours, which is about one person's share of the country's electric output for an entire year. Compared to large quantities of other harmful materials, the volume of nuclear waste is minuscule.

What Mr. Zarb fails to mention is that, unlike a real aspirin tablet, his radioactive one is sufficiently toxic to kill 100 people.

Nuclear wastes are persistent. Their radioactivity will remain at a very harmful level, and will need to be meticulously isolated from people and the environment for about 200,000 years. This fact provokes a melancholy question: Who is to stand watch over this radioactive legacy? What social institution can promise to last that long? One reply, from perhaps the most thoughtful proponent of nuclear power, A. M. Weinberg, is that the task must be assumed by a kind of nuclear priesthood:

> We nuclear people have made a Faustian bargain with society. On the one hand we offer—in the catalytic nuclear burner [the breeder]—an inexhaustible source of energy. . . . But the price that we demand of society for this magical energy source is both a vigilance and longevity of our social institutions that we are quite unaccustomed to. . . . In a sense we have established a military priesthood which guards against inadvertent use of nuclear weapons . . . peaceful nuclear energy probably will make demands of the same sort on our society.

This concept—which cloaks the devil in a laboratory coat and the soldier in a cassock—is almost as forbidding as the fact to which it seeks to respond.

The current status of the waste-disposal problem is described in the latest government report on the nuclear-power industry. A diagram in the report depicts the movement of uranium from the mines through the successive phases of the nuclear-power system. A final arrow marked "high-level solid waste" points to an impressive building labeled "Federal Repository." The possible contents of such a repository are described in three accompanying diagrams, but their effect is rather spoiled by the notation that they are an "artist's concept." In fact there is no Federal repository for the permanent storage of highly radioactive waste. The final disposition of this enormously dangerous material remains, indeed, an "artist's concept."

Proposals abound, none of them satisfactory. One idea is to improve the present reprocessing method. This now leaves in the waste 0.5 percent of the long-lived radioactive isotopes originally present in the spent fuel; the proposed new method would reduce this residue to .0001 percent of the original material. That would shorten the time during which the waste is too dangerous for human contact from about 200,000 years to perhaps 1000 years. Depending on one's outlook, this might perhaps bring the storage problem within what one nuclear expert has called the "time horizon of present rational planning." Since the present reprocessing system is already so difficult that none of the three plants that are supposed to handle commercial-reactor wastes is now in operation, this approach does not seem to be a very practical one.

Another idea—to store the radioactive waste in the Antarctic ice—would violate a specific prohibition in the Antarctic Treaty of 1959. At one time the AEC proposed to store the waste in deep salt mines in Kansas. The people of Kansas rejected the idea, since no one was able to assure them that the radioactivity would not eventually leak into underground water supplies. The most elaborate and redundantly fearsome idea has been proposed by experts at the Lawrence Livermore Laboratory, one of the nation's leading nuclear-research institutions. They would set off an underground nuclear bomb beneath the waste-reprocessing plant, creating a large hole, into which the radioactive waste would be poured, to be contained—it is hoped—within the glassy walls created by the intense heat of the nuclear explosion.

The entire waste-disposal situation has been summed up by two experts who, as it happens, are optimistic about solving it, with the comment that AEC efforts "have yet to produce, after a decade and a half, one operational long-term storage facility—a sign of both commendable caution and inadequate work."

With no acceptable outlet for its radioactive waste, the nuclear-power system's temporary storage facilities have become heavily overloaded. Temporary storage is provided next to each reactor so that the spent fuel can be safely stored while its initially intense radioactivity decays somewhat. Without an operational waste-disposal system, these temporary facilities have been used routinely to hold spent fuel. There are enough such storage facilities for about 930 metric tons of spent fuel. A recent survey shows that storage space for all but 50 metric tons of fuel is now occupied; many reactors have been deprived of their temporary spent-fuel storage site. Our nuclear cup runneth over.

It is instructive to imagine how a nuclear reactor would be designed if its fuel were as innocuous as, let us say, coal—and the wastes as harmless as Mr. Zarb's aspirin—and to compare it with the actual design that is required by the radioactive realities. Such an imagined non-radioactive reactor could consist of the core of fuel rods, immersed in a tank of water, contained in a metal boiler. Steam produced in the boiler would be conducted to a turbine; the spent steam would be condensed by cooling in the usual way and the resulting water conducted back to the boiler. Control rods would govern the rate of heat output from the core. Every few years, fresh fuel rods would replace the spent ones, which would be readily disposed of (they weigh only a few thousand pounds), perhaps by burying them. The only danger would be the possibility of accidental overheating in the core or a failure in the water-circulation system, for either event could result in excessive boiler pressure and a steam explosion. Such an accident could be reliably prevented by existing boiler safety devices. (Boiler explosions plagued steam-engine operations 100 years ago—for example, on Mississippi River steamboats—but since then the technology has been thoroughly mastered and, although high-pressure steam is widely used today, boiler explosions are rare.)

When the intense radioactivity of the actual nuclear-fuel system is added to this benign imaginary device, it becomes enormously more complex—and dangerous. The core is surrounded by a heavy shield to protect workers from emitted radiation. The entire reactor is sealed into a massive containment vessel—a concrete hemisphere 150 feet across. In the vessel there are spray systems to drain off radioactive materials if the core should rupture into it. A complex system is provided for cooling down the core if the normal water-circulating system should fail. There are elaborate control and warning systems, often in multiples to reduce the risk of failure. Safety and environmental-control measures account for a large part of the cost of a nuclear reactor. All this is to avoid the consequences of a failure that might cause the core to overheat. If it became hot enough to melt, after a day the molten core could burn a hole through the bottom of the container and then release massive amounts of radioactive material into the environment.

VICTOR GILINSKY

 # A Common-Sense Approach to Nuclear Waste

The Achilles heel of nuclear power may turn out to be the lack of a satisfactory means of storing the highly radioactive spent fuel piling up at reactor sites around the country. Congress tackled the issue in the Nuclear Waste Policy Act of 1982, setting 1998 as the date when a deep underground repository could begin receiving used nuclear fuel for permanent disposal. After many years of vacillation, that action was to be a sign that the waste problem was finally under control. Unfortunately, the process of finding a suitable underground site has been delayed, and it is increasingly unlikely that the deadline will be met.

No aspect of nuclear power concerns people more than disposal of nuclear waste. In the case of deep underground disposal, this concern is underscored by uncertainties about below-surface geology, and what could happen over the long term to buried nuclear waste, as well as by the irrevocable nature of the decision. These public worries translate into demands for extraordinary precautions and siting standards so severe that it is unclear whether any site could qualify. We have taken on too great a burden in committing ourselves exclusively to a deep underground repository on a very tight schedule laid down by law. There is in fact no way of predicting when—if ever—we will have such a permanent disposal site.

One way out of this dilemma would be to build a surface or near-surface repository for semipermanent storage of nuclear waste. Such a facility would provide us with a safe means of storage while we continue to explore sites for permanent underground disposal.

Ironically, that is what the Atomic Energy Commission (AEC) concentrated its efforts on 12 years ago—developing a surface or near-surface repository. In fact, the AEC announced in 1972 that it would have such a repository available in 1979. Unfortunately, this approach was abandoned in 1975 by the newly formed Energy Research and Development Administration—for reasons not of health and safety but of psychology.

The conventional view then, as now, was that anything but permanent underground storage left proponents of nuclear power vulnerable to the charge that there was no "solution" to the waste problem. These advocates feared that, unless a permanent solution could be found, their opponents would find legal means to have plants shut down. Accordingly, the government shifted its goal to permanaent underground storage, and all sides have since been obsessed with burying the waste, or at least showing that this could be done.

The key to success would be cooperation between the Department of Energy (DOE) and the six states, mostly in the West, who are candidates for a nuclear disposal site. However, officials in these states find that their constituents balk at accepting a waste disposal facility; they worry about potential problems such as contamination of underground waters and the proximity of proposed sites to national parks and recreation areas. The states intend to make full use of the Nuclear Waste Policy Act's requirements for state participation in site selection, and they do have clout. A state veto can be overriden only by a joint congressional resolution.

If the prolonged and sometimes bitter wrangling over step one in this process—preparation of guidelines for selecting underground sites—is a sign of things to come, we are in deep trouble. One of the most controversial issues has been whether DOE should make a "preliminary determination" of suitability before it actually does geologic tests at the potential sites. The states wanted the tests done first; the DOE disagreed. Benard Rusche, DOE's new director of civilian radioactive waste management,[1] resolved the dispute last June with a timely compromise: he agreed to conduct tests first.

But underlying problems remain. The states are still deeply suspicious of the DOE site selection process, and they have little faith in the hearings on safety and environmental effects to be held before the Nuclear Regulatory Commission (NRC) grants a license to build a facility. State officials reason that if things get that far, the site will already have been approved by the DOE, the president, and Congress. That's a pretty big steamroller to stop.

No Technical Unknowns

Given the current state of affairs, the alternative of building a semipermanent repository would make good sense. Such a facility offers two important advantages: technical simplicity, and the fact that any mistakes in packaging the waste could be easily corrected. There are important safety advantages in a facility that allow inspection and maintenance of the waste, whether it is above or below ground. And since there are essentially no technical unknowns to argue about, building such a facility should be simple and inexpensive.

[1]Rusche was director in 1985. [Ed.]

A variety of schemes have been proposed for semipermanent storage. One widely accepted approach would be to build structurally enclosed concrete cavities near the surface of the ground, fill them with water, and put the spent fuel in the water. After some years, water cooling would be unnecessary, and the spent fuel could be placed in concrete canisters for extended storage. Maintenance people would be able to spot and fix any flaws and repackage the waste if necessary.

Spent fuel is now being stored at nuclear reactor sites under similar conditions. But moving the waste off the reactor sites and into sound containers in central facilities would be an improvement. Not only could the waste then be managed by specially trained staffs, but it would cease to be a distraction for the utilities that operate reactors. They have enough to worry about.

Surface repositories have another advantage: their effectiveness does not depend on special geology, so the constraints on their siting are far fewer. Officials would not, for example, have to choose a site next to a national park in Utah (a candidate for a deep repository) simply because it offered a nice salt formation.

Indeed, the law requires DOE to submit a proposal to Congress by June 1985 on establishing such a semipermanent facility under the rubric "monitored retrievable storage." Although DOE has until now downplayed the MRS option (technical bureaucracies naturally shy away from low-cost solutions), there are signs that the department is changing its mind and will support MRS as an integral part of its overall program.

Interestingly, this is the approach that Sweden has taken. That country is in the process of completing a near-surface facility—concrete-lined cavities in granite—that should be ready in a year or two.

Will the American people accept this avenue as well? We should not expect it to be embraced; no waste facility is likely to be very popular. But as long as people are reassured that a surface repository can be closely monitored and that mistakes will be corrected promptly, I think they would be more likely to accept its construction. I firmly believe that what disturbs many people about permanent underground storage is its irrevocable nature.

Unfortunately, federal officials have not factored that concern into their plans and schedules for a permanent repository. For example, DOE plans to ask for a limited work authorization so it can start construction at a site before obtaining a license. That means that by the time the NRC decides on whether to approve a construction application, DOE will have been building the facility for three years.

On paper, this is a way of allowing DOE to meet the nuclear waste act's 1998 deadline. In practice, it is a recipe for trouble. It means that sensitive issues such as geologic uncertainties will be reviewed under the pressure of construction commitments and investments. This is precisely the kind of thing that scares the states.

A principal argument against near-surface storage has been that such a program would slow down efforts to establish a permanent geologic repository. That may happen, but we should be more worried about putting all our eggs into one basket and then failing to build any storage facility. It makes sense to start with something we already know how to do.

Exercises and Projects

CHECKING YOUR COMPREHENSION

1. What does Commoner point to as the greatest problem in disposing of radioactive waste?

2. Commoner writes, "Proposals [for disposal of nuclear waste] abound, none of them satisfactory." How does he support this statement?

3. Why is Commoner doubtful that improving the reprocessing system will substantially reduce the radioactivity hazard of waste materials?

4. According to Gilinsky, what kind of site could be used for temporary disposal while permanent disposal sites are being explored?

5. In Gilinsky's view, what are the advantages of a semipermanent waste storage facility?

6. In 1972 the Atomic Energy Commission planned to have a near-surface repository ready by 1979. Why was this project abandoned, according to Gilinsky?

7. Summarize the essential difference between Commoner's and Gilinsky's views toward waste disposal safety.

FOR DISCUSSION AND DEBATE

1. Are you convinced that a near-storage waste facility would be safe enough? Why or why not?

2. Why does Commoner feel that having a "scientific priesthood" oversee atomic waste disposal operations would cloak "the devil in a laboratory coat"? Discuss the accuracy of this analogy.

3. How might Commoner react to Gilinsky's argument about the use of temporary storage facilities?

FOR YOUR NOTEBOOK

1. Keep a list of all the contaminants you hear about that are associated with nuclear waste, or with nuclear energy production. Later on, you may wish to do background reading on the properties of these contaminants to find out which are the most dangerous to human and animal life.

2. Jot down what you consider to be the benefits of nuclear energy; next, jot down all the dangers you can think of. After doing some background reading on the subject, return to your list. What do you wish to add to one list or the other? What do you wish to delete?

FOR WRITING

1. Review the current status of atomic waste disposal safety. Has there been any significant progress in lessening the risk of leakage or of radioactivity level? Report your findings and arrive at a conclusion in a three- to five-page paper. The following sources may provide you with the necessary information: *Bulletin of the Atomic Scientists, Physics Review, Journal of Applied Physics.* Also see Samuel Glasstone, *Sourcebook on Atomic Energy* (New York: D. Van Nostrand, 1967).

2. Write an essay in which you answer the question, Is atomic energy worth the risks involved? Consider, in addition to the difficulties of nuclear waste disposal, the likelihood of reactor core meltdown, radiation leakage, political sabotage, and geological instability. You may wish to refer to Three Mile Island or Chernobyl as a case in point.

3. Defend or challenge the following claim in a five- to six-page essay: "The benefits of atomic energy justify the hazards." Cite specific examples of nuclear power benefits (compared to the benefits of alternative energy sources) as well as hazardous features of nuclear power plants. You might wish to begin your research by looking up "atomic energy" in an encyclopedia such as *Encyclopaedia Britannica* or the *McGraw-Hill Encyclopedia of Science and Technology.*

Animal Rights

Each year roughly 60 million animals, from mice to primates, are used for laboratory experimentation—and subsequent sacrifice—for anything from cancer research to testing cosmetics. An editorial in *USA Today* (August 5, 1983) mentions an experiment conducted by the military in which dogs were shot with a high-powered 9 mm. Swedish Mauser to test that weapon's damaging effects. The widespread public outrage over this and similar experiments stems from the strong suspicion that many of these experiments—even if they are important to human welfare—could have been conducted without using live animals.

On the other hand, some animal rights advocates wish to put an end to all live animal experiments. But is it possible to do this without jeopardizing human welfare? At Stanford University hundreds of animals are used for many different medical research programs—dogs and primates for heart-lung transplant research, cats for brain research, rabbits for antibody research, and, of course, mice and rats for many kinds of research projects. Should all of this research come to a halt?

Some animal rights advocates seek a middle ground: Yes, they say, use animals in vital research, but treat them humanely, minimizing their fear and suffering. But above all, put a stop to all nonvital experiments, such as the heavily publicized experiment in which thousands of unanesthetized rabbits were blinded in testing a mascara dye. The difficulty is, who decides what is a vital experiment? And on what basis is the decision made? Any scientific research has many unknowns: Many experiments may prove futile, while others may produce breakthroughs. The vital nature of an experiment is often not known beforehand.

In light of this, how should animal experimentation be regulated? The following selections may provide useful clues. Peter Singer is the author of *Animal Liberation* (1977), from which the following reading is taken. He is a professor of philosophy and Director of the Centre for Human Bioethics at Monash University in Australia. John Mastalski is a Jesuit priest who wrote his article while he was a senior at Santa

Clara University. Denis Collins is a staff writer for the *San Jose Mercury News*.

TERMS TO LEARN

speciesism: discrimination against a species of animal life, based on ungrounded assumptions about intelligence, physiological complexity, and so forth

extrapolation: conceptualizing a state of affairs in a hypothetical context, based on what is observed in an actual one. The belief that human eyes will become inflamed by a cosmetic dye because that dye inflamed rabbits' eyes is an example of extrapolation.

PETER SINGER

 When Are Experiments on Animals Justifiable?

When are experiments on animals justifiable? Upon learning of the nature of many contemporary experiments, many people react by saying that all experiments on animals should be prohibited immediately. But if we make our demands as absolute as this, the experimenters have a ready reply: Would we be prepared to let thousands of humans die if they could be saved by a single experiment on a single animal?

This question is, of course, purely hypothetical. There never has been and there never could be a single experiment that saves thousands of lives. The way to reply to this hypothetical question is to pose another: Would the experimenter be prepared to carry out his experiment on a human orphan under six months old if that were the only way to save thousands of lives?

If the experimenter would not be prepared to use a human infant then his readiness to use nonhuman animals reveals an unjustifiable form of discrimination on the basis of species, since adult apes, monkeys, dogs, cats, rats, and other mammals are more aware of what is happening to them, more self-directing, and, so far as we can tell, at least as sensitive to pain as a human infant. (I specified that the human infant be an orphan to avoid the complications of the feelings of parents, although in so doing I am being overfair to the experimenter, since the nonhuman animals used in experiments are not orphans and in many species the separation of mother and young clearly causes distress for both.)

There is no characteristic that human infants possess to a higher degree than adult nonhuman animals, unless we are to count the infant's potential as a characteristic that makes it wrong to experiment on him. Whether this characteristic should count is controversial—if we count it, we shall have to condemn abortion along with experiments on infants, since the potential of the infant and the fetus is the same. To avoid the complexities of this issue, however, we can alter our original question a little and assume that the infant is one with severe and irreversible brain damage that makes it impossible for him ever to develop beyond the level of a six-month-old infant. There are, unfortunately, many such human beings, locked away in special wards throughout the country, many of them long since abandoned by their parents. Despite their mental deficiencies, their anatomy and physiology is in nearly all respects identical with that of normal humans. If, therefore, we were to force-feed them with large quantities of floor polish, or drip concentrated solutions of cosmetics into their eyes, we would have a much more reliable indication of the safety of these products for other humans than we now get by attempting to extrapolate the results of tests on a variety of other species. The radiation experiments, the heatstroke experiments, and many other experiments . . . could also have told us more about human reactions to the experimental situation if they had been carried out on retarded humans instead of dogs and rabbits.

So whenever an experimenter claims that his experiment is important enough to justify the use of an animal, we should ask him whether he would be prepared to use a retarded human at a similar mental level to the animal he is planning to use. If his reply is negative, we can assume that he is willing to use a nonhuman animal only because he gives less consideration to the interests of members of other species than he gives to members of his own—and this bias is no more defensible than racism or any other form of arbitrary discrimination.

Of course, no one would seriously propose carrying out the experiments . . . on retarded humans. Occasionally it has become known that some medical experiments have been performed on humans without their consent, and sometimes on retarded humans; but the consequences of these experiments for the human subjects are almost always trivial by comparison with what is standard practice for nonhuman animals. Still, these experiments on humans usually lead to an outcry against the experimenters, and rightly so. They are, very often, a further example of the arrogance of the research worker who justifies everything on the grounds of increasing knowledge. If experimenting on retarded, orphaned humans would be wrong, why isn't experimenting on nonhuman animals wrong? What difference is there between the two, except for the mere fact that, biologically, one is a member of our species and the other is not? But *that,* surely, is not a morally relevant difference, any more than the fact that a being is not a member of our race is a morally relevant difference.

Actually the analogy between speciesism and racism applies in practice as well as in theory in the area of experimentation. Blatant speciesism leads to painful experiments on other species, defended on the grounds of its contribution to knowledge and possible usefulness for our species. Blatant racism has led to painful experiments on other races, defended on the grounds of its contribution to knowledge and possible usefulness for the experimenting race. Under the Nazi regime in Germany, nearly 200 doctors, some of them eminent in the world of medicine, took part in experiments on Jews and Russian and Polish prisoners. Thousands of other physicians knew of these experiments, some of which were the subject of lectures at medical academies. Yet the records show that the doctors sat through medical reports of the infliction of horrible injuries on these "lesser races" and then proceeded to discuss the medical lessons to be learned from them without anyone making even a mild protest about the nature of the experiments. The parallels between this attitude and that of experimenters today toward animals are striking. Then, as now, the subjects were frozen, heated, and put in decompression chambers. Then, as now, these events were written up in a dispassionate scientific jargon. The following paragraph is taken from a report by a Nazi scientist of an experiment on a human being, placed in a decompression chamber; it could equally have been taken from accounts of recent experiments in this country on animals:

> After five minutes spasms appeared; between the sixth and tenth minute respiration increased in frequency, the TP [test person] losing consciousness. From the eleventh to the thirtieth minute respiration slowed down to three inhalations per minute, only to cease entirely at the end of that period . . . about half an hour after breathing had ceased, an autopsy was begun.

Then, as now, the ethic of pursuing knowledge was considered sufficient justification for inflicting agony on those who are placed beyond the limits of genuine moral concern. Our sphere of moral concern is far wider than that of the Nazis; but so long as there are sentient beings outside it, it is not wide enough.

To return to the question of when an experiment might be justifiable. It will not do to say: "Never!" In extreme circumstances, absolutist answers always break down. Torturing a human being is almost always wrong, but it is not absolutely wrong. If torture were the only way in which we could discover the location of a nuclear time bomb hidden in a New York City basement, then torture would be justifiable. Similarly, if a single experiment could cure a major disease, that experiment would be justifiable. But in actual life the benefits are always much, much more remote, and more often than not they are nonexistent. So how do we decide when an experiment is justifiable?

We have seen that the experimenter reveals a bias in favor of his own species whenever he carries out an experiment on a nonhuman for a purpose that he would not think justified him in using a human being, even a retarded human being. This principle gives us a guide toward an answer to our question. Since a speciesist bias, like a racist bias, is unjustifiable, an experiment cannot be justifiable unless the experiment is so important that the use of a retarded human being would also be justifiable.

This is not an absolutist principle. I do not believe that it could *never* be justifiable to experiment on a retarded human. If it really were possible to save many lives by an experiment that would take just one life, and there were *no other way* those lives could be saved, it might be right to do the experiment. But this would be an extremely rare case. Not one tenth of one percent of the experiments now being performed on animals would fall into this category. . . .

It should not be thought that medical research would grind to a halt if the test I have proposed were applied, or that a flood of untested products would come onto the market. So far as new products are concerned it is true that, as I have already said, we would have to make do with fewer of them, using ingredients already known to be safe. That does not seem to be any great loss. But for testing really essential products, as well as for other areas of research, alternative methods not requiring animals can be and would be found. Some alternatives exist already and others would develop more rapidly if the energy and resources now applied to experimenting on animals were redirected into the search for alternatives.

At present scientists do not look for alternatives *simply because they do not care enough about the animals they are using*. I make this assertion on the best possible authority, since it has been more or less admitted by Britain's Research Defence Society, a group which exists to defend researchers from criticism by animal welfare organizations. A recent article in the *Bulletin* of the National Society for Medical Research (the American equivalent of the Research Defence Society) described how the British group successfully fought off a proposed amendment to the British law regulating experiments that would have prohibited any experiment using live animals if the purpose of that experiment could be achieved by alternative means not involving animals. The main objections lodged by the Research Defence Society to this very mild attempt at reform were, first, that in some cases it may be cheaper to use animals than other methods, and secondly, that: "in some cases alternatives may exist but they may be unknown to an investigator. With the vast amount of scientific literature coming out of even a very narrow field of study it is possible that an investigator may not know all that is now known about techniques or results in a particular area." (This ignorance would make the experimenter liable to prosecution under the proposed amendment.)

What do these objections amount to? The first can mean only one thing: that economic considerations are more important than the suffering of animals; as for the second, it is a strong argument for a total moratorium on animal experiments until every experimenter has had time to read up on the existing reports of alternatives available in his field and results already obtained. Is it not shocking that experimenters may be inflicting agony on animals only because they have not kept up with the literature in their field—literature that may contain reports of methods of achieving the same results without using animals? Or even reports of similar experiments that have been done already and are being endlessly repeated?

JOHN R. MASTALSKI

Animal Rights in Perspective

Over the past several decades, a passionate liberation movement has arisen directed at the discrimination of animals. Joining other well-intentioned and justified groups that lobby for the underrepresented and exploited members of our society, the animal rights movement has succeeded in raising a few eyebrows and, at times, the judge's gavel.

The proponents of animal rights are usually intelligent, sensitive people. They argue that animals and human beings are equal in, among other things, the ability to reason, a position that justifies their staunch, morally based stance against the killing, eating, or using of animals in any way and for any reason—including for research.

I do not agree with their argument. Though not a biologist (or a philosopher), I have observed that animals are not equal to humans.

Unlike animals, human beings have the ability to reason—to decide between right and wrong, good and bad, past and present and future. Moreover, we have the abilities to question, to ponder, to reflect, to distinguish cause and effect relations, and to predict outcomes of certain events or behaviors. I haven't met an animal yet that shows any prolonged signs of guilt—a truly human quality.

So far as I am able to observe and science has been able to determine, animals do not have these reasoning faculties.

Many modern philosophers, on the other hand, favor a close relationship between humans and animals, and, in fact, would argue that what makes us comparable is not our ability to reason but our capacity to suffer.

Peter Singer, author of *Animal Liberation,* maintains that "if a being suffers, there can be no moral justification for refusing to take that suffering into consideration, and, indeed, to count it equally with the like suffering (if rough comparisons can be made) of any other being."

Anyone can observe the external indications of pain and suffering in animals. Animals, on the contrary, cannot make reasonable assumptions about the pain.

Surely a dog can determine that the pain it feels in its hindquarters resulted from its owner swatting it with a rolled newspaper. Further-more, the dog can even determine that the punishment somehow is related to the wet spot on its owners' new living room carpet. (Science has proved that animals can learn behavior.) But the dog cannot interpret or question—that is, reason—the right or wrong of the impulses behind the punishment (pain) in the same way that humans can.

Yet, animal advocates continue their campaign because they have witnessed too many injustices against the relatively defenseless animal kingdom—all for the betterment or senseless pleasure of mankind.

I, like them, agree that we should take some measures to ensure the proper treatment and care of animals. The basis of my stance, however, rests on the belief that since all animals are God's creatures, they have certain, intrinsic rights, including the right to freedom from suffering and the right to cleanliness; therefore, we are obligated to exercise tutelage and responsibility in our relationship with them. But this is not the same thing as treating them as equals.

The intensity of the animal rights lobby varies, though most of the activists lobby avidly without compromise. Over the decades, they have helped pass some very worthy laws that now protect the intrinsic rights of all animals.

Currently, they argue against the use of animals in scientific research, claiming that the pain involved in some experiments isn't justifiable. They also cite improper care given animals in research facilities.

Their protests range from staged demonstrations to an effective lobby for legislation that presently regulates, but will eventually ban, such research. Their righteousness, however, could stifle significant advances in all scientific fields—like medicine and psychology— dependent on developmental research.

The history of experimenting with animals lends itself to a small record of abuses, usually grounded on ignorance later dispelled with further research. On the contrary, partly because of research with animals, beneficial cures, therapies, medicines, and surgical procedures exist that have not only improved the fate of animals themselves but have helped humans in our treatment of polio, diabetes, heart defects, and a number of other diseases.

Scientists, surgeons, and physicians partly owe their success to animal research because few advances in their fields have emerged without such research. Moreover, the rest of us—and the animals themselves—are indebted to previous scientific research with animals, for almost solely through such research can we escape the threat of polio, survive most operations, and ingest all medicines.

Without such research, scientists would have to rely on artificial resources, like the computer, that would certainly jeopardize the near-absolute validity of their present research methods—and hamper today's advances in the treatment and cure of cancer, heart disease, AIDS, and the other polios of our day.

A majority of the arguments against animal-related research is directed at the probability that most experiments cause pain to the animals. In his essay "Animal Rights Versus Human Health," however, biologist Albert Rosenfeld professes that "the day is long past when a researcher can take any animal and do anything he pleases to it with a total disregard for its welfare and comfort."

On the contrary, researchers must bow before strict ethical codes that protect the basic rights of the animals, including a requirement to anesthetize them against unnecessary pain. According to Rosenfeld, every research facility in the United States is subject to the scrutinizing inspection of, among others, the National Institutes of Health and a roaming team of veterinarians from the U. S. Department of Agriculture.

Actually, he continues, the research "most objected to by the animal advocates are those required by the government." He cites the controversial LD-50 test (short for "lethal dose for 50 percent"). Because of the LD-50 law, all new drugs must be tested wherein "a great many animals are given a lot of the stuff to find out how much it takes to kill half of them—and the survivors aren't exactly in the pink."

The daily care of research animals also concerns the animal advocates. Fortunately, some cases of abuse have been brought to the public's attention. In 1981, for example, a research biologist from Maryland's Institute for Behavioral Research was charged with six counts of "unnecessarily failing to provide veterinary care" for the seventeen monkeys he was using in his research.

Cited for improper ventilation and cleanliness of the animal cages, he was fined $3,000 by the government and stripped of his $200,000 research grant from the National Institute of Health—thus ending 25 years of important research in the interest of stroke victims and sufferers of spinal injuries.

In fact, most scientists are aware of the obvious correlation between the controlled, sanitary care of their research animals and the validity of their research. Few scientists would jeopardize their research—not to mention their grants and licenses—by overlooking the proper care of their subjects.

I do believe that if researchers violate the intrinsic rights of their research subjects, they should be prosecuted and their research should be carried on by other competent scientists.

The advocates of animal rights, however, appear to ignore the necessary contribution that our co-habitants are helping to make for the betterment of their species and ours. Moreover, they wrongly base their arguments on the unrealistic premise of animal-human equality.

Rosenfeld wisely laments that "it would be tragic indeed—when medical science is on the verge of learning so much more that is essential to our health and welfare—if already regulation-burdened and budget-crushed researchers were further hampered" by the increasingly effective lobby of the animal rights protesters.

Sadly, they continue to frustrate significant scientific progress while failing to accept the necessity of animals in research and the essential contributions they make toward alleviating suffering for humans and animals alike.

DENIS COLLINS

 ## Animal Rights vs. Medical Research

Dr. Thomas Hamm might begin the movie version of his life story with a close-up of a red-haired kid plucking a thorn from the paw of a neighborhood dog. He would end it, after a lifetime of scholarship, with his discovery of a cure for AIDS, heart disease or cancer.

"I know it sounds corny, but my goal is to make this a better planet," says Hamm, the 44-year-old director of animal research at Stanford University. "And I think I've already achieved my goal."

There would be other, less flattering versions of the Dr. Hamm story. In the harshest, Hamm and his colleagues at Stanford's Division of Laboratory Animal Medicine would be depicted performing un-speakable acts upon dogs, cats and monkeys. Lassie eviscerated. Garfield electrocuted. And all for the sake of specious science and personal enrichment.

"It bothers my staff that they're thought of that way. There is that image of us down here as torturers," says Hamm, who claims he has received death threats from animal-rights activists. "The whole idea of it is to drive people out of research. We really don't understand this controversy."

The controversy at Stanford, which is focusing for the moment on a planned expansion of Stanford's Animal Research Facility, is just one skirmish in a nationwide war between animal-rights advocates and biomedical researchers. It is a conflict of moral principle, stained with the blood of laboratory mice. And it has been waged at times with more than words.

During the last six years there have been break-ins at more than a dozen research facilities across the country. Research animals have been "liberated" and equipment destroyed. In April of this year, the underground Animal Liberation Front claimed credit for a fire that caused $3.5 million in damage at an unfinished veterinary lab at the University of California at Davis.

Like the debate over abortion, the animal rights-vs.-research controversy has polarized its adversaries into hostile camps. Hamm refers to the most radical animal-rights activists as "terrorists." And he distrusts even the avowed centrists in the movement.

"I think people are really being fooled by the person who stands up and says, 'We're not against research. We just want it done

185

properly,' " Hamm insists. "If they were sincere, they'd say, 'Way to go, Stanford.' Because we do it right."

The extremists in the animal-rights movement, who oppose any use or domination of animals including pet ownership, depict researchers such as Hamm as callous, misguided or immoral. At last spring's biannual demonstration at Stanford to protest research on animals, one protester summed up that attitude.

"Most of them," said Emily Halber of Los Altos, referring to the researchers, "are sadists."

The mainstream of the animal-welfare movement wants conditions in research facilities, which undeniably have been gruesome in years past, made more humane. There is, though, much disagreement over whose standard of humaneness should apply.

Caught in this clash of moral and ethical values, biomedical researchers say, are the lives of human beings not yet born. Nearly every major medical breakthrough in the last half century from the development of polio vaccines and antibiotics to the pioneer work in organ transplants, has been made possible by research performed on mice, rabbits, dogs, cats and primates. Outlaw animal research, they say, and you outlaw future medical discoveries.

"We have to look at the consequences of giving animals rights," Laurence McCullough of Georgetown University's Kennedy Center for Bioethics told Washingtonian Magazine last year. "Are you ready to say to the thousands of human beings in this country who have heart attacks every year that we're more obligated not to use those dogs than we are to you?"

Helen McCloskey, president of the Palo Alto Humane Society and the leader in the effort to keep Stanford from expanding its animal-research facility, insists that there can be both research and respect for animal rights in the nation's laboratories.

"I'm definitely more of a centrist on this whole issue," says McCloskey, wife of former California Republican congressman Pete McCloskey. "I think most people (in the animal-rights movement) say yes, there is some research that is vital and there is a need to use animals for the foreseeable future. But there is a tremendous amount of research that is not vital. There is much that is incredibly duplicative. In some instances, the use of animals is almost promiscuous."

McCloskey sits on the board of review for animal use at Letterman Army Institute for Research in San Francisco. Kim Sturla, a director of the Peninsula Humane Society, sits on a similar review board at the University of California at Berkeley. Both women ask why Stanford

University will not allow a member of the "movement" to occupy a similar spot.

"I think the public has an absolute right to know what is going on there," Sturla says. "To deny that kind of accessibility to the (Stanford) research lab is inexcusable."

Hamm opposes the inclusion of an animal-rights representative on an oversight committee at his facility, even though he knows "it makes it look like we're trying to hide something."

"I'm not saying they're all terrorists," says Hamm, sitting in his office at the Stanford facility, which is beneath a medical-center parking lot. "But we don't know who is and who isn't. We don't know who belongs to the Animal Liberation Front."

Hamm, who has graduate degrees in zoology, veterinary medicine, laboratory animal medicine and comparative pathology, is impatient with activists who have no formal education in animal behavior, yet tell him what animals need to be happy. "Just because someone owns a dog, that does not make them an expert," he says.

He conducts tours of his facility for anyone who asks, including animal-rights advocates. But the advocates complain those prearranged tours are too easily stage-managed.

"I went on a tour with a group of people from various humane organizations perhaps a year and a half ago and this tour showed me absolutely nothing," says Jane Hutchison, director of communications for the Humane Society of Santa Clara Valley. "All I could do was peer through a small window in a door to where the animals were housed. Basically, we have to take Stanford's word for it."

Hamm counters that Stanford is the "state of the art" research facility in the country, and he points to the glowing reports from six inspections (two of them unannounced) by the U. S. Department of Agriculture this year to prove it.

But activists counter that the USDA has not exactly been a harsh inspector in years past. The USDA approved conditions at a University of Pennsylvania's Head Injury Clinic in 1984, for example, just months before revelations concerning abuse of baboons at that facility led to the suspension of funding for the project by then-Secretary of Health and Human Services Margaret Heckler.

"I can't guarantee there will be no abuses. I'm sure there are some because we're human," Hamm says during a tour of his facility. "But we have a vested interest in avoiding that. You can't do good science unless you take care of your animals. You can't get good research from animals that are stressed or diseased."

Hamm spoke as he gave a tour of the facility. Hairless rats with induced tumors occupied one corner of a room lined with glass cages. Across from them sat large white rats, in apparent good health, awaiting their call to service. "These rats are just sitting around getting old," Hamm says.

In the "narcoleptic" room, dogs born with sleeping sickness barked, fell asleep, then woke to bark again with startling speed.

Twenty years ago, Hamm and his colleagues at Stanford might have been lionized by a public grateful for their lifesaving discoveries. Today, ask to speak to some of the Stanford researchers, and Hamm's answer reveals how much the status quo has changed.

"I'm willing to talk. That's my job. But as far as getting somebody else to, it's always hard," Hamm says. "As soon as somebody does, they become the focus. People here are afraid."

Are they afraid enough to abandon careers?

"I shouldn't say it, because the animal-rights people would love to hear it, but yes, people in my field have quit. They don't believe it's worth putting up with this kind of harassment. The problem is," Hamm says, "if you quit, they've won."

Exercises and Projects

CHECKING YOUR COMPREHENSION

1. What is the basis for Singer's comparison of human infants with nonhuman animals?

2. According to Singer, when is an animal experiment justifiable?

3. Mastalski asserts that animals are not equal to humans. What reasons does he give?

4. How does Mastalski reconcile the necessity for animal experimentation with what he calls "the intrinsic rights" of animals?

5. Collins's report on the Stanford controversy is intended to present the views of the medical researchers and the animal rights activists equally. Without taking sides, summarize each view as objectively as you can.

FOR DISCUSSION AND DEBATE

1. Defend or challenge one of the following assertions:
   a. "If the experimenter would not be prepared to use a human infant, then his readiness to use nonhuman animals reveals an unjustifiable form of discrimination on the basis of species." (Singer)
   b. "The history of experimenting with animals lends itself to a small record of abuses, usually grounded on ignorance later dispelled with further research." (Mastalski)
   c. "Most of them [animal researchers] are sadists." (Emily Halber, quoted by Collins).

2. Should animal experimentation be limited to vital research only? In arguing, be sure to stipulate your definition of *vital*. Just as important, address the point that seemingly nonvital research can, in the long run, prove to be of vital importance—that scientists often have no way of knowing where a line of inquiry will lead.

3. Debate Singer's claim that scientists do not look for alternatives to experimenting on animals "simply because they do not care enough about the animals they are using" (paragraph 13).

FOR YOUR NOTEBOOK

1. Over the next few days, use your notebook to record your own views about animal rights. Do rapid freewrites on the following: using animals to test cosmetic products; using the hides of animals for fur coats, shoes, or other articles of clothing; hunting higher-order animals such as whales and dolphins for food, in light of the fact that (a) they are part of the basic diet of those who hunt them and (b) they are endangered and of comparatively high intelligence.

2. Make a list of animals that, in your opinion, should never be used for laboratory experiments; now make a list of animals that are most appropriate for laboratory experiments. How would you defend your choices?

3. Is it possible to support animal rights and eat meat without being hypocritical? Explore this common dilemma in a notebook entry.

FOR WRITING

1. Write an essay in which you convey your personal feelings about the importance of animal rights in the context of necessary medical research.

2. It has been suggested that animal rights advocates be allowed to sit in on oversight committees that regulate the use of animals for research projects. Do you agree or disagree? Argue your premise in a three- to four-page essay.

3. Write a short essay in which you draw a clear distinction between humane treatment and abuse with regard to animals used for experiments. Be sure to take a stand on some of the "gray areas" you encounter. For example, if you argue that any animal sacrificed for a nonessential experiment is abused, you must be prepared to explain what you mean by a nonessential experiment.

The Uses of Genetic Engineering

Genetic control has been a stock theme in science fiction since Aldous Huxley in 1934 created his nightmare vision of a genetically predetermined society in *Brave New World*. During the following two decades, the secrets of the gene did indeed begin to be revealed, climaxed by the discovery of the structure of DNA in 1953. Before long, biochemists learned to manipulate genes, to "splice" pieces of one organism's DNA onto that of another organism, thereby creating entirely new life-forms.

Understandably, many people were alarmed. Science fiction stories often tell of mutated organisms that are transformed into monsters. Would the new findings in genetic research lead to disaster?

The following forum, moderated by Lewis Lapham, editor of *Harper's*, is based on a discussion held at the Cooper Union for the Advancement of Science and Art in New York City. It addresses the ethical issues that arise from this far-reaching, complex technology. Three topics are discussed: (1) fetal brain implants, (2) sex determination before conception, and (3) genetic profiles of test-tube babies. The discussions make clear how inseparable are human welfare and scientific research and how important it is that nonscientists understand the complexities involved.

Lewis Lapham is joined by Nancy Dubler, director of the Division of Legal and Ethical Issues in Health Care at New York City's Montefiore Medical Center; Thomas Murray, director of the Center for Bioethics, Case Western Reserve University School of Medicine; Jeremy Rifkin, author of *Declarations of a Heretic* (1985) and *Entropy* (1980) and president of the Foundation on Economic Trends in Washington D. C.; and Lee Salk, professor of child development at Brown University and clinical professor of psychology and pediatrics at Cornell University Medical School.

TERMS TO LEARN

Parkinson's disease: a neural disorder characterized by hand tremors and muscular stiffness

Alzheimer's disease: a disorder of the brain's frontal and temporal lobes, causing serious impairment of speech and memory

insulin: a hormone, secreted by the pancreas, that enables the body to utilize sugar

diabetes: a disease resulting from an insulin deficiency and consequent excess of sugar in the blood

survival of the fittest: a principle of evolution whereby the strongest and healthiest of a species survive (and hence reproduce) while the weak and sickly die before they can reproduce

Down's syndrome: a congenital birth defect affecting the brain, marked by physical malformation and retardation

eugenics: the systematic improvement of the human species through natural or technological genetic control

LEWIS H. LAPHAM
NANCY NEVELOFF DUBLER
THOMAS H. MURRAY
JEREMY RIFKIN
LEE SALK

 Ethics in Embryo

Fetal Brain Implants

CURRENT TECHNOLOGY
Swedish scientists have relieved the symptoms of Parkinson's disease
by implanting fetal brain tissue in patients' brains. The fetal tissue
causes regeneration in the surrounding brain tissue.

PROPOSED TECHNOLOGY
Scientists discover that fetal brain implants restore mental lucidity in
Alzheimer's disease patients.

LAPHAM: Let's say the breakthrough of using fetal brains to reverse
Alzheimer's was announced this morning. This means the demand
for fetal brain tissue will no longer be confined to the small number
of Parkinson's patients. Now almost everyone will have a grandfather
or grandmother who could benefit. Nancy Dubler, do you think
there's a problem with the widespread use of fetal brains as a
routine therapy?

DUBLER: That depends on the restrictions applied, the assumptions
about the fetus, and the context. Fetuses deserve respect. I don't
think that principle conflicts with the right of a woman to an
abortion. But it would demand that nothing demeaning or repugnant
be done with the fetus.

Let us assume a woman opts for an abortion and the fetus that is
removed has brain tissue which could be effectively transplanted.
If the mother had no objection, then it could be used. There should
be a requirement that the arrangement not be commercial. The
woman should not profit from the procedure. The issue of profit to
the physician is slightly more complicated.

SALK: I agree with Nancy that the context is important. What would
make it repugnant would be if a woman became pregnant in order
to sell the aborted fetus.

LAPHAM: Tom Murray, why is the profit motive repugnant? We sell
blood.

193

MURRAY: Actually we sell very little blood in this country. The overwhelming majority is donated. We used to think that you had to pay people to get them to give blood. But that turns out not to be true. The American public is overwhelmingly against a commercial system for blood. They would probably feel the same repugnance to a market in fetal brains.

One of the primary reasons we donate blood, organs, and other kinds of tissues is to affirm our ties with the strangers among whom we live. It is one of the few ways left open for us, in a mass bureaucratic society, to minister to their needs, particularly their health needs.

LAPHAM: I really don't understand the objection to the profit motive. We're talking about a waste product here: thousands of fetuses are discarded every day.

DUBLER: We would not want to live in a society where women became pregnant for the purpose of making money.

LAPHAM: For Mary Beth Whitehead, we already do live in that kind of society.

DUBLER: That's different. And some of us want to see that practice halted.

But if you go back to blood donation—and I think Tom is right, that is the closest analogy—we discovered that to maintain the highest quality blood supply it was unwise to have people sell their blood. The profit motive, it turns out, encourages blood donations from hepatitis carriers. But more than that, you don't want to encourage commerce in human parts. That's a bad idea.

LATHAM: Let's say there's no commercial motivation: Should you use discarded fetal brains to treat Alzheimer's?

DUBLER: In organ donations, when someone dies, we approach the family. We say, "Now that this person is dead, someone else may benefit from what remains physiologically of this person." We ask the family for their consent. That seems to me to be the closest analogy we have.

LAPHAM: So that you would ask women coming into abortion clinics routinely to sign a waiver allowing the fetal tissue to be used?

DUBLER: Yes. It would be a two-step process. First, society reaches a judgment, either through its legislative process or through a combination of political and administrative processes, that this is a good for society and should be encouraged. Step two, the individual involved—the gestational mother—can refuse or consent to have those fetal parts used.

LAPHAM: Jeremy Rifkin, do you agree?

RIFKIN: There's a broader question that needs to be looked at. For the last hundred years in Western medical science, there has been a shift toward utilitarianism, toward short-term benefits to individuals. However, utilitarianism has thrived at the expense of a gradual desacralization of the life process. In this kind of procedure, two different values conflict: the short-term utilitarian value to the individual versus the long-run systematic desacralization of human life itself.

Science and technology in Western civilization have increasingly reduced living things to dead material for manipulation. We need to ask ourselves: Is life more than the chemicals that make it up? Is life more than tissues and cells and nucleic acid sequences?

MURRAY: I don't think utilitarianism or reductionism is the issue here. In fact, if you consider how the theologians have approached organ transplantation—theologians such as Paul Ramsey—they can, in the end, justify organ transplantation precisely because they believe in the sacredness of life.

DUBLER: I am a bit surprised, Jeremy, by your answer. When you sign an organ-donation card, or when a family agrees to an organ transplant after a person is brain-dead, that is a benefit to others and not a detriment to the individual. I would argue it enhances the sanctity of life by permitting others to enjoy a better quality of life.

RIFKIN: Let me try to place this in another time context. I'm not talking about the immediate moment because one could advance very good arguments for each immediate moment over the last fifty to seventy-five years of medical advances in Western culture. I'm arguing about a longer time span. If we look at this period anthropologically we find that, step-by-step, we are reducing life to the chemical components that make it up. And we're doing it in the name of good, in the name of providing benefits for our fellow human beings. But we're going to have to look at the long-term implications of doing that. I think they are profound and disturbing, and again they get to the heart of our world view.

In public policy in Washington, ethical concerns always play a secondary role to commercial considerations. By the time the ethics of a new technology are debated, it's generally too late to change course. The technology is already ensconced in the marketplace. The religious community, the social philosophers, and the ethicists—much to my chagrin—have been edged out of public deliberation in any meaningful way on these technologies.

MURRAY: You could make those arguments about almost any earlier technology. Penicillin was a new technology once; it was discovered in 1928 and made available in the '40s. At the same time you could have said: We don't know all the effects—more children will survive childhood and that will affect housing markets; more old people will live longer because we can now cure them of pneumonia at age seventy-three instead of just letting them die. We could have faced exactly the same questions.

SALK: Take the case of diabetes: Insulin treatment has allowed millions of people to reach reproductive age who have a diabetic tendency. Insulin has introduced into the population a high incidence of people prone to diabetes.

My own research on adolescent suicide suggests that complications during pregnancy, labor, and delivery seem to increase the likelihood of suicide during adolescence and perhaps later in life. Now that we can save more babies, we might be, in a sense, tampering with nature's quality control.

Thirty years ago we did not engage in heroics in the delivery room. Newborns were allowed to die if there were any complications. Today those same babies survive and seem to be at risk for problems later. Maybe we're introducing certain weaknesses into the species. That's the disadvantage and it suggests a much larger question.

Survival of the fittest in the evolutionary process and natural selection may no longer be the only factors influencing the course of life. We have reached the point where we can control our evolution and change the world we live in without waiting for natural forces to operate. We have become the force that can control our evolution. The problem is *how* we are going to shape it. We will indeed be doing that and manipulating things that were once considered totally unacceptable. Implanting fetal brains in adults' brains is only the beginning.

Sex Determination Before Conception

CURRENT TECHNOLOGY
Male-and female-producing sperm can be separated by machine. Artificial insemination then gives parents the opportunity to choose the sex of their child. The success rate is 95 percent when seeking boys, slightly less for girls.

PROPOSED TECHNOLOGY
A spermicide that kills either male-or female-producing sperm and provides near statistical certainty in determining the sex of the child.

LAPHAM: Let's suppose that this spermicide—let's call it Sexselex—can determine at intercourse the sex of the child.

MURRAY: I suppose it comes in pink and blue tubes?

LAPHAM: Exactly. Now I'm the father of, say, three sons, and I want to have a daughter. I want to buy Sexselex. What do you tell me?

DUBLER: You can't buy it. I tell you to read all the pertinent literature and to arrange intercourse at that time and in that position recommended by the literature to produce the boy or girl you want.

LAPHAM: What's the difference? I can buy it for $5 in a blue or pink tube. Otherwise it could take ten years and I could miss. Maybe I'm not athletic enough.

DUBLER: I'm telling you there are certain technologies which could be so disruptive to the basic fabric of society that we will say they are excluded from the marketplace. Whatever shadow of that technology you can achieve through more natural processes, you're welcome to do.

Given the ongoing problem of female infanticide in China and India, it seems clear that the technology would be used to discriminate mainly against females.

SALK: I have no doubt that we will use this technology, but I have real problems with it. If we begin to manipulate the existing balance between genders in any society, we will have a major disruptive effect on society.

If a man and a woman want to bring a child into this world only if it is a certain gender, they shouldn't have a child in the first place. When it comes to French poodles, they can choose. But the nurturing of a child should not depend on its gender.

LAPHAM: Wait. I'm allowed to take an aspirin. I'm allowed to take penicillin. I'm allowed to take all kinds of products that are not natural. But now you're telling me that to conceive a child I must return to the state of nature.

DUBLER: You're also allowed to take medication that will prevent conception. But there are certain parts of the reproductive process that properly lie beyond individual manipulation by scientific technology.

LAPHAM: Do you think you have any chance explaining that to a desperate father?

DUBLER: I think that there are some plights of the human condition for which there are impermissible answers. This is one. I'm sorry that you have only three sons. I agree that daughters are highly valuable. But it is not a problem to which society permits a specific and effective solution.

LAPHAM: Even though I can buy it in the drugstore?

DUBLER: No, no. I'm not letting you buy it in the drugstore.

SALK: You're not going to be able to stop him.

DUBLER: I would make every effort to keep it out of the drugstore by having the FDA refuse to license it.

LAPHAM: If you pass that law, I'll make a fortune. I'll make much more with Sexselex on the black market than I could over the counter.

RIFKIN: This example forces us to address what's really happening here. As we move out of the Industrial Age into the Biotechnical Age, we're increasingly able to manipulate living things for our own advantage. What we're really talking about is engineering the life process. So let's begin by understanding what engineering is.

We are introducing technological principles into reproduction. We are exploiting living things with the same methodology used during the Industrial Age to exploit inanimate things.

Engineering is about quality controls, design, and building predictability into the product.

SALK: It is disruptive to any culture to interfere with the balance of male and female. But it's inevitable; it's going to happen. With so many new technologies, we look back and wonder "How did we ever adapt?" Well, we did adapt.

LAPHAM: But would you try to legislate this technology out of existence?

SALK: If we did, we would indeed make some people rich by creating a black market. My approach would be for public education to convince people it's unwise to do this. It may be better to develop a conscience than to develop legislation. People may act on their conscience.

MURRAY: We shouldn't let this product on the market. The reason Lee Salk and Nancy Dubler offer is cogent, but it's not the only reason.

If we let you choose your child's sex, we're saying it is socially legitimate to get pregnant, test the fetus, and decide whether to keep it or not.

LAPHAM: Don't we do that already?

MURRAY: We do for certain limited purposes. We use amniocentesis to look for certain serious detectable disorders. Should we also use it to screen for gender? I think not. Look what the baby becomes—a commodity just like your car. You want it with air-conditioning? This one doesn't have air-conditioning, so you return it to the manufacturer.

LAPHAM: Our society already treats its citizenry like commodities.

MURRAY: Do you really believe we can buy and sell each other?

LAPHAM: That's exactly what we do every day.

DUBLER: This sounds like Sweeney Todd's London.

LAPHAM: No, it sounds like Donald Trump's New York.

Genetic Profiles of Test-tube Babies

CURRENT TECHNOLOGY
In vitro fertilization involves the withdrawal of about six eggs from a woman. All the eggs are fertilized with the father's sperm. Those eggs which show abnormal cell division in the early stages are destroyed. The remaining fertilized eggs are returned to the mother's womb for development.

PROPOSED TECHNOLOGY
The woman takes fertility drugs, or is "superovulated," to produce around thirty eggs. These are fertilized and genetically profiled to determine whether the embryo has diseases, such as Huntington's chorea; afflictions, such as Down's syndrome, or even simple astigmatism; and finally for characteristics such as eye color, skin color, and physical imperfections.

LAPHAM: I've got thirty fertilized eggs here. Ms. Dubler, am I allowed to throw out the embryos with Down's syndrome or serious disorders?

DUBLER: Yes. We look to find out if there is Down's syndrome or any other affliction that we recognize as exceptionally painful and difficult, those that are not a "good" in human beings.

LAPHAM: How do we know which traits are "not a good in human beings"?

RIFKIN: Exactly. Every year we locate more and more genetic markers for single-gene diseases. When the technology exists to remove them, there will be parental pressure to do so. Soon parents are going to have a genetic read-out of all the traits they can potentially pass on to their children. Parents will become statisticians. They're going to ask, "Do I want to burden my child with a particular trait?"

Where do you draw the line? There are several thousand recessive traits. Leukemia can kill your child at three, heart disease at thirty, and Alzheimer's at fifty. At what point do you say no? Society might even legislate or compel parents not to pass on certain traits because of the health costs likely to be incurred.

We're forcing a profound change in the parent-child relationship. As we introduce predictability, we create more pressure for perfect eggs, perfect sperm, and perfect embryos.

MURRAY: Let's make a distinction. With a disease, a child is sick and in pain. And there are a relative handful of genetic disorders that cause great suffering. But with a recessive trait the gene is not expressed, so the child is not ill. There are thousands of those, so why remove them?

LAPHAM: Let's get back to my petri dish. You've got thirty fertilized eggs. You're going to allow me to take out Down's. What else are you going to let me take out?

DUBLER: Tay-Sachs, Huntington's. If we have the same information about early-onset Alzheimer's as we do about Tay-Sachs, I would include early-onset Alzheimer's.

LAPHAM: I'm down to twenty-six. Now let's suppose the twenty fifth one has got a harelip. Am I allowed to take that one out?

DUBLER: You're not going to test for that, so you're not going to know.

LAPHAM: As soon as I get the technology I'm going to test for that. Mr. Rifkin is right. Once you let me take out Tay-Sachs, there's no stopping.

DUBLER: I don't agree with that at all. There is a fundamental assumption in this discussion with which I disagree profoundly: that we as a society cannot make and enforce decisions. We as a society could have a reproductive policy which stated that we could test for those conditions that burden the life to such a degree that it is permissible to exclude them. The number of conditions would be limited. Aside from those, you would not gather the information. It would be regulated the same way we now regulate research.

RIFKIN: How do you determine "the conditions that burden life"? What about a disease that kills at age five or one that kills at age thirty?

DUBLER: Dying of Huntington's is a terrible death, and I think that society has a shared perception on certain diseases. We can draw lines. We are human beings; we deal with difficult problems all the time.

MURRAY: Jeremy, you lack faith in our ability to make judgments, yet we make judgments all the time. We decide what is a disease and what is not a disease, what's a deformity and what's not a deformity. For example, society says: "If you have a harelip, that's a deformity, and it's enough of one to warrant trying to correct it. We'll even help you pay for it."

That's a social consensus. Whereas if you want a tummy tuck because you don't like your paunch, we say we'll let you do it, but we sure as hell won't pay for it. We draw that line. You may want to argue with me about how to draw it, but we draw it nonetheless.

LAPHAM: But our "society" is defined by the marketplace. And a capitalist ethic does not allow the state to say: Do this, do that.

DUBLER: Sure it does. Let me give you an example. On the black market, you can buy or sell anything. You can torture people. You can pay to have them killed. You can sell human flesh. I don't want to argue that criminals don't exist. On the open market, though, what society professes to believe guides our behavior.

Over the last decade we as a society have said there are certain values in medical research which we will support and ones we will prohibit.

For example, you can't do research on children where there is more than a "minimal risk to the child" unless there is an overwhelming compensating benefit. So we've taken medical research, which is also driven by the marketplace, by gain, by ego, by position, and we've said, *no,* there are certain things that you can't do.

Let me come back to our petri dish. There are certain things you can't do. You can take out Huntington's and you can take out early Alzheimer's and then you are left with a certain number of fertilized eggs. Here's what you do: You will line them up, you will take the first one in line, and you will implant it. I don't think that's any more difficult than regulating research. The black market will exist, but that doesn't invalidate my argument.

RIFKIN: What we're really talking about is eugenics. Professional ethicists keep looking out the front door saying, "I hope this technology isn't abused by a particular government or a particular ideological system. I hope another Adolf Hitler doesn't come along."

Meanwhile a new eugenics has quietly slipped in the back door. You can hear it in our conversation today. We're talking about commercial eugenics. We want perfect babies. We want perfect plants and animals. We want a better economy. There's no evil intent here. The road to the Brave New World is paved with good intentions.

Step-by-step, we are deciding to engineer parts of the genetic code of living things. Two important questions emerge: If we're going to engineer the genetic code, what criteria does this society establish for determining good and bad, useful and dysfunctional genes? And I would like to know whether there is an institution anyone here would trust with the ultimate authority to decide the genetic blueprints for a living thing?

MURRAY: Wait. You asked me to come up with a criterion for a disease everyone thinks should be engineered out. Here it is: a disease that causes a prolonged, painful, and undignified death. How does that sound?

RIFKIN: Would you feel qualified to be on the President's Commission set up to advise on this?

MURRAY: You never answer a question.

RIFKIN: Would you feel qualified to give advice and consent as to what genetic changes in the biological code of human beings are permissible?

MURRAY: Yes. I wouldn't feel qualified to make the ultimate judgment, but I would feel qualified to become part of the discussion. The alternative is to do nothing. Again, Jeremy, you hold no faith in our ability to make any distinctions, any reasonable judgments.

RIFKIN: I have faith in humanity's ability to make reasonable judgments. The question is who is making the judgments and on behalf of whom? What are the preconceptions and central assumptions that we're using?

SALK: Let's look for a moment at a technology developed two decades ago and see where that's taken us. Neonatology, the medical science devoted to troubled newborns, emerged as a subspecialty about 1965 and created a new breed of physicians. Have we made any reasonable judgments in this field? What I see is a technology driving these doctors to save babies at the lowest birth weight possible. Today I see babies born in our hospital with multiple handicaps. We can save a 600-gram baby, but I don't think the doctors are as concerned with the quality of life as they should be.

DUBLER: I disagree with that entirely. They're very concerned, although puzzled as to how to determine it. They're very aware that it would be unethical to save a 200-gram infant.

SALK: But I'm not sure it's ethical to save a 1,000-gram infant with multiple handicaps.

DUBLER: Many neonatologists would agree.

SALK: But no one is setting up any criteria that they can abide by. Thirty years ago, when a baby was born with respiratory distress, other than giving it oxygen, they would just put it in the corner and let nature take its course. Mothers were told, "This is God's will. You would have had a multiply handicapped child. It's better to let it go." And people accepted that. They had no problems with that at all.

DUBLER: I disagree with almost every one of your statements. There are some babies who are so clearly in intractable pain that they cannot lead any sort of reasonable life. At that point they are let go. Those decisions are made carefully and adequately on moral bases by the medical team and the parents.

Neonatology is a good example where principles—incorporating both science and ethics—have provided real guideposts for caregivers. Similarly, I think a standard for genetic decisions could be developed along the lines of Tom Murray's criterion: when suffering and disease and an undignified death are inevitable.

MURRAY: It's hard to imagine a culture that would not spare people suffering and painful death, as long as it didn't come at a terrible moral price.

LAPHAM: What I hear Nancy and Tom saying is that you are prepared to breed out pain or death in our petri dish but you're not prepared to breed anything in.

DUBLER: Correct.

MURRAY: Right.

LAPHAM: Why not breed in? We could solve the problem of racism, for instance. Let's take out skin color in my petri dish. Why won't you let me do that?

MURRAY: Is that the way to respond to a social problem like discrimination?

LAPHAM: You let me prevent hideous death, but you won't let me put in any "positive" traits.

RIFKIN: When the day comes that we can make these decisions, we will probably be less tolerant of the disabled because we will perceive them as defective *products*.

Also, we're likely to see the beginning of a prejudice based on genetic type, on genetic read-out, which is likely to be just as virulent as prejudice based on race or ethnic background.

Should your employer know that you have a tendency toward Alzheimer's? Should your school system know the genetic read-out of your child? Should a government have these records? I suspect we're going to see the beginning of a biological caste system in the next two to three centuries. We may be seeing the gradual emergence of eugenics in civilization.

MURRAY: You're using the word "eugenics" a little too cavalierly here. Eugenics means the management of the genetic stock of a population.

RIFKIN: To improve it.

MURRAY: To "improve" it, as if we know what that means.

RIFKIN: That's the problem with engineering for improvement. Do you know of any engineer who only wants to make technology *somewhat* efficient but not *perfectly* efficient? Do you know of any engineer who stops midway through the process and decides to accept less than the most efficient solution? I don't. Engineers want to continue the process until they have *perfected* the technology. Why would it be any different in genetic engineering than it is in mechanical or electrical or nuclear engineering?

DUBLER: Because people are not bolts of steel.

RIFKIN: But we are beginning to perceive living things as indistinguishable from bolts of steel.

DUBLER: I don't accept that judgment.

RIFKIN: It depends on what your highest value is. If your highest value is respect for life, then I would agree that we've got a fighting chance here. If, however, the highest value in civilization is efficiency, expediency, and engineering values, then I would say we're in trouble.

MURRAY: If that's the way the values line up, we're in deep trouble. I think fortunately the values don't line up that way.

RIFKIN: The problem with these different values is that they are being developed into a new sociology, one that goes hand-in-hand with genetic engineering. Increasingly we open up the newspaper and find articles saying we have located the newest gene governing personality or social behavior (a good example is the much celebrated but recently discredited "depression" gene).

We're beginning to believe that our social behavior is a direct result of our genetic typing. Social biologists don't come right out and say, "It's all genetics; it's all inheritance." What they do say is more subtle: That genetic inheritance is the *broad determinant* of your personality. Environment, institutions, and values play some role, they say, but it's a smaller role than we had thought.

What happens in a society that has both the technology to manipulate the genetic code and a social biology that suggests that we are no more or less than the genes that make us up? It's a dangerous combination, moving us ever closer to a eugenic civilization.

MURRAY: This is not the first sweeping intellectual change that mankind has experienced. I think Jeremy is right in saying that this challenges the way we think about ourselves. But then again so did Copernicus, so did Darwin, so did Freud. They challenged us to think about ourselves in entirely new ways—in ways at least as profound as those imposed by the genetic-engineering revolution. We still look at ourselves as creatures capable of dignity, capable of meaning, capable of morality.

DUBLER: One example of individual choice—and a simple form of genetic engineering—is choosing your spouse. If you think, for example, that sociological characteristics are linked to behaviors that are determined by genes, then you ought not to choose someone to reproduce with who has a history of assaults or burglaries or murders.

LAPHAM: You're allowing me free choice with my spouse but not my child.

DUBLER: Yes, absolutely. Even though over 50 percent of us in this country make bad decisions in our choice of a spouse, we will not limit that foolishness even when it's repetitive foolishness. That's because there are values inherent in individual choice.

LAPHAM: I don't understand what value system anybody at this table lives by. You'll allow me free choice with a spouse, but not with a child.

SALK: We'll allow you free choice about whether or not to have children.

LAPHAM: And you'll allow me to design my child with enormously expensive neonatal care, private schools, child psychiatrists, Yale University.

DUBLER: That's coping with your decisions.

LAPHAM: No. It's trying to imprint on my descendant a certain set of traits.

DUBLER: You get to rear your child, that's all.

LAPHAM: I get to rear—not design—my child?

DUBLER: Yes.

RIFKIN: But wait a minute. What I gather from you is that some design is permissible and some isn't.

DUBLER: To manipulate for a good—such as ruling out Huntington's—is different than designing.

RIFKIN: To plan in advance the outcome of something: That's what design is. So what you really want is to eliminate the word "design."

DUBLER: Because language helps us distinguish among processes even when they are similar.

RIFKIN: Haven't you introduced design by eliminating one gene? It seems to me you're not taking full responsibility for this. You're saying you are willing to design for some things but not others. It's not semantics. It's a question of whether you're willing to plan any part of the genetic makeup of your offspring in advance.

MURRAY: I'm willing to spare my offspring the horrors of a few terrible diseases.

RIFKIN: It's interesting how we use language. Scientists used the term "genetic engineering" up until the late 1970s. When the controversy over genetics emerged the word was changed from "engineering" to "therapy." Suddenly we're talking about gene therapy. What's the difference between engineering and therapy?

LAPHAM: From this discussion it seems obvious. Therapy connotes taking away the negatives, and engineering connotes putting in the positives. The sentiment here is that it's okay to take away the negatives; that's therapy. It's not okay to put in the positives; that's engineering.

RIFKIN: So when an engineer takes a defect out of a machine, that's not engineering—that's therapy.

MURRAY: We're not talking about engineering; we are talking about eliminating a disease.

RIFKIN: You're talking here about changing the blueprint of life itself.

MURRAY: When a physician cures a disease, is that engineering?

RIFKIN: Yes, if the physician engineers changes into the genetic blueprint. When an engineer eliminates a defect in the design of a tool, that's engineering. Because you're going right to the heart of the actual technology that you've created. Remember, just because something can be done doesn't mean it inevitably should be done. Throughout history many more technologies have been rejected by various cultures than accepted. It's only in the last 200 years of the Western world view that we have come to believe that if it can be done, it's inevitable—a fait accompli. As if new technologies come here in some mysterious way, by the gods, and we just stumble across them and therefore have to live with them as we do the changing seasons. That view allows us not to take responsibility. I don't assume that any of these things are a fait accompli.

DUBLER: It's a wonderful moment: Jeremy and I agree. There is no technological imperative. That's exactly what I've been arguing. Simply because a technology exists is no reason that we must use it or that we can use it.

RIFKIN: But what are you going to do? You have to have a change in world views to deal responsibly with this technology. You can't use this world view to critique this technology because this world view is the architect of this technology.

DUBLER: I believe that scholarly discussion serves as the basis for public discussion and that is how our society should proceed. Ideas are addressed by scholars, which are then discussed by legislators, which then become the subject of articles in the public press. Eventually, but not without great difficulty, this debate will produce a consensus on what our overriding values should be.

Exercises and Projects

CHECKING YOUR COMPREHENSION

1. Why does Nancy Dubler object to the potential profit motive regarding the use of aborted fetuses?

2. What does Jeremy Rifkin mean by "desacralization of the life process"? How does Dubler attempt to refute Rifkin's premise?

3. What dangers do Dubler and Salk see in the technology that enables parents to predetermine the sex of their children? How does Lapham attempt to refute their views?

4. Rifkin imagines a time when parents will receive a list of all the traits they could potentially pass on to their children—any of which could be eliminated if it poses a threat to the child's well-being. Why does Rifkin find this troublesome?

5. How does Lapham distinguish between genetic therapy and genetic engineering?

FOR DISCUSSION AND DEBATE

1. What disturbs Rifkin about the connotations of the word *engineering* in the context of eugenics? To what extent do you share these concerns?

2. Debate the following: Parents have the right to predetermine as much of their child's genetic makeup as technology allows.

3. Is it always possible to draw the line between "good" and "bad" genetic traits? Discuss.

4. Salk states, "If a man and a woman want to bring a child into this world only if it is a certain gender, they shouldn't have a child in the first place." Do you agree or disagree?

FOR YOUR NOTEBOOK

1. What frightens or intrigues you the most about genetic engineering? Record your candid feelings in your notebook.

2. If you could determine the sex of your children before birth, would you? Why or why not?

FOR WRITING

1. Distinguishing between "natural" and "artificial" is sometimes difficult. Discuss the distinction, as you perceive it, in a three- to five-page essay. In developing your ideas, think about concepts like "human nature." If it is true that the desire for new knowledge is natural, does it follow that the results of such knowledge—say medical technology—are also natural? Where does one draw the line—or should one draw the line?

2. Defend or refute in a three- to five-page essay Dubler's claim that "there are certain parts of the reproductive process that properly lie beyond individual manipulation by scientific technology."

3. Write an essay in which you alert your readers to the dangers or the benefits of eugenics. Suggested strategy: Begin with a clear definition of eugenics, then describe ways in which eugenics has been beneficial. Finally, point out possible dangers and argue that they either warrant suspending further research or not.

Creationism Versus Evolution

People are often surprised to learn that during the Renaissance, the Church, far from being "antiscience," encouraged inquiry into the natural world and felt that such inquiry would potentially strengthen faith in God. The Papal Office even included an astronomer (in Galileo's day it was Father Christopher Clavius). It is no exaggeration to say that the Church contributed in its own way to the rise of modern science.

But natural phenomena, in the eyes of the Church, were subordinate to scripture: Scripture revealed that human beings, made in God's image, were above nature. Charles Darwin demonstrated that human beings were as subject to biological laws as any other species and were nurtured by their physical environment over a vast period of time.

Today, 130 years after Darwin's *On the Origin of Species,* the debate between the "creationists" (those who assert that human beings were literally created by God in a separate, miraculous act) and the "evolutionists" (those who assert that human beings evolved from simpler life-forms over time, in exclusive accordance with biological laws) is just as intense as ever, as evidenced by the following confrontation between Duane Gish, director of the Institute for Creation Research in San Diego, and Isaac Asimov, a distinguished and prolific science and science-fiction writer. Both Asimov and Gish hold doctorates in biochemistry, from Boston University and from the University of California, Berkeley, respectively.

TERMS TO LEARN

paleontology: a branch of geology focusing on the study of prehistoric plant and animal life via the fossil record

morphology: in biology, the study of the shape and structure of plants and animals

natural selection: in evolutionary theory, the "favoring," via a gradual increase in numbers (over successive generations) of a more durable species variant over a less durable one

cosmology: the branch of astronomy that studies the physical nature of the universe as a whole

cosmogony: the branch of cosmology that studies the origin of the universe

DUANE GISH
ISAAC ASIMOV

 The Genesis War

Gish Argues/Asimov Responds

There are two general explanations for the origin of the Universe and the living things it contains. Either the Universe arose through naturalistic, mechanistic evolutionary processes, or it was created supernaturally. There were no human witnesses to the origin of the Universe, the origin of life or the origin of a single living thing. These were unique, unrepeatable events of the past that cannot be observed in nature or recapitulated in the laboratory. Thus, neither creation nor evolution qualifies as a scientific theory, and each is equally religious. As the philosopher Sir Karl Popper has stated, evolution is not a testable scientific theory but a metaphysical research program. To teach only one explanation to the exclusion of the other in tax-supported public schools in our pluralistic democratic society is a violation of academic and religious freedoms and, furthermore, it is poor science and poor education. It is imperative that students be exposed to arguments supporting each explanation. The following facts support creation:

Thermodynamics. The second law of thermodynamics states unequivocally that within an isolated system order and complexity can only decrease with time, *never* increase. No one has stated our argument here more eloquently than Asimov himself. He writes, "Another way of stating the second law, then, is: 'The Universe is constantly getting more disorderly!' Viewed that way we can see the second law all about us.... How difficult to maintain houses and machinery and our own bodies in perfect working order; how easy to let them deteriorate. In fact, all we have to do is nothing and everything deteriorates, collapses, breaks down, wears out, all by itself—and that is what the second law is all about." Indeed, if that is what the second law of thermodynamics is all about, then evolution is a contradiction to everything in science. By what means of tortured logic is it possible to maintain that the very principles and processes that inexorably lead to the destruction of all order and complexity in the Universe were responsible for its origin in the first place?

Evolutionists maintain, however, that the Universe is an isolated system that began in a disordered, chaotic state and transformed itself into its present highly ordered and complex state[1]* If science is science, that is simply impossible. Since the Universe could not have created itself naturally, it had to be created supernaturally.[2]

[1]*Astronomers do not believe the Universe began in a disordered, chaotic state. It began, in fact, in a condition of high order. A departure from this order, an inhomogeneity, led to the formation of stars and galaxies* in accordance *with the second law. Scientists do not know how the condition of high order began, but scientists are accustomed to lack of knowledge. It is their aim to steadily reduce that lack. To suppose that because we don't know we must assume a "Creator" is to give up the game—to settle for ignorance. To foolish people who don't know what keeps the sun shining, the answer is a "Sun God." To those who don't know what makes the rain fall, the answer is a "Rain God."*

[2]*Having falsely assumed that the Universe could not have created itself naturally, creationists draw the false conclusion that it was created supernaturally.*

Probability laws. The human body contains about 30 trillion cells of over 200 varieties. Twelve billion of these cells are found in the brain, which contains about 120 trillion connections. All of this was supposedly generated through millions of mistakes, beginning with a single cell. Using all the assumptions employed by evolutionists, including natural selection, it can be shown that such a process would have required longer than the assumed 5 billion years of earth's history.

The probability of getting the first cell is even less, however. Using information theory, the biologist H. P. Yockey calculated that the longest piece of DNA that could be expected with 95 percent confidence to form naturally would code for only 49 amino acids (most genes code for proteins that consist of 100 to 300 amino acids). This is, as he said, much too short to provide even a start toward life. It is light-years short, in fact. Furthermore, even if the subunits composing the DNA could be lined up in the right order, these calculations do not take into account the improbability of their linking spontaneously. H. J. Morowitz calculated the probability of matter arranging itself as a bacterium to be $10^{-10^{11}}$. That is one chance out of one followed by 100 billion zeros! Evolutionary theories on the origin of life are nothing more than twentieth-century mythology.[3]

---

*Superscript numbers in the argument indicate the statements to which the response (preceded by the same superscript number) refers. [Ed.]

³Throughout the section, people are quoted—out of context—as expressing doubts and wonder about the insufficiencies of evidence and theory. There are always doubts and wonder, always insufficiencies. That is what science is all about. Creationists take these doubts and this wonder and use them as an excuse to throw everything away. One might as well seek out in all the books written about the Kennedy assassination a half-dozen quotes expressing doubts about Lee Harvey Oswald's role and use them to show that the only way out is to suppose that a "Creator" killed President Kennedy. As for the improbability of forming life, that depends on what conditions and assumptions you use, and creationists carefully seek out those that suit them best.

Molecular biology. As we learn more and more, the facts of molecular biology are turning against evolution theory. Since we now know, for example, that the mode of synthesis of messenger RNA is drastically different in procaryotes (cellular organisms without distinct nuclei) and eucaryotes (organisms whose cells have nuclei), it is no longer tenable to claim that one evolved from the other.[4] Furthermore, as we learn more about DNA synthesis, two general facts have emerged: DNA synthesis is vastly more complex than previously supposed, and the mode of synthesis in different types of organisms is significantly different. In fact, it is quite likely that when more facts are known about DNA synthesis it will be possible to positively exclude the notion that all forms of life have arisen from a common ancestor.[5]

⁴That is the kind of unsupported conclusion a creationist would naturally make. Creationists follow the advance of science, and as soon as a single item comes up that they can seize on, they say, "This proves. . . ." Scientific investigation continues. If procaryotes and eucaryotes are different in some ways, that is exciting news giving scientists additional leads for finding out the true connection. No one actually in the field of procaryote/eucaryote research has decided that the differences are so great as to preclude evolution.
⁵"Quite likely" is the wishful thinking of a creationist.

Embryology. The idea of embryological recapitulation—that at successive stages of development a fetus resembles a fish, amphibian, reptile and, finally, mammal—is now a thoroughly discredited theory and should be expunged from textbooks.[6]

⁶I don't know what aspect of embryological recapitulation is now "thoroughly discredited" in the eyes of a creationist. However, the human fetus in the course of its development has a tail and has indications of gills. These have not disappeared, and if the "Creator" put them there I can only wonder why.

Homology. The idea that homologous, or similar, structures and organs exist in different animals due to inheritance from common ancestors is so thoroughly contradicted by the scientific evidence that Sir Gavin de Beer titled his 1971 book on the subject *Homology: An Unsolved Problem.*[7] In fact, the genetic evidence related to homologous structures is directly contradictory to what is predicted on the basis of evolution theory. Homologous structures ought to be governed by homologous genes. This doesn't prove to be the case, however. Both the fish and man have the same kind of eye, but the genetic apparatus of each creature is different.

[7]*"Thoroughly contradicted" only to creationists. You quote a problem and give up the game. If every last point about homology isn't certain, you postulate the existence of a "Creator."*

The fossil record. If millions of species have gradually evolved through hundreds of millions of years, the fossil record must contain an immense number of transitional forms—museums should be overflowing with them.[8] The fossil record shows, however, an explosive appearance of a great variety of highly complex creatures for which no ancestors can be found and systematic gaps between all higher categories of plants and animals.[9] The fossil record is thus highly contradictory to evolution but remarkably in accord with creation.[10]

[8]*There are an immense number of transitional forms, and museums are overflowing with them. A creationist prefers to look the other way.*
[9]*Fossils were formed rarely and haphazardly. We don't expect a complete story. Some people may not know the names of all eight of their great-great-grandfathers or even the name of one of them. That does not mean that they are not members of the human race and have been specially formed by a "Creator."*
[10]*A mere statement based on other statements persuades only those who are creationists to begin with.*

There is absolutely no doubt about the gaps. In no case has a single transitional form been found. For example, 100 million years was supposedly required for an invertebrate to evolve into a vertebrate, but the fossil record produces no transitional forms whatsoever.[11] The evolutionary family tree simply does not exist.

[11]*Nonsense! There are even living transitional forms between vertebrates and invertebrates. Balanoglossus, a kind of sea worm, and the tunicates, a subphylum of marine animal, show clear signs of echinoderm (the phylum that includes starfish) ancestry, and yet they are indisputably related to the vertebrates.*

Evolutionary paleontologists are finally beginning to admit that they have little or no evidence for gradual change. The record they have been looking for ever since Darwin is simply not there. From evolutionary literature of the past decade we see statements such as "Evolution requires intermediate forms between species, and paleontology does not provide them" and "The fossil record with its abrupt transitions offers no support for gradual change" and "All paleontologists know that the fossil record contains precious little in the way of intermediate forms; transitions between major groups are characteristically abrupt" and "Different species usually appear and disappear from the record without showing the transitions Darwin postulated."[12]

[12]*What is all this? Unattributed quotes? Shall I search religious literature of the past decade for isolated statements seeming to imply doubts about the existence of a "Creator"?*

In spite of several highly imaginative transitional forms suggested for man, the record here is no better. Lord Solly Zuckerman, after years of research in this field, states in *Beyond the Ivory Tower* that if creation is excluded, then obviously man must have evolved from an apelike creature, but if he did, he hasn't left a trace in the fossil record.[13] To escape the dilemma, evolutionists are suggesting radical new theories such as punctuated equilibria, the idea that periodic environmental upheaval hastens the creation of species, or even a return to the "hopeful monster" mechanism of Richard Gold-schmidt, the notion that evolution occurs in fits and starts, occasionally yielding a mutation that works—such as man. The evidence of genetics is against both notions. The first bird could not have hatched from a reptilian egg, for example: the genetic apparatus of a lizard is devoted 100 percent to producing another lizard.

Evolution theory suffers fatal weaknesses, while the concept of creation explains the evidence admirably. Thousands of scientists are convinced creationists, and the number grows rapidly.

[13]*"Hasn't left a trace":* Homo neanderthalensis, Homo erectus, Australopithecus africanus—*what are all these and others? Imaginary? As usual, the creationist argument consists entirely of pointing out "flaws" in evolutionary theory. Not one word in* support *of the*

"Creator" except as a court of last resort with the plaintive question, "What else could it be, since evolutionary arguments don't seem perfect to me?" Give us some information about the "Creator." When did he create the Universe? Six thousand years ago? In how many days did he create it? Six? Did he create the earth ahead of the sun or vice versa? Tell us about Adam and Eve. Was Eve really created out of Adam's rib? Or are you throwing out the Bible altogether and speaking only about a "Creator" you know nothing about? Come on, take a chance and speak up.

Asimov Argues/Gish Responds

The first hints of biological evolution arose through efforts to classify living things.

Aristotle was among the first to find that all living things could be divided into plants and animals; animals into those with gills and those with lungs; animals with lungs into those that lay eggs and those that bear live young; and so on and so on.

Ultimately, it was found that living things could be arranged into different kinds (species), and similar species could be gathered into groups, then groups of similar groups, and so on. It is, in fact, possible to draw a diagram separating life forms into finer and finer subdivisions, ending with the individual species, rather like the individual leaves of a tree.

Imagine that through some magic, all we could see of a real tree were its individual leaves distributed in space. Would we suppose that somehow those leaves had just sprung into existence where they were? Surely not! We would suppose that they were supported by an unseen trunk, branches and stems, dividing and subdividing, and that the leaves hung at the end of the finest, final stems.

Through the nineteenth century, paleontologists discovered and studied steadily increasing numbers of fossils, petrified remnants of past life. They found many extinct species unmistakably different from any now living but resembling them sufficiently to be added to the "tree of life." Extinct reptiles, for example, are like no living reptiles, but they are clearly reptiles just the same. Fossils fill many of the empty spaces between living species, making the tree of life denser and revealing more intermediate species.[1]

---

[1] The fact that paleontologists can almost immediately and without difficulty assign newly discovered fossils to existing categories is contradictory to evolutionary expectations, which would predict gradual blending of one creature into another. Since only tips of the branches exist, with branches and trunk missing, the

evolutionary "tree of life" exists only in the minds of evolutionists, not in the fossil record.

The chance that all life forms, living and extinct, could have come into being independently is so small as to be virtually nonexistent. If life forms had come into being independently, then we might reasonably suspect that the fossil record, if lined up chronologically, would occassionally be out of developmental order. But it isn't.

Thus, we find in the fossil record a series of horselike creatures that, if we arrange them in order of age, show a steadily increasing size and a steadily decreasing number of toes per foot, right down to the present large, solid-hoofed horse. We don't find a four-toed horse, then a solid-hoofed horse, then a three-toed horse.

In fact, in the entire fossil record, and among all living species, there is nothing, no inconsistency, that could seriously upset the classification in any fundamental way. Scientists have no choice but to consider evolution a fact.

Only by evolution, the slow and more or less gradual change of one species into another, could we end up with the fossil record as we have it and the classification of life forms as we observe it.[2]

[2]*Asimov seems unaware of the current uproar in evolutionary circles incited by those paleontologists who are suggesting radical new evolutionary mechanisms ("punctuated equilibria," Goldschmidt's "hopeful monster" mechanism) precisely because the fossil record offers no evidence for slow, gradual change.*

Having the fact of evolution before us (and the few paragraphs in which I sketch the main argument barely begin to list the millions of careful individual observations that exist, from the biochemical to the mophological, all of which, without exception, strengthen the force of the argument), the next problem is that of determining by what mechanism evolution has taken place. What causes species to change?

Scientists who deal with evolution as their field of specialization may argue over the mechanism behind evolutionary development, but none questions the fact of evolution itself. It is possible to argue over the number of stories constituting the Empire State Building—does the observation deck count as a story?—without questioning whether the Empire State Building exists.

The first successful suggestion about the mechanism behind evolutionary development came from Charles Darwin in 1859: the "theory of evolution by natural selection." The word *theory* does not mean a wild guess or baseless speculation. It is a scientific term that refers to a system of thought based on careful observation and deduction, thoroughly tested by numerous scientists in numerous ways,

Darwin's theory has been greatly modified in the century and a quarter since it was put forth, thanks to knowledge gained since his death.

For instance, it was after Darwin had advanced his theory that Mendel's laws of inheritance became known. It was after Mendel's work that de Vries devised his theory of mutations; after de Vries that Sutton pinpointed the chromosomes as the site of mutations and inheritance, and after Sutton that Crick and Watson worked out the structure of DNA and explained the details accounting for much that had been puzzling before.

All subsequent findings have only served to amplify, elaborate and improve Darwin's theory without in any way upsetting its fundamentals. In the past few years, for instance, scientists such as Stephen Jay Gould have suggested that evolution proceeds to a greater extent in small isolated groups of organisms than in large ones, that chance plays a larger role and that changes can take place in small groups more rapidly than had been thought (in thousands of years rather than millions). This further refines the evolutionary mechanism without in any way abandoning either the fact of evolution or the overall importance of natural selection.[3] Today, we can even observe natural selection in action when we breed varieties of domestic animals.

[3]*According to theory, ultimately all of evolution is due to mutations, which are strictly chance events (accidents, mistakes). It has been shown that such an evolutionary process would require billions of times longer than 5 billion years to convert a single-celled organism into complex creatures such as man.*

Scientific findings outside the field of biology also strengthen Darwin's theory. In the twentieth century, we have learned how to determine the age of rocks by measuring radioactive changes within them—a technique that has nothing directly to do with either fossils or evolution. Through this technique we learned that the earth is about 4.6 billion years old—plenty of time for evolution. We learned that, in every detail, the newly authenticated ages of the strata in which fossils were found fit those fossils firmly into the scheme of evolution.[4]

[4]*The question of the age of the earth does not affect arguments for creation. Evolution, however, demands an immensity of time. It is significant, therefore, that scores of physical chronometers establish*

an upper limit for the age of the earth and cosmos that is vastly less than 5 billion years.

Again, twentieth-century findings in astronomy, cosmology and cosmogony all led to the working out of an evolutionary theory for the Universe as a whole, and for individual stars such as our sun, and into this the evolution of life fits perfectly well.[5]

[5]*Apparently Asimov has not been reading current literature. "The standard Big Bang model does not give rise to lumpiness [galaxies, stars, and so on]. . . . If you apply the laws of physics to this model, you get a Universe that is uniform. . . . Needless to say, the night sky . . . says otherwise," says Philip Seiden, an IBM sky scientist. The astronomer Hermann Bondi says, "As an erstwhile cosmologist, I speak with feeling of the fact that theories of the origin of the Universe have been disproved by present-day empirical evidence, as have various theories of the origin of the solar system." In fact, it can be shown that a star could never form spontaneously by the collapse of a cloud of gas, since the gas pressure pushing out would exceed the gravitational force pulling in by 50 to 100 times. Furthermore, the complete absence of organic material on Mars; many "anomalous" isotope ratios (the Argon-36 to Argon-40 ratio on Venus is 300 times greater than that on earth); the intrinsic magnetic field of Mercury; Jupiter's small moon Io with its dense nitrogen atmosphere; the braided rings of Saturn; and many other facts from our space program are contradictory to evolutionary predictions. The evidence is directly opposed to the idea that these objects evolved from the same cloud of dust and gas but rather indicates that the solar system is a manufactured article.*

The most recent findings of geology, including plate tectonics, have also worked to explain evolutionary mechanisms in improved ways without upsetting any of the fundamentals.[6]

[6]*About 20 years ago, practically every geologist accepted a model of earth's history involving static continents. Now, practically every geologist accepts a model with continents drifting all over the world. The fact that evolution theory could be so readily accomodated to such drastically different models attests to the fact that it is so plastic it can be made to fit no matter what the data may be.*

In fact, the strongest of all indications as to the fact of evolution and the truth of the theory of natural selection is that all the independent findings of scientists in every branch of science, when they have anything to do with biological evolution at all, *always* strengthen the case and *never* weaken it. (The second law of thermodynamics is sometimes quoted against evolution, but only by those who don't understand—or choose not to understand—the law.)[7]

[7]*This statement is simply absurd, and Asimov ought to know that.*

And the summary is this:

Evolution is a fact and it cannot be upset without discarding all of modern biology, biochemistry, geology, astronomy—in short, without discarding all of science.

Exercises and Projects

CHECKING YOUR COMPREHENSION

1. Summarize the four facts that, according to Gish, support the argument for supernatural creation.

2. How does Asimov refute Gish's assertion that the fossil record shows "a great variety of complex creatures for which no ancestors can be found"?

3. How does Gish refute Asimov's assertion that the 4.6 billion-year age of the earth—determined through radioactive dating techniques—is "plenty of time for evolution"?

4. According to Asimov, how can we observe evolution in action?

FOR DISCUSSION AND DEBATE

1. Gish states that both creation and evolution are "equally religious." Do you agree? Why or why not?

2. Asimov frequently criticizes Gish for flaws in logic and technique of argument. Pinpoint at least two of them and discuss whether or not these are indeed flaws.

3. Assuming that a human fetus actually acquires a tail and gills in the course of its development (as Asimov insists it does), how might a creationist explain that phenomenon?

4. Some states have banned biology textbooks that discuss evolutionary theory from use in public schools. Defend or challenge this action.

FOR YOUR NOTEBOOK

1. Begin a notebook entry with a statement of your personal views regarding the origin of the human species. Next, defend your view as convincingly as you can. Has the Asimov–Gish debate influenced your views in any way? How?

2. Over the next several days, gather as much data as you can in support of creationism or evolution. Record this information in your notebook, making sure to include your sources. After a while, you may wish to compare your notes with those of your classmates.

FOR WRITING

1. According to Gish, "to teach only one explanation to the exclusion of another in tax-supported public schools . . . is a violation of academic and religious freedoms and . . . is poor science and poor education." Support or refute this assertion in a three- to five-page essay.

2. Some theologians, such as Teilhard de Chardin, an anthropologist as well as a Jesuit priest, not only accept biological evolution but also include it in a divine model of the cosmos. Read a representative work by one of these theologians—for example, Teilhard's *The Phenomenon of Man* (1955)—then argue whether such a view is plausible from both a religious and a scientific point of view.

3. Write an essay on the tension between science and religion in the modern world. You may wish to favor one over the other or attempt to find a synthesis between them

Computer Technology

Think about the word *computer* for a while. Most likely, you will envision glowing screens filled with columns or rows of numbers and letters. You might also think of "computerese" terms such as *megabyte, ROM, RAM, baud, download, pixel, digitized,* and *interactive software* that have been influencing not only our language but also our manner of thinking. Carrying the association even further you might see supersmart artificial intelligence (AI) machines programming themselves and revolting against humankind, maintaining control in a future society with inflectionless, metallic voices—or, worse yet, perhaps, with motherly voices that disguise their inhuman power.

Not since 1456 when Johannes Gutenberg began to use moveable type to print books has a technological innovation so radically transformed the way we receive and assimilate information. And since 1977—the year the personal computer made its debut—the computer has become an integral part of our lives. What is more, the computer has given us a new perspective on what it means to think. Information and logic are quantifiable, we have discovered. Complex ideas can be broken down into discreet "bits" and transformed into a "program" that the computer can "run"—much the same way that sounds can be digitized (transformed into binary code) on a compact disc, which the CD player then "reads" in order to reproduce the sounds.

According to J. David Bolter—professor of classics at the University of North Carolina, visiting fellow in computer science at Yale, and author of *Turing's Man: Western Culture in the Computer Age* (1984), from which the following selection is taken—human beings appear to be redefining themselves in relation to computers. We are perceiving ourselves, he writes, as "information processors" and perceiving nature as "information to be processed." In short, we are becoming what Bolter calls "Turing's men." The reference is to the famous logician and mathematician A. M. Turing, who in 1936 described the theoretical basis for a "logic machine." And in 1950, in a controversial paper entitled "Computing Machinery and Intelligence," Bolter reports that Turing "stated his conviction that computers were capable of imitating human intelligence perfectly and that indeed they would do so by the year 2000."

Surprisingly, Bolter argues that Turing's man has cultural roots that extend not only into the Renaissance but also into classical Greece and Rome, having an awareness of human limitations and a preoccupation with the immediate and the observable.

In contrast (but not necessarily in opposition) to Bolter's view that computers are turning us into Turing's men, Lewis Thomas, in an engaging and lighthearted manner, describes the insurmountable gap he sees between computer nature and human nature, asserting that human nature is ultimately unquantifiable.

Dr. Thomas is a pediatrician, biologist, cancer researcher, chancellor of the Memorial Sloan-Kettering Cancer Institute in New York City, and winner of the National Book Award for his first collection of essays, *The Lives of a Cell* (1974), from which "Computers" is taken.

TERMS TO LEARN

fixed stars: unmoving stars in the medieval model of the universe. In this model, the earth was believed to be at the center, and all celestial bodies revolved around it in their respective "crystalline spheres." The sun occupied one sphere, the moon another, and each planet its own; finally, there was the outermost sphere (beyond which lay Heaven), of fixed stars—"fixed" because they seemed never to move. We know today that all stars move (revolve around the axis of whatever galaxy they are in), but their relative motions, because of their vast distances from us, cannot be detected except over thousands of years.

syncytium: (pronounced sin-SIH-shum) a unified mass of protoplasm not organized into separate cells but nonetheless containing distinct nuclei

J. DAVID BOLTER

 From Socrates to Faust to Turing

The ancient ideal was characterized by balance, proportion, a sense of sane limits in human affairs—an ideal announced humbly enough by the Greek potter (molding his wares with careful symmetry and decorating them in a spare, linear fashion) but reverberating throughout society and literature. The two famous Greek proverbs "nothing in excess" and "know yourself" are both admonitions for the life of balance and limits. Aristotle made the first the keystone of his ethical system, which set a mean between extremes in most human activities. The second, so closely associated with Socrates, was not a plea for psychoanalytic or Christian soul-searching: it meant instead that men must know their limits, particularly as mortals in relation to the divine, and be careful not to overstep them. What happened when men did overstep their limits was the favorite, indeed the definitive, subject of Greek tragedy.

With an appreciation of formal balance in art and life came the tendency to be superficial; and the Greeks would not have regarded this as a criticism. The idea of, in fact the obsession with, plumbing the depths of any experience belonged rather to Western European culture. The ancients appreciated the linear, the superficial, the immediate, and the tactile in mathematics, art, and ethics as well. Hence conscience played a relatively small role in ancient ethics: crimes against individuals or the state and impiety toward the gods were acts committed at a definite time and place; sins thought but not acted upon did not matter. Another aspect of the superficial was that the Greeks had comparatively little concern for history. The past did not weigh heavily upon them, as it did upon the men of Western Europe, for the ancient world itself had no ancient world against which to measure its achievements. Nor did the ancient man care to look far into the future, for there was nothing like the Christian concept of millennium or the secular notion of progress to direct his gaze. As Spengler put it, "The Classical Life exhausted itself in the completeness of the moment."

The limit of the ancient gaze was not only a temporal one. Most philosophers had no difficulty finding the physical limits of the universe: it was the sphere of the fixed stars, beyond which there was absolutely nothing. In social terms, a contentment with limited resources expressed itself in a steady-state economy and in a disinterest in technological innovation. The inventor at least had an honored, if not prominent, place in Greek mythology, but the explorer was a character type seldom found in ancient literature or ancient history. Odysseus was not really an explorer, but a wanderer, trying his best to get home, and Alexander the Great marched from Macedonia to India as a conqueror, not an explorer. The Greeks were gifted sailors and brazen enough to face the sea in small, wooden boats, yet they seldom ventured beyond the Pillars of Heracles. How complacent they seem when judged by the Western European standard.

In fact, the ancient character differed from the Western European in every respect I have mentioned. The Western European character came, of course, in a dozen varieties, as did the ancient, but common to all was a fascination with depth, a desire to penetrate the surface of reality. In art, this led to the invention of linear perspective· the technique of organizing a whole picture around a single deep focus, giving the illusion of three dimensions. In moral terms, it led to the Christian preoccupation with the human soul as something deep and mysterious beneath the facade of human behavior. In later, secular times, psychology took up where Christianity left off, exploring the depths of conscious and unconscious human experience. This self-searching was a principal theme of literature from the Middle Ages on: the quest for the Grail in medieval romance or for salvation in Dante later became the search for knowledge of oneself and the world in the nineteenth-century novel, as such critics as Northrop Frye have taught us. Nor was the drive limited to fiction. The great explorers of the fifteenth, sixteenth, and seventeenth centuries were answering the same call, as were the creators of modern science.

Spengler called this Western character "Faustian," after Goethe's rendering of the scientist-magician who seeks ultimate power and knowledge. He argued that the Faustian character was far more conscious of its place in history than the ancient man. And he emphasized, justly I think, the fact that Faustian men had an appreciation for the idea of infinity, which the ancients did not. The point is obvious in a comparison of ancient and modern mathematics, but it emerges in other ways, too. Because of Christian dogma, Western men were accustomed to regard infinity as a good thing (was not God infinitely good and powerful?), but the ancients often associated the infinite with something unintelligible and therefore evil.

Where does the computer age fit in this scheme? It constitutes another turning point, another major change in sensibilities. As I have argued, computer technology is a curious combination of ancient and Western European technical qualities. Developing through modern science and engineering, it nonetheless encourages its users to think in some ways in ancient technical terms. Turing's man has in fact inherited traits from both the ancient and Western European characters, and the very combination of these traits makes him different from either. Those of us who belong to the last generation of the Western European mentality, who still live by the rapidly fading ideals of the previous era, must reconcile ourselves to the fact that electronic man does not in all ways share our view of self and world.

In one fundamental sense, Turing's man has only taken Western European thinking one step further. He has forced to one extreme the dividing line between nature and the artificial. Throughout the industrializing period, our culture was busy making the world an ever more artificial place: making technologies out of matters that originally belonged to nature. Agriculture, metallurgy, textiles, and inanimate prime movers are all instances. With less and less that was unimproved, the result of a total artificial world, a complete change from nature to artifact, became thinkable. Samuel Butler stated the obvious with magnificent hyperbole in his "Book of the Machines": "Man's very soul is due to the machines: it is a machine-made thing: he thinks as he thinks, and feels as he feels, through the work that machines have wrought upon him, and their existence is quite as much a *sine qua non* for his, as for theirs." . . . In the computer age, when hyperbole has become commonplace, man has no difficulty regarding even himself as an artifact, and with him nearly everything of interest in nature has been made over by technology.

This is the point of programs for artificial intelligence, and Herbert Simon has said as much in his book *The Sciences of the Artificial.* The evidence suggests, he writes soberly, "that there are only a few 'intrinsic' characteristics of the inner environment of thinking man that limit the adaptation of his thought to the shape of the problem environment. All else in his thinking and problem-solving behavior is artificial—is learned and is subject to improvement through the invention of improved designs." . . . Man is born an information processor with an empty memory store, and he programs himself to become an adult problem solver.

This new twist on Locke's old empiricism is the defining philosophy of the computer age. It certainly reflects the optimism of the Enlightenment. By ignoring the complex and hard-to-fathom aspects of human nature—what Simon calls in typical behaviorist fashion the "inner environment"—computer man can bend himself to any task, find a rational path to any goal. Surely human beings are not as flexible as that or as artificial. Recent hard-won knowledge in neurology and genetics shows us how little control we still have over those aspects of nature that most immediately affect our thought and action. It may be hundreds of years before man can really make himself over genetically, if ever. But Turing's man is so caught up in the computer metaphor that he refuses to wait for the genetic solution; he chooses to regard man as software more than hardware, as the program run by the computer more than the hard-wired machine itself. So he speaks of programming techniques (means-ends analysis, simulation, optimization, and so on) just as Enlightenment figures spoke of reason. The mind programs itself and through programming solves problems, achieves goals, molds itself to its environment. The making of man into an electronic artifact goes beyond the dreams of any nineteenth-century entrepreneur or materialist philosopher. For Turing's man, the ancient rift between the human and the natural is mended in a startlingly different way. It is not that man is a part of nature so much as the reverse—nature and man are both artifacts. For what is nature but a brilliantly designed "ecosystem," whose beauty and significance for mankind lies in its operational success?

In going to such extremes, Turing's man parts company with his predecessor. His concern with functions, paths, and goals overrides an interest in any deeper kind of understanding. In general, men of the computer age seem destined to lose the Faustian concern with depth. The rejection of depth for considerations of surface and form, long a feature of modern art, is now spreading throughout our intellectual life. The so-called sciences of human behavior make it their creed not to look at human experience below the surface. Indeed, they sometimes deny the existence of any experience that is not immediately and superficially demonstrable. Behaviorist psychology regards a man as a complex of sensing and responding elements that are wired together to produce human action; there is no question of deep, perhaps unfathomable motives and unconscious thoughts. Sociologists treat aggregates of human beings in the same operational terms, and economists treat them as unambivalent pleasure machines. Although computer technology did not single-handedly call forth this view, which has been developing at least since the turn of the century, it has nonetheless encouraged it, providing by far the most compelling metaphor in the social scientists' vocabulary.

Turing's men are by no means all strict behaviorists. Noam Chomsky is famous for his attack on the behaviorist view of language as a simple matter of stimulus and response. In fact, many programmers in artificial intelligence regard their work as "humanistic" psychology because their programs are meant to simulate the human mind as it manipulates symbols in sophisticated ways, not to mimic the simple reactions of chains of neurons. But programmers with their semantic networks and behaviorists with their Skinner boxes agree on this vital point: everything that happens in the mind or the brain is played out according to the rules of a formal system. These rules are finite, and they can someday be specified. Douglas Hofstadter, one of the most thoughtful of Turing's men, has made this a central theme of his book *Gödel, Escher, Bach*. For him the paradox is that the brain is a formal system of neurons underlying an apparently informal system, "which can, for instance, make puns, discover patterns, forget names, make awful blunders in chess, and so forth." ... Here is the classic philosophical problem of mind and matter expressed in a way practically incomprehensible to anyone before the twentieth century. To a Western European metaphysician or a Platonist, it would have seemed an utterly superficial approach to the problem. How could a mere set of formal rules underlie the human intellect, with its access to universal notions of truth and divinity? Yet Marvin Minsky, the artificial intelligence specialist, writes: "To me 'intelligence' seems to denote little more than the complex of performances which we happen to respect, but do not understand. So it is, usually, with the question of 'depth' in mathematics. Once the proof of a theorem is really understood its content seems to become trivial." ...

The goal of artificial intelligence is to demonstrate that man is all surface, that there is nothing dark or mysterious in the human condition, nothing that cannot be lit by the even light of operational analysis. Like any program an artificial intelligence program is a set of instructions to manipulate symbolic data: every symbol and every instruction is as clearly defined and accessible as the next. There are no shades or degrees, and nothing can remain undefined. A dislike of mystery is ingrained in every programmer by hard experience; for every one has spent untold hours "debugging" his programs, tracking down subtle errors that have crept into his commands as he wrote or copied them. Unexplained or unknown lines of code do not add variety or give his work a pleasantly unpredictable turn; they simply mean failure to perform. It is no surprise, then, that Minsky claims: "It may be so with *man*, as with *machine*, that, when we understand finally the structure and program, the feeling of mystery (and self-approbation) will weaken." ... To put it another way, the symbolic logic by which the machine functions demands total unidimensional understanding. The goal of logicians at least since Leibniz has been to shine the light of mathematical reason upon the widest possible area of human experience. Artificial intelligence programmers have pursued that end further than even Leibniz envisioned, for they even devise algorithms to imitate human paranoia, thus reducing the irrational to a set of machine instructions.

In his own way, computer man retains and even extends the Faustian tendency to analyze. Yet the goal of Faustian analysis was to understand, to "get to the bottom" of a problem; it divided an issue painstakingly into parts in order to build a clear picture of the interrelations. Turing's man analyzes not primarily to understand but to act. A computer program is not a static description but a series of instructions. This we have seen all along—a program is a logical theorem that proves itself by its execution. The computer gives mathematical and verbal symbols a life of their own, sets them dancing to a prearranged tune, and the programmer is never sure that the tune is correct until he can witness the dance. For Turing's man, knowledge is a process, a skill. A man or a computer knows something only if he or it can produce the right answer when asked the right question. The approach to any problem is still highly analytical but utterly superficial, for depth in the Faustian sense adds nothing to a program's operational success. Electronic man creates convenient hierarchies of action by dividing tasks into subtasks, routines into subroutines. The end is reached when the "subproblems" become trivial manipulations of data that are clear at a glance. In this way, all complexity is drained from a problem, and mystery and depth vanish, defined out of existence by the programmer's operational cast of thought.

LEWIS THOMAS

 Computers

You can make computers that are almost human. In some respects they are superhuman; they can beat most of us at chess, memorize whole telephone books at a glance, compose music of a certain kind and write obscure poetry, diagnose heart ailments, send personal invitations to vast parties, even go transiently crazy. No one has yet programmed a computer to be of two minds about a hard problem, or to burst out laughing, but that may come. Sooner or later, there will be real human hardware, great whirring, clicking cabinets intelligent enough to read magazines and vote, able to think rings around the rest of us.

Well, maybe, but not for a while anyway. Before we begin organizing sanctuaries and reservations for our software selves, lest we vanish like the whales, here is a thought to relax with.

Even when technology succeeds in manufacturing a machine as big as Texas to do everything we recognize as human, it will still be, at best, a single individual. This amounts to nothing, practically speaking. To match what we can do, there would have to be 3 billion of them with more coming down the assembly line, and I doubt that anyone will put up the money, much less make room. And even so, they would all have to be wired together, intricately and delicately, as we are, communicating with each other, talking incessantly, listening. If they weren't *at* each other this way, all their waking hours, they wouldn't be anything like human, after all. I think we're safe, for a long time ahead.

It is in our collective behavior that we are most mysterious. We won't be able to construct machines like ourselves until we've understood this, and we're not even close. All we know is the phenomenon: we spend our time sending messages to each other, talking and trying to listen at the same time, exchanging information. This seems to be our most urgent biological function; it is what we do with our lives. By the time we reach the end, each of us has taken in a staggering store, enough to exhaust any computer, much of it incomprehensible, and we generally manage to put out even more than we take in. Information is our source of energy; we are driven by it. It has become a tremendous enterprise, a kind of energy system on its own. All 3 billion of us are being connected by telephones, radios, television sets, airplanes, satellites, harangues on public-address systems, newspapers, magazines, leaflets dropped from great heights, words got in edgewise. We are becoming a grid, a circuitry around the earth. If we keep at it, we will become a computer to end all computers, capable of fusing all the thoughts of the world into a syncytium.

Already, there are no closed, two-way conversations. Any word you speak this afternoon will radiate out in all directions, around town before tomorrow, out and around the world before Tuesday, accelerating to the speed of light, modulating as it goes, shaping new and unexpected messages, emerging at the end as an enormously funny Hungarian joke, a fluctuation in the money market, a poem, or simply a long pause in someone's conversation in Brazil.

We do a lot of collective thinking, probably more than any other social species, although it goes on in something like secrecy. We don't acknowledge the gift publicly, and we are not as celebrated as the insects, but we do it. Effortlessly, without giving it a moment's thought, we are capable of changing our language, music, manners, morals, entertainment, even the way we dress, all around the earth in a year's turning. We seem to do this by general agreement, without voting or even polling. We simply think our way along, pass information around, exchange codes disguised as art, change our minds, transform ourselves.

Computers cannot deal with such levels of improbability, and it is just as well. Otherwise, we might be tempted to take over the control of ourselves in order to make long-range plans, and that would surely be the end of us. It would mean that some group or other, marvelously intelligent and superbly informed, undoubtedly guided by a computer, would begin deciding what human society ought to be like, say, over the next five hundred years or so, and the rest of us would be persuaded, one way or another, to go along. The process of social evolution would then grind to a standstill, and we'd be stuck in today's rut for a millennium.

Much better we work our way out of it on our own without governance. The future is too interesting and dangerous to be entrusted to any predictable, reliable agency. We need all the fallibility we can get. Most of all, we need to preserve the absolute unpredictability and total improbability of our connected minds. That way we can keep open all the options, as we have in the past.

It would be nice to have better ways of monitoring what we're up to so that we could recognize change while it is occurring, instead of waking up as we do now to the astonished realization that the whole century just past wasn't what we thought it was, at all. Maybe computers can be used to help in this, although I rather doubt it. You can make simulation models of cities, but what you learn is that they seem to be beyond the reach of intelligent analysis; if you try to use common sense to make predictions, things get more botched up than ever. This is interesting, since a city is the most concentrated aggregation of humans, all exerting whatever influence they can bring to bear. The city seems to have a life of its own. If we cannot understand how this works, we are not likely to get very far with human society at large.

Still, you'd think there would be some way in. Joined together, the great mass of human minds around the earth seems to behave like a coherent, living system. The trouble is that the flow of information is mostly one-way. We are all obsessed by the need to feed information in, as fast as we can, but we lack sensing mechanisms for getting anything much back. I will confess that I have no more sense of what goes on in the mind of mankind than I have for the mind of an ant. Come to think of it, this might be a good place to start.

Exercises and Projects

CHECKING YOUR COMPREHENSION

1. What effect is computer technology having on our sense of the natural and the artificial, according to Bolter? How are current attitudes different from those common during the Industrial Revolution?

2. What are "Faustian tendencies?" Do Turing's men manifest them at all?

3. According to Bolter, what is the goal of artificial intelligence technology?

4. Why is a computer so much unlike a human being, in Thomas's opinion?

5. Thomas writes, "We need all the fallibility we can get." How does he defend this rather surprising statement?

FOR DISCUSSION AND DEBATE

1. Challenge or defend Bolter's assertion that Turing's men's "concern with functions, paths, and goals overrides an interest in any deeper kind of understanding." What do you suppose Bolter means by "deeper" in this context?

2. Discuss the implications behind Thomas's statement that sending messages seems to be "our most urgent biological function."

3. Lewis Thomas wrote his essay on computers in the early 1970s, before microcomputers appeared. In view of today's computer technology, do you suppose Thomas would change his mind about the relation between computer and human intelligence?

4. Compare Thomas's writing style to Bolter's. What relationship, if any, do you perceive between style and content of each writer?

5. How effective is Thomas's opening sentence, "You can make computers that are almost human." Does it make you want to read on? Why or why not? How convincingly does Thomas support this claim in what follows?

FOR YOUR NOTEBOOK

1. How accurate a term is *artificial intelligence,* in your opinion? Can computers be intelligent in a literal sense? Explore your views in a notebook entry.

2. List the potential benefits and dangers of artificial intelligence.

FOR WRITING

1. There is no question that computers are extremely valuable in business, science, and industry. But what about in the arts? Write an essay that discusses the use of computers in one of the arts (music, painting, graphic design, writing, and so on). Focus on specific applications, artistic innovations that may have resulted from the computerized applications, problems, and outlooks for the future.

2. Write an essay in which you express your faith or doubt in the idea that AI computers will someday be able to mimic human intelligence in every respect.

3. Computers have been a part of elementary education for some time now. Visit an elementary school in your area and observe the ways in which children are being taught to work with computers. Prepare a detailed report on your observations. You may wish to include some or all of the following items:
     • particular kinds of learning activities for which the computers are used
     • kinds of software programs
     • detailed description and evaluation of one program
     • attitude of the children toward the computers and the programs they are working with
     • role of the teacher

Suggestions for Further Reading

I. THE SEARCH FOR EXTRATERRESTRIAL LIFE

Christian, James L., ed. *Extra-Terrestrial Intelligence.* Boston: Prometheus Books, 1976
  Includes articles by Ray Bradbury, Leonard Nimoy, Isaac Asimov, and others.

Clarke, Arthur C. "When the Aliens Come." In *Report on Planet Three and Other Speculations.* New York: Signet, 1972.

McDonough, Thomas R. *The Search for Extraterrestrial Intelligence: Listening for Life in the Cosmos.* New York: Wiley, 1987.

Shklovskii, I. S., and Carl Sagan. *Intelligent Life in the Universe.* New York: Dell, 1966.

II. NUCLEAR WASTE DISPOSAL

Chiles, James. "Learning to Live with Plutonium." *Science Digest* (July 1984):49–51, 88–89.

Gofman, John W., and Arthur R. Tamplin. *Poisoned Planet: The Case Against Nuclear Power Plants Before and After Three Mile Island.* Rodale, Pa.: Emmamus Press, 1979.

Rosenthal, Elizabeth. "The Hazards of Everyday Radiation." *Science Digest* 92 (March 1984):38–43, 96–97.

Yulsman, Tom. "Burying Nuclear Waste." *Science Digest* 93 (July 1985):16.

III. ANIMAL RIGHTS

Fox, Michael Allen. *The Case for Animal Experimentation: An Evolutionary and Ethical Perspective.* Berkeley: University of California Press, 1986.

Lockett, Landon. "Whales off the Faeroe Islands." *Newsweek* Nov. 23, 1987:11
Argues that those who love nature should accept the brutality inherent in whale hunting that is essential to a people's subsistance.

Morrow, Lance. "Thinking Animal Thoughts." *Time* (Oct. 3, 1983):85–86.

Quammen, David. "Animal Rights and Beyond." In *Natural Acts: A Sidelong View of Science and Nature.* New York: Dell, 1985.
A critical response to the ideas of animal rights activists Peter Singer and Tom Regan.

Regan, Tom. *The Case for Animal Rights.* Berkeley: University of California Press, 1983.

Rose, Kenneth Jon. "How Animals Think." *Science Digest* (Feb. 1984):59–61, 89.

Satchell, Michael. "Should You Buy That Doggie in the Window? A Report on Cruelty in 'Puppy Mills.'" *Parade* (July 19, 1987):4–7.

IV. GENETIC ENGINEERING

Brownlee, Sharon. "Lords of the Flies." *Discover* (April 1987):26–40.
By genetically altering fruit flies, scientists are learning how genes control growth.

Chinnici, Madeline. "The Promise of Gene Therapy." *Science Digest* (May 1985):48–51, 88–89.

Hall, Stephen S. *Invisible Fortress: The Race to Synthesize a Human Gene.* Boston: Atlantic Monthly Press, 1987.

Lawren, Bill. "1990's Designer Genes." *Omni* (Nov. 1985):57–61.
Details genetic experiments on animals.

Penrose, L. S. "Ethics and Eugenics." In *The Biological Revolution* edited by Watson Fuller. New York: Anchor Books, 1972.

Rifkin, Jeremy. *Algeny.* New York: Viking, 1983.
Discusses the "desacralization" of human life as a result of increasing technological control, with genetic engineering posing a special threat.

V. EVOLUTION VERSUS CREATIONISM

Coffin, Harold G., with Robert H. Brown. *Origin by Design.* Washington, D. C.: Review and Herald Publishing Association, 1983.

Gorman, James. "Would You Vote for a Man Who Says He's No Kin to an Ape?" *Discover* (Dec. 1986):25–27.

Gould, Stephen Jay. "Our Greatest Evolutionary Step." In *The Panda's Thumb: More Reflections in Natural History.* New York: Norton, 1980.

Gould, Stephen Jay. "Evolution as Fact and Theory." In *Hen's Teeth and Horse's Toes: More Reflections in Natural History.* New York: Norton, 1983.

McGowan, Chris. *In the Beginning . . . : A Scientist Shows Why the Creationists Are Wrong.* Buffalo, N.Y.: Prometheus Books, 1984.

Sanders, Alain L. "Tilting at 'Secular Humanism.' " *Time* (July 28, 1986):68.

Scopes, John T., and James Presley. *Center of the Storm: Memoirs of John T. Scopes.* New York: Holt, Rinehart & Winston, 1967.

Stein, Kathleen. "Censoring Science." *Omni* (Feb. 1987):42–49, 94–99.

Teilhard de Chardin, Pierre. *Christianity and Evolution.* Translated by Rene Hague. New York: Harcourt Brace Jovanovich, 1969.

Tierney, John, et al., "The Search for Adam and Eve." *Newsweek* (Jan. 11, 1988):46–52.
Reports on the genetically based hypothesis that all human beings share a common Homo sapiens ancestor, which appeared no earlier than 200,000 years ago, thus challenging the older scientific view that humans have a much older lineage.

VI. COMPUTER TECHNOLOGY

Dreyfus, Hubert L. *What Computers Can't Do: A Critique of Artificial Reason.* New York: Harper & Row, 1972.

Larson, Erik. "Neural Chips." *Omni* (Nov. 1986):113–16, 168–69.
Describes the problems involved in developing computers that can see accurately.

Peat, F. David. *AI: How Machines Think.* New York: Baen Books, 1988.

Schauk, Roger C. *The Cognitive Computer: On Language, Learning, and Artificial Intelligence.* Reading, Mass.: Addison-Wesley, 1984.

Turkle, Sherry. *The Second Self: Computers and the Human Spirit.* New York: Simon & Schuster, 1984.
An absorbing study of the psychological impact of computers, particularly on children.

Zinsser, William. *Writing with a Word Processor.* New York: Harper & Row, 1983.
A veteran writer delightfully describes his grudging conversion to word processing.

PART FOUR

The Literary Dimension:

Short Stories, Poetry, and Personal Essays on Scientific Themes

We interact with the world emotionally as well as intellectually. Emotion, no less than reason, shapes and gives significance to our lives. The enchantment we feel before a full moon rising above a mountain lake should be just as important to us as our factual knowledge of the moon—a world devoid of life, utterly desolate, whose rocks reveal to the scientific eye the early history of our solar system. To be sure, the secrets that nature yields to us simply beget more secrets. "Science does not dispel mystery," writes Loren Eiseley, "but opens vaster mysteries to our gaze." Imagination and curiosity, along with a great deal of sheer wonder, lurk behind the most incisive intellectual inquiry.

The sense of wonder is the link between rational inquiry and creative imagining. Science gives us the raw material for thinking about humanity in exciting new contexts. It entices us to ask the question, What if . . . ? and to come up with bold responses. These responses may take the form of stories, poems, essays—and, as is the case with the selections that follow, transform readers into *sharers* of the experiences depicted.

While it is true that these works can illuminate our understanding of the scientific or psychological concepts that they build upon, their primary purpose is to engage us emotionally, to make us feel like participants, not spectators, in the dramas they unfold.

In "The Birthmark," for example, Hawthorne enables us, through the magic of his storytelling, to experience the reality of Aylmer's obsession with physical perfection; Hawthorne doesn't merely tell us about Aylmer—he takes us deep inside Aylmer's consciousness. We aren't merely given an abstract premise about Aylmer's compulsion to control scientifically that which is beyond such control—instead, we *feel* his compulsion.

Similarly, in "The Judgment of the Birds," Loren Eiseley enables us to feel what it is like to walk alone through the desolate Badlands and to witness a series of events that are both natural and supernatural. In May Swenson's poem, "The DNA Molecule," science (in this case molecular biology) and modern art become complements of one another in a poetic tapestry that unravels like the DNA molecule itself.

It is through the medium of literature—of artistic expression in general—that scientific ideas have their deepest influence upon the human spirit.

READING INTRODUCTION

In a Hawthorne tale, emotions and intellect are continually in opposition, with the welfare of the soul at stake. Hester Prynne, Roger Chillingworth, and Arthur Dimmesdale of *The Scarlet Letter* (1850); Judge Pyncheon of *The House of the Seven Gables* (1851); Hilda, Miriam, and Donatello of *The Marble Faun* (1860)—these characters are memorable because Hawthorne takes us into the depths of their psyches. Hawthorne began with an effort to determine the nature of sin as the Puritans defined it, but he ends up exploring the complexities of human motivation. The following tale, written in 1843, is a case in point. Aylmer rationalizes the practicality of removing his wife's birthmark—the only blemish on her flawless beauty—but we soon suspect that the real motive behind his compulsion to operate goes far beyond any practical considerations.

TERMS TO LEARN

natural philosophy: the pre-nineteenth-century term for science

Eve of Powers: reference to a statue of Eve by Hiram Powers, a nineteenth-century American sculptor

Pygmalion: the legendary king of Cyprus who fell in love with the statue of a beautiful woman that he sculpted. Aphrodite, pitying him, gave the statue life.

elixir (of life): a mythical drug capable of prolonging life indefinitely

nostrum: a homemade medicine, often sold by quacks

NATHANIEL HAWTHORNE

 The Birthmark

In the latter part of the last century there lived a man of science, an eminent proficient in every branch of natural philosophy, who not long before our story opens had made experience of a spiritual affinity more attractive than any chemical one. He had left his laboratory to the care of an assistant, cleared his fine countenance from the furnace smoke, washed the stain of acids from his fingers, and persuaded a beautiful woman to become his wife. In those days, when the comparatively recent discovery of electricity and other kindred mysteries of Nature seemed to open paths into the region of miracle, it was not unusual for the love of science to rival the love of woman in its depth and absorbing energy. The higher intellect, the imagination, the spirit, and even the heart might all find their congenial aliment in pursuits which, as some of their ardent votaries believed, would ascend from one step of powerful intelligence to another, until the philosopher should lay his hand on the secret of creative force and perhaps make new worlds for himself. We know not whether Aylmer possessed this degree of faith in man's ultimate control over Nature. He had devoted himself, however, too unreservedly to scientific studies ever to be weaned from them by any second passion. His love for his young wife might prove the stronger of the two; but it could only be by intertwining itself with his love of science and uniting the strength of the latter to his own.

Such a union accordingly took place, and was attended with truly remarkable consequences and a deeply impressive moral. One day, very soon after their marriage, Aylmer sat gazing at his wife with a trouble in his countenance that grew stronger until he spoke.

"Georgiana," said he, "has it never occurred to you that the mark upon your cheek might be removed?"

"No, indeed," said she, smiling; but, perceiving the seriousness of his manner, she blushed deeply. "To tell you the truth, it has been so often called a charm that I was simple enough to imagine it might be so."

"Ah, upon another face perhaps it might," replied her husband; "but never on yours. No, dearest Georgiana, you came so nearly perfect from the hand of Nature that this slightest possible defect, which we hesitate whether to term a defect or a beauty, shocks me, as being the visible mark of earthly imperfection."

"Shocks you, my husband!" cried Georgiana, deeply hurt; at first reddening with momentary anger, but then bursting into tears. "Then why did you take me from my mother's side? You cannot love what shocks you!"

To explain this conversation, it must be mentioned that in the center of Georgiana's left cheek there was a singular mark, deeply interwoven, as it were, with the texture and substance of her face. In the usual state of her complexion—a healthy though delicate bloom— the mark wore a tint of deeper crimson, which imperfectly defined its shape amid the surrounding rosiness. When she blushed it gradually became more indistinct, and finally vanished amid the triumphant rush of blood that bathed the whole cheek with its brilliant glow. But if any shifting motion caused her to turn pale there was the mark again, a crimson stain upon the snow, in what Aylmer sometimes deemed an almost fearful distinctness. Its shape bore not a little similarity to the human hand, though of the smallest pygmy size. Georgiana's lovers were wont to say that some fairy at her birth hour had laid her tiny hand upon the infant's cheek, and left this impress there in token of the magic endowments that were to give her such sway over all hearts. Many a desperate swain would have risked life for the privilege of pressing his lips to the mysterious hand. It must not be concealed, however, that the impression wrought by this fairy sign manual varied exceedingly according to the difference of temperament in the beholders. Some fastidious persons—but they were exclusively of her own sex—affirmed that the bloody hand, as they chose to call it, quite destroyed the effect of Georgiana's beauty and rendered her countenance even hideous. But it would be as reasonable to say that one of those small blue stains which sometimes occur in the purest statuary marble would convert the Eve of Powers to a monster. Masculine observers, if the birthmark did not heighten their admiration, contented themselves with wishing it away, that the world might possess one living specimen of ideal loveliness without the semblance of a flaw. After his marriage—for he thought little or nothing of the matter before—Aylmer discovered that this was the case with himself.

Had she been less beautiful—if Envy's self could have found aught else to sneer at—he might have felt his affection heightened by the prettiness of this mimic hand, now vaguely portrayed, now lost, now stealing forth again and glimmering to and fro with every pulse of emotion that throbbed within her heart; but, seeing her otherwise so perfect, he found this one defect grow more and more intolerable with every moment of their united lives. It was the fatal flaw of humanity which Nature, in one shape or another, stamps ineffaceably on all her productions, either to imply that they are temporary and finite, or that their perfection must be wrought by toil and pain. The crimson hand expressed the ineludible grip in which mortality clutches the highest and purest of earthly mould, degrading them into kindred with the lowest, and even with the very brutes, like whom their visible frames return to dust. In this manner, selecting it as the symbol of his wife's liability to sin, sorrow, decay, and death, Aylmer's somber imagination was not long in rendering the birthmark a frightful object, causing him more trouble and horror than ever Georgiana's beauty, whether of soul or sense, had given him delight.

At all the seasons which should have been their happiest he invariably, and without intending it, nay, in spite of a purpose to the contrary, reverted to this one disastrous topic. Trifling as it at first appeared, it so connected itself with innumerable trains of thought and modes of feeling that it became the central point of all. With the morning twilight Aylmer opened his eyes upon his wife's face and recognized the symbol of imperfection; and when they sat together at the evening hearth his eyes wandered stealthily to her cheek, and beheld, flickering with the blaze of the wood fire, the spectral hand that wrote mortality where he would fain have worshipped. Georgiana soon learned to shudder at his gaze. It needed but a glance with the peculiar expression that his face often wore to change the roses of her cheek into a deathlike paleness, amid which the crimson hand was brought strongly out, like a bas-relief of ruby on the whitest marble.

Late one night, when the lights were growing dim so as hardly to betray the stain on the poor wife's cheek, she herself, for the first time, voluntarily took up the subject.

"Do you remember, my dear Aylmer," said she, with a feeble attempt at a smile, "have you any recollection, of a dream last night about this odious hand?"

"None! none whatever!" replied Aylmer, starting; but then he added, in a dry, cold tone, affected for the sake of concealing the real depth of his emotion, "I might well dream of it; for, before I fell asleep, it had taken a pretty firm hold of my fancy."

"And you did dream of it?" continued Georgiana, hastily; for she dreaded lest a gush of tears should interrupt what she had to say. "A terrible dream! I wonder that you can forget it. Is it possible to forget this one expression?—'It is in her heart now; we must have it out!' Reflect, my husband; for by all means I would have you to recall that dream."

The mind is in a sad state when Sleep, the all-involving, cannot confine her specters within the dim region of her sway, but suffers them to break forth, affrighting this actual life with secrets that perchance belong to a deeper one. Aylmer now remembered his dream. He had fancied himself with his servant Aminadab, attempting an operation for the removal of the birthmark; but the deeper went the knife, the deeper sank the hand, until at length its tiny grasp appeared to have caught hold of Georgiana's heart; whence, however, her husband was inexorably resolved to cut or wrench it away.

When the dream had shaped itself perfectly in his memory Aylmer sat in his wife's presence with a guilty feeling. Truth often finds its way to the mind close muffled in robes of sleep, and then speaks with uncompromising directness of matters in regard to which we practice an unconscious self deception during our waking moments. Until now he had not been aware of the tyrannizing influence acquired by one idea over his mind, and of the lengths which he might find in his heart to go for the sake of giving himself peace.

"Aylmer," resumed Georgiana, solemnly, "I know not what may be the cost to both of us to rid me of this fatal birthmark. Perhaps its removal may cause cureless deformity; or it may be the stain goes as deep as life itself. Again: do we know that there is a possibility, on any terms, of unclasping the firm grip of this little hand which was laid upon me before I came into the world?"

"Dearest Georgiana, I have spent much thought upon the subject," hastily interrupted Aylmer. "I am convinced of the perfect practicability of its removal."

"If there be the remotest possibility of it," continued Georgiana, "let the attempt be made, at whatever risk. Danger is nothing to me; for life, while this hateful mark makes me the object of your horror and disgust—life is a burden which I would fling down with joy. Either remove this dreadful hand, or take my wretched life! You have deep science. All the world bears witness of it. You have achieved great wonders. Cannot you remove this little, little mark, which I cover with the tips of two small fingers? Is this beyond your power, for the sake of your own peace, and to save your poor wife from madness?"

"Noblest, dearest, tenderest wife," cried Aylmer, rapturously, "doubt not my power. I have already given this matter the deepest thought—thought which might almost have enlightened me to create a being less perfect than yourself. Georgiana, you have led me deeper than ever into the heart of science. I feel myself fully competent to render this dear cheek as faultless as its fellow; and then, most beloved, what will be my triumph when I shall have corrected what Nature left imperfect in her fairest work! Even Pygmalion, when his sculptured woman assumed life, felt not greater ecstasy than mine will be."

"It is resolved, then," said Georgiana, faintly smiling. "And Aylmer, spare me not, though you should find the birthmark take refuge in my heart at last."

Her husband tenderly kissed her cheek—her right cheek—not that which bore the impress of the crimson hand.

The next day Aylmer apprised his wife of a plan that he had formed whereby he might have opportunity for the intense thought and constant watchfulness which the proposed operation would require; while Georgiana, likewise, would enjoy the perfect repose essential to its success. They were to seclude themselves in the extensive apartments occupied by Aylmer as a laboratory, and where, during his toilsome youth, he had made discoveries in the elemental powers of Nature that had roused the admiration of all the learned societies in Europe. Seated calmly in this laboratory, the pale philosopher had investigated the secrets of the highest cloud region and of the profoundest mines; he had satisfied himself of the causes that kindled and kept alive the fires of the volcano; and had explained the mystery of fountains, and how it is that they gush forth, some so bright and pure, and others with such rich medicinal virtues, from the dark bosom of the earth. Here, too, at an earlier period, he had studied the wonders of the human frame, and attempted to fathom the very process by which Nature assimilates all her precious influences from earth and air, and from the spiritual world, to create and foster man, her masterpiece. The latter pursuit, however, Aylmer had long laid aside in unwilling recognition of the truth—against which all seekers sooner or later stumble—that our great creative Mother, while she amuses us with apparently working in the broadest sunshine, is yet severely careful to keep her own secrets, and, in spite of her pretended openness, shows us nothing but results. She permits us, indeed, to mar, but seldom to mend, and, like a jealous patentee, on no account to make. Now, however, Aylmer resumed these half-forgotten investigations; not, of course, with such hopes or wishes as first suggested them; but because they involved much physiological truth and lay in the path of his proposed scheme for the treatment of Georgiana.

As he led her over the threshold of the laboratory, Georgiana was cold and tremulous. Aylmer looked cheerfully into her face, with intent to reassure her, but was so startled with the intense glow of the birthmark upon the whiteness of her cheek that he could not restrain a strong convulsive shudder. His wife fainted.

"Aminadab! Aminadab!" shouted Aylmer, stamping violently on the floor.

Forthwith there issued from an inner apartment a man of low stature, but bulky frame, with shaggy hair hanging about his visage, which was grimed with the vapors of the furnace. This personage had been Aylmer's underworker during his whole scientific career, and was admirably fitted for that office by his great mechanical readiness, and the skill with which, while incapable of comprehending a single principle, he executed all the details of his master's experiments. With his vast strength, his shaggy hair, his smoky aspect, and the indescribable earthiness that incrusted him, he seemed to represent man's physical nature; while Aylmer's slender figure, and pale, intellectual face, were no less apt a type of the spiritual element.

"Throw open the door of the boudoir, Aminadab," said Aylmer, "and burn a pastil."

"Yes, master," answered Aminadab, looking intently at the lifeless form of Georgiana; and then he muttered to himself, "If she were my wife, I'd never part with that birthmark."

When Georgiana recovered consciousness she found herself breathing an atmosphere of penetrating fragrance, the gentle potency of which had recalled her from her deathlike faintness. The scene around her looked like enchantment. Aylmer had converted those smoky, dingy, somber rooms, where he had spent his brightest years in recondite pursuits, into a series of beautiful apartments not unfit to be the secluded abode of a lovely woman. The walls were hung with gorgeous curtains, which imparted the combination of grandeur and grace that no other species of adornment can achieve, and as they fell from the ceiling to the floor, their rich and ponderous folds, concealing all angles and straight lines, appeared to shut in the scene from infinite space. For aught Georgiana knew, it might be a pavilion among the clouds. And Aylmer, excluding the sunshine, which would have interfered with his chemical processes, had supplied its place with perfumed lamps, emitting flames of various hue, but all uniting in a soft, impurpled radiance. He now knelt by his wife's side, watching her earnestly, but without alarm; for he was confident in his science, and felt that he could draw a magic circle around her within which no evil might intrude.

"Where am I? Ah, I remember," said Georgiana, faintly; and she placed her hand over her cheek to hide the terrible mark from her husband's eyes.

"Fear not, dearest!" exclaimed he. "Do not shrink from me! Believe me, Georgiana, I even rejoice in this single imperfection, since it will be such a rapture to remove it."

"O, spare me!" sadly replied his wife. "Pray do not look at it again. I never can forget that convulsive shudder."

In order to soothe Georgiana, and as it were, to release her mind from the burden of actual things, Aylmer now put in practice some of the light and playful secrets which science had taught him among its profounder lore. Airy figures, absolutely bodiless ideas, and forms of unsubstantial beauty came and danced before her, imprinting their momentary footsteps on beams of light. Though she had some indistinct idea of the method of these optical phenomena, still the illusion was almost perfect enough to warrant the belief that her husband possessed sway over the spiritual world. Then again, when she felt a wish to look forth from her seclusion, immediately, as if her thoughts were answered, the procession of external existence flitted across a screen. The scenery and the figures of actual life were perfectly represented, but with that bewitching yet indescribable difference which always makes a picture, an image, or a shadow so much more attractive than the original. When wearied of this, Aylmer bade her cast her eyes upon a vessel containing a quantity of earth. She did so, with little interest at first; but soon was startled to perceive the germ of a plant shooting upward from the soil. Then came the slender stalk; the leaves gradually unfolded themselves; and amid them was a perfect and lovely flower.

"It is magical," cried Georgiana. "I dare not touch it."

"Nay, pluck it," answered Aylmer, "pluck it, and inhale its brief perfume while you may. The flower will wither in a few moments and leave nothing save its brown seed vessels; but thence may be perpetuated a race as ephemeral as itself."

But Georgiana had no sooner touched the flower than the whole plant suffered a blight, its leaves turning coal-black as if by the agency of fire.

"There was too powerful a stimulus," said Aylmer, thoughtfully.

To make up for this abortive experiment, he proposed to take her portrait by a scientific process of his own invention. It was to be effected by rays of light striking upon a polished plate of metal. Georgiana assented; but, on looking at the result, was affrighted to find the features of the portrait blurred and indefinable; while the minute figure of a hand appeared where the cheek should have been. Aylmer snatched the metallic plate and threw it into a jar of corrosive acid.

Soon, however, he forgot these mortifying failures. In the intervals of study and chemical experiment he came to her flushed and exhausted, but seemed invigorated by her presence, and spoke in glowing language of the resources of his art. He gave a history of the long dynasty of the alchemists, who spent so many ages in quest of the universal solvent by which the golden principle might be elicited from all things vile and base. Aylmer appeared to believe that, by the plainest scientific logic, it was altogether within the limits of possibility to discover this long-sought medium; "but," he added, "a philosopher who should go deep enough to acquire the power would attain too lofty a wisdom to stoop to the exercise of it." Not less singular were his opinions in regard to the elixir vitae. He more than intimated that it was at his option to concoct a liquid that should prolong life for years, perhaps interminably; but that it would produce a discord in Nature which all the world, and chiefly the quaffer of the immortal nostrum, would find cause to curse.

"Aylmer, are you in earnest?" asked Georgiana, looking at him with amazement and fear. "It is terrible to possess such power, or even to dream of possessing it."

"O, do not tremble, my love," said her husband. "I would not wrong either you or myself by working such inharmonious effects upon our lives; but I would have you consider how trifling, in comparison, is the skill requisite to remove this little hand."

At the mention of the birthmark, Georgiana, as usual, shrank as if a red-hot iron had touched her cheek.

Again Aylmer applied himself to his labors. She could hear his voice in the distant furnace room giving directions to Aminadab, whose harsh, uncouth, misshapen tones were audible in response, more like the grunt or growl of a brute than human speech. After hours of absence, Aylmer reappeared and proposed that she should now examine his cabinet of chemical products and natural treasures of the earth. Among the former he showed her a small vial, in which, he remarked, was contained a gentle yet most powerful fragrance, capable of impregnating all the breezes that blow across a kindgom. They were of inestimable value, the contents of that little vial; and, as he said so, he threw some of the perfume into the air and filled the room with piercing and invigorating delight.

"And what is this?" asked Georgiana, pointing to a small crystal globe containing a gold-colored liquid. "It is so beautiful to the eye that I could imagine it the elixir of life."

"In one sense it is," replied Aylmer; "or rather, the elixir of immortality. It is the most precious poison that ever was concocted in this world. By its aid I could apportion the lifetime of any mortal at whom you might point your finger. The strength of the dose would determine whether he were to linger out years, or drop dead in the midst of a breath. No king on his guarded throne could keep his life if I, in my private station, should deem that the welfare of millions justified me in depriving him of it."

"Why do you keep such a terrific drug?" inquired Georgiana in horror.

"Do not mistrust me, dearest," said her husband, smiling; "its virtuous potency is yet greater than its harmful one. But see! here is a powerful cosmetic. With a few drops of this in a vase of water, freckles may be washed away as easily as the hands are cleansed. A stronger infusion would take the blood out of the cheek, and leave the rosiest beauty a pale ghost."

"Is it with this lotion that you intend to bathe my cheek?" asked Georgiana, anxiously.

"O, no," hastily replied her husband; "this is merely superficial. Your case demands a remedy that shall go deeper."

In his interviews with Georgiana, Aylmer generally made minute inquiries as to her sensations, and whether the confinement of the rooms and the temperature of the atmosphere agreed with her. These questions has such a particular drift that Georgiana began to conjecture that she was already subjected to certain physical influences, either breathed in with the fragrant air or taken with her food. She fancied likewise, but it might be altogether fancy, that there was a stirring up of her system—a strange, indefinite sensation creeping through her veins, and tingling, half painfully, half pleasurably, at her heart. Still, whenever she dared to look into the mirror, there she beheld herself pale as a white rose with a crimson birthmark stamped upon her cheek. Not even Aylmer now hated it so much as she.

To dispel the tedium of the hours which her husband found it necessary to devote to the processes of combination and analysis, Georgiana turned over the volumes of his scientific library. In many dark old tomes she met with chapters full of romance and poetry. They were the works of the philosophers of the middle ages, such as Albertus Magnus, Cornelius Agrippa, Paracelsus, and the famous friar who created the prophetic Brazen Head.[1] All these antique naturalists stood in advance of their centuries, yet were imbued with some of their credulity, and therefore were believed, and perhaps imagined themselves to have acquired from the investigation of Nature a power above Nature, and from physics a sway over the spiritual world. Hardly less curious and imaginative were the early volumes of the Transactions of the Royal Society,[2] in which the members, knowing little of the limits of natural possibility, were continually recording wonders or proposing methods whereby wonders might be wrought.

---

[1]The "famous friar" is the Franciscan, Roger Bacon (1214–1294), who achieved fame as a scholastic philosopher and scientist. According to a legend, Friar Bacon created a brass head that had the power of prophecy. Albertus Magnus (1206–1280), Cornelius Agrippa (1468–1535), and Aureolus Philippus von Hohenheim, more commonly known as Paracelsus (1493–1541), all combined medieval philosophy and science in their writings.

[2]The Royal Society, devoted to the advancement of science, was founded in London in 1662 by Thomas Sprat (1635–1713).

But to Georgiana, the most engrossing volume was a large folio from her husband's own hand, in which he had recorded every experiment of his scientific career, its original aim, the methods adopted for its development, and its final success or failure, with the circumstances to which either event was attributable. The book, in truth, was both the history and emblem of his ardent, ambitious, imaginative, yet practical and laborious life. He handled physical details as if there were nothing beyond them; yet spiritualized them all and redeemed himself from materialism by his strong and eager aspiration toward the infinite. In his grasp the veriest clod of earth assumed a soul. Georgiana, as she read, reverenced Aylmer and loved him more profoundly than ever, but with a less entire dependence on his judgment than heretofore. Much as he had accomplished, she could not but observe that his most splendid successes were almost invariably failures, if compared with the ideal at which he aimed. His brightest diamonds were the merest pebbles, and felt to be so by himself, in comparison with the inestimable gems which lay hidden beyond his reach. The volume, rich with achievements that had won renown for its author, was yet as melancholy a record as ever mortal hand had penned. It was the sad confession and continual exemplification of the shortcomings of the composite man, the spirit burdened with clay and working in matter, and of the despair that assails the higher nature at finding itself so miserably thwarted by the earthly part. Perhaps every man of genius, in whatever sphere, might recognize the image of his own experience in Aylmer's journal.

So deeply did these reflections affect Georgiana that she laid her face upon the open volume and burst into tears. In this situation she was found by her husband.

"It is dangerous to read in a sorcerer's books," said he with a smile, though his countenance was uneasy and displeased. "Georgiana, there are pages in that volume which I can scarcely glance over and keep my senses. Take heed lest it prove detrimental to you."

"It has made me worship you more than ever," said she.

"Ah, wait for this one success," rejoined he, "then worship me if you will. I shall deem myself hardly unworthy of it. But come. I have sought you for the luxury of your voice. Sing to me, dearest."

So she poured out the liquid music of her voice to quench the thirst of his spirit. He then took his leave with a boyish exuberance of gaiety, assuring her that her seclusion would endure but a little longer, and that the result was already certain. Scarcely had he departed when Georgiana felt irresistibly impelled to follow him. She had forgotten to inform Aylmer of a symptom which for two or three hours past had begun to excite her attention. It was a sensation in the fatal birthmark, not painful, but which induced a restlessness throughout her system. Hastening after her husband, she intruded for the first time into the laboratory.

The first thing that struck her eye was the furnace, that hot and feverish worker, with the intense glow of its fire, which by the quantities of soot clustered above it seemed to have been burning for ages. There was a distilling apparatus in full operation. Around the room were retorts, tubes, cylinders, crucibles, and other apparatus of chemical research. An electrical machine stood ready for immediate use. The atmosphere felt oppressively close, and was tainted with gaseous odors which had been tormented forth by the processes of science. The severe and homely simplicity of the apartment, with its naked walls and brick pavement, looked strange, accustomed as Georgiana had become to the fantastic elegance of her boudoir. But what chiefly, indeed almost solely, drew her attention, was the aspect of Aylmer himself.

He was pale as death, anxious and absorbed, and hung over the furnace as if it depended upon his utmost watchfulness whether the liquid which it was distilling should be the draught of immortal happiness or misery. How different from the sanguine and joyous mien that he had assumed for Georgiana's encouragement!

"Carefully now, Aminadab; carefully, thou human machine; carefully, thou man of clay," muttered Aylmer, more to himself than his assistant. "Now, if there be a thought too much or too little, it is all over."

"Ho! ho!" mumbled Aminadab. "Look, master! look!"

Aylmer raised his eyes hastily, and at first reddened, then grew paler then ever, on beholding Georgiana. He rushed toward her and seized her arm with a grip that left the print of his fingers upon it.

"Why do you come hither? Have you no trust in your husband?" cried he, impetuously. "Would you throw the blight of that fatal birthmark over my labors? It is not well done. Go, prying woman! go!"

"Nay, Aylmer," said Georgiana with the firmness of which she possessed no stinted endowment, "it is not you that have a right to complain. You mistrust your wife; you have concealed the anxiety with which you watch the development of this experiment. Think not so unworthily of me, my husband. Tell me all the risk we run, and fear not that I shall shrink; for my share in it is far less than your own."

"No, no, Georgiana!" said Aylmer, impatiently; "it must not be."

"I submit," replied she, calmly. "And Aylmer, I shall quaff whatever draught you bring me; but it will be on the same principle that would induce me to take a dose of poison if offered by your hand."

"My noble wife," said Aylmer, deeply moved, "I knew not the height and depth of your nature until now. Nothing shall be concealed. Know, then, that this crimson hand, superficial as it seems, has clutched its grasp into your being with a strength of which I had no previous conception. I have already administered agents powerful enough to do aught except to change your entire physical system. Only one thing remains to be tried. If that fail us we are ruined."

"Why did you hesitate to tell me this?" asked she.

"Because, Georgiana," said Aylmer, in a low voice, "there is danger."

"Danger? There is but one danger—that this horrible stigma shall be left upon my cheek!" cried Georgiana. "Remove it, remove it, whatever be the cost, or we shall both go mad!"

"Heaven knows your words are too true," said Aylmer, sadly. "And now, dearest, return to your boudoir. In a little while all will be tested."

He conducted her back and took leave of her with a solemn tenderness which spoke far more than his words how much was now at stake. After his departure Georgiana became rapt in musings. She considered the character of Aylmer and did it completer justice than at any previous moment. Her heart exulted, while it trembled, at his honorable love—so pure and lofty that it would accept nothing less than perfection nor miserably make itself contented with an earthlier nature than he had dreamed of. She felt how much more precious was such a sentiment than that meaner kind which would have borne with the imperfection for her sake, and have been guilty of treason to holy love by degrading its perfect idea to the level of the actual; and with her whole spirit she prayed that, for a signal moment, she might satisfy his highest and deepest conception. Longer than one moment she well knew it could not be; for his spirit was ever on the march, ever ascending, and each instant required something that was beyond the scope of the instant before.

The sound of her husband's footsteps aroused her. He bore a crystal goblet containing a liquor colorless as water, but bright enough to be the draught of immortality. Aylmer was pale; but it seemed rather the consequence of a highly-wrought state of mind and tension of spirit than of fear or doubt.

"The concoction of the draught has been perfect," said he, in answer to Georgiana's look. "Unless all my science have deceived me, it cannot fail."

"Save on your account, my dearest Aylmer," observed his wife, "I might wish to put off this birthmark of mortality by relinquishing mortality itself in preference to any other mode. Life is but a sad possession to those who have attained precisely the degree of moral advancement at which I stand. Were I weaker and blinder, it might be happiness. Were I stronger, it might be endured hopefully. But, being what I find myself, methinks I am of all mortals the most fit to die."

"You are fit for heaven without tasting death!" replied her husband. "But why do we speak of dying? The draught cannot fail. Behold its effect upon this plant."

On the window seat there stood a geranium diseased with yellow blotches which had overspread all its leaves. Aylmer poured a small quantity of the liquid upon the soil in which it grew. In a little time, when the roots of the plant had taken up the moisture the unsightly blotches began to be extinguished in a living verdure.

"There needed no proof," said Georgiana, quietly. "Give me the goblet. I joyfully stake all upon your word."

"Drink, then thou lofty creature!" exclaimed Aylmer, with fervid admiration. "There is no taint of imperfection on thy spirit. Thy sensible frame, too, shall soon be all perfect."

She quaffed the liquid and returned the goblet to his hand.

"It is grateful," said she, with a placid smile. "Methinks it is like water from a heavenly fountain; for it contains I know not what of unobtrusive fragrance and deliciousness. It allays a feverish thirst that had parched me for many days. Now, dearest, let me sleep. My earthly senses are closing over my spirit like the leaves around the heart of a rose at sunset."

She spoke the last words with a gentle reluctance, as if it required almost more energy than she could command to pronounce the faint and lingering syllables. Scarcely had they loitered through her lips ere she was lost in slumber. Aylmer sat by her side, watching her aspect with the emotions proper to a man the whole value of whose existence was involved in the process now to be tested. Mingled with this mood, however, was the philosophic investigation characteristic of the man of science. Not the minutest symptom escaped him. A heightened flush of the cheek, a slight irregularity of breath, a quiver of the eyelid, a hardly perceptible tremor through the frame—such were the details which, as the moments passed, he wrote down in his folio volume. Intense thought had set its stamp upon every previous page of that volume; but the thoughts of years were all concentrated upon the last.

While thus employed, he failed not to gaze often at the fatal hand, and not without a shudder. Yet once, by a strange and unaccountable impulse, he pressed it with his lips. His spirit recoiled, however, in the very act; and Georgiana, out of the midst of her deep sleep, moved uneasily and murmured as if in remonstrance. Again Aylmer resumed his watch. Nor was it without avail. The crimson hand, which at first had been strongly visible upon the marble paleness of Georgiana's cheek, now grew more faintly outlined. She remained not less pale than ever, but the birthmark, with every breath that came and went lost somewhat of its former distinctness. Its presence had been awful; its departure was more awful still. Watch the stain of the rainbow fading out of the sky, and you will know how that mysterious symbol passed away.

"By Heaven! it is well nigh gone!" said Aylmer to himself, in almost irrepressible ectasy. "I can scarcely trace it now. Success! success! And now it is like the faintest rose color. The lightest flush of blood across her cheek would overcome it. But she is so pale!"

He drew aside the window curtain and suffered the light of natural day to fall into the room and rest upon her cheek. At the same time he heard a gross, hoarse chuckle, which he had long known as his servant Aminadab's expression of delight.

"Ah, clod! ah, earthly mass!" cried Aylmer, laughing in a sort of frenzy, "you have served me well! Matter and spirit—earth and heaven—have both done their part in this! Laugh, thing of the senses! You have earned the right to laugh."

These exclamations broke Georgiana's sleep. She slowly unclosed her eyes and gazed into the mirror which her husband had arranged for that purpose. A faint smile flitted over her lips when she recognized how barely perceptible was now that crimson hand which had once blazed forth with such disastrous brilliancy as to scare away all their happiness. But then her eyes sought Aylmer's face with a trouble and anxiety that he could by no means account for.

"My poor Aylmer!" murmured she.

"Poor? Nay, richest, happiest, most favored!" exlaimed he. "My peerless bride, it is successful! You are perfect!"

"My poor Aylmer," she repeated, with a more than human tenderness, "you have aimed loftily; you have done nobly. Do not repent that, with so high and pure a feeling, you have rejected the best the earth could offer. Aylmer, dearest Aylmer, I am dying!"

Alas! it was too true! The fatal hand had grappled with the mystery of life, and was the bond by which an angelic spirit kept itself in union with the mortal frame. As the last crimson tint of the birthmark—that sole token of human imperfection—faded from her cheek, the parting breath of the now perfect woman passed into the atmosphere, and her soul, lingering a moment near her husband, took its heavenward flight. Then a hoarse, chuckling laugh was heard again! Thus ever does the gross fatality of earth exult in its invariable triumph over the immortal essence which, in this dim sphere of half development, demands the completeness of a higher state. Yet, had

Aylmer reached a profounder wisdom, he need not thus have flung away the happiness which would have woven his mortal life of the selfsame texture with the celestial. The momentary circumstance was too strong for him; he failed to look beyond the shadowy scope of time, and, living once for all in eternity, to find the perfect future in the present.

Exercises and Projects

CHECKING YOUR COMPREHENSION

1. Relate, in a sentence or two, the basic story line of "The Birthmark."

2. How does Georgiana's attitude toward her birthmark differ from her husband's?

3. Summarize Aylmer's dream. How is it important to the story?

4. At one point Aylmer says to his wife that he rejoices in her one imperfection. Is he contradicting himself? Explain.

5. Aylmer admits that the drug he wishes to administer to Georgiana is a poison. Why does he want to use it on her?

FOR DISCUSSION AND DEBATE

1. One of Hawthorne's great talents as a storyteller is his ability to create mood (or atmosphere). Describe the mood of "The Birthmark" and try to pinpoint what Hawthorne does to create that mood, particularly in the opening paragraphs.

2. Discuss the effectiveness of the ending. Some find it melodramatic. Do you agree or disagree?

3. Early in the tale we learn that Aylmer's passion for scientific studies was such that he could scarcely "be weaned from them by any second passion." Do you see this as a defect in Aylmer's character or the inevitable consequence of pursuing scientific research?

4. It becomes apparent that Georgiana's birthmark is more than a superficial blemish. What does it come to represent, in your opinion? Is there any special significance you associate with its shape?

FOR YOUR NOTEBOOK

1. Think about your own tolerance for imperfection. Do you get unusually distressed when things aren't perfect (such as when you receive a score of 99 instead of 100 on an exam)? List as many of these incidents as you can, and explain why you reacted the way you did.

2. Outline or write out a sequel to "The Birthmark." What kind of fate would (or should) Aylmer have?

FOR WRITING

1. Imagine Aylmer as a famous scientist of the late 1980s. What would he be investigating with a passion? How dangerous would his research be? Write a story in which your modern-day Aylmer encounters a life-or-death situation arising from his explorations.

2. Over the next several days observe how scientists (including medical professionals) are portrayed by the press, on television, and in films. Report and evaluate your findings in an essay.

3. Write a personal essay about the human need to unravel the mysteries of nature versus the need to preserve mystery. Questions to consider: What is the value of mystery in a scientific age? What value does it have for you personally? Does the mysteriousness of a phenomenon always disappear when the phenomenon is explained?

The tales of Edgar Allan Poe are often horrific, steeped in mystery, creating what Poe called a single effect upon the reader—a uniform sense of dread or terror. Poe is also master of verisimilitude—the technique of making any situation seem utterly real. First published in 1845, the following tale reflects one of Poe's favorite themes: the cheating of death. The tale hinges on what was then a medical (and, also, theatrical) marvel: mesmerism—what we today call hypnotism. Physicians and magicians alike had been zealously experimenting with this strange psychological phenomenon, and the possibilities seemed endless. The Poe scholar Stephen Peithman (see "Suggestions for Further Reading" at the end of this part) notes that a New York physician, Sidney Doane, announced in 1845 that he had removed a tumor from a woman under hypnosis; and Chauncey Townshend in *Facts in Mesmerism* (1844) reported that hypnosis had prolonged a dying man's life by two months.

TERMS TO LEARN

clairvoyance: the ability to see beyond what is ordinarily visible. Poe apparently was the first author to use this word in English writings.

emaciation: a state of abnormal weight loss

aneurism: a weakened and enlarged section of an artery wall

stertorous (breathing): snoring

ichor: the watery discharge from a sore; in mythology, the "blood" of the gods

EDGAR ALLAN POE

 The Facts in the Case of M. Valdemar

Of course I shall not pretend to consider it any matter for wonder, that the extraordinary case of M. Valdemar has excited discussion. It would have been a miracle had it not—especially under the circumstances. Through the desire of all parties concerned, to keep the

affair from the public, at least for the present, or until we had farther opportunities for investigation—through our endeavors to effect this—a garbled or exaggerated account made its way into society, and became the source of many unpleasant misrepresentations, and, very naturally, of a great deal of disbelief.

It is now rendered necessary that I give the *facts*—as far as I comprehend them myself. They are, succinctly, these:

My attention for the last three years, had been repeatedly drawn to the subject of Mesmerism; and, about nine months ago, it occurred to me, quite suddenly, that in the series of experiments made hitherto, there had been a very remarkable and most unaccountable omission: no person had as yet been mesmerized *in articulo mortis.*[1] It remained to be seen, first, whether, in such condition, there existed in the patient any susceptibility to the magnetic influence; secondly, whether, if any existed, it was impaired or increased by the condition; thirdly, to what extent, or for how long a period, the encroachments of Death might be arrested by the process. There were other points to be ascertained, but these most excited my curiosity—the last in especial, from the immensely important character of its consequences.

In looking around me for some subject by whose means I might test these particulars, I was brought to think of my friend, M. Ernest Valdemar, the well-known compiler of the "Bibliotheca Forensica," and author (under the nom de plume of Issachar Marx) of the Polish version of "Wallenstein" and "Gargantua." M. Valdemar, who has resided principally at Harlaem, N. Y., since the year 1839, is (or was) particularly noticeable for the extreme spareness of his person—his lower limbs much resembling those of John Randolph; and, also, for the whiteness of his whiskers, in violent contrast to the blackness of his hair—the latter, in consequence, being very generally mistaken for a wig. His temperament was markedly nervous, and rendered him a good subject for mesmeric experiment. On two or three occasions I had put him to sleep with little difficulty, but was disappointed in other results which his peculiar constitution had naturally led me to anticipate. His will was at no period positively, or thoroughly, under my control, and in regard to *clairvoyance,* I could accomplish with him nothing to be relied upon. I always attributed my failure at these points to the disordered state of his health. For some months previous to my becoming acquainted with him, his physicians had declared him in a confirmed phthisis. It was his custom, indeed, to speak calmly of his approaching dissolution, as of a matter neither to be avoided nor regretted.

[1]At the moment of death. [Ed.]

When the ideas to which I have alluded first occurred to me, it was of course very natural that I should think of M. Valdemar. I knew the steady philosophy of the man too well to apprehend any scruples from *him*; and he had no relatives in America who would be likely to interfere. I spoke to him frankly upon the subject; and, to my surprise, his interest seemed vividly excited. I say to my surprise; for, although he had always yielded his person freely to my experiments, he had never before given me any tokens of sympathy with what I did. His disease was of that character which would admit of exact calculation in respect to the epoch of its termination in death; and it was finally arranged between us that he would send for me about twenty-four hours before the period announced by his physicians as that of his decease.

It is now rather more than seven months since I received, from M. Valdemar himself, the subjoined note:

My Dear P_____ ,

You may as well come *now*. D_____ and F_____ are agreed that I cannot hold out beyond to-morrow midnight; and I think they have hit the time very nearly.

VALDEMAR.

I received this note within half an hour after it was written, and in fifteen minutes more I was in the dying man's chamber. I had not seen him for ten days, and was appalled by the fearful alteration which the brief interval had wrought in him. His face wore a leaden hue; the eyes were utterly lusterless; and the emaciation was so extreme that the skin had been broken through by the cheek-bones. His expectoration was excessive. The pulse was barely perceptible. He retained, nevertheless, in a very remarkable manner, both his mental power and a certain degree of physical strength. He spoke with distinctness—took some palliative medicines without aid— and, when I entered the room, was occupied in penciling memoranda in a pocket-book. He was propped up in the bed by pillows. Doctors D_____ and F_____ were in attendance.

After pressing Valdemar's hand, I took these gentlemen aside, and obtained from them a minute account of the patient's condition. The left lung had been for eighteen months in a semi-osseous or cartilaginous state, and was, of course, entirely useless for all purposes of vitality. The right, in its upper portion, was also partially, if not thoroughly, ossified, while the lower region was merely a mass of purulent tubercles, running one into another. Several extensive perforations existed; and, at one point, permanent adhesion to the ribs had taken place. These appearances in the right lobe were of comparatively recent date. The ossification had proceeded with very unusual rapidity; no sign of it had been discovered a month before, and the adhesion had only been observed during the three previous days. Independently of the phthisis, the patient was suspected of aneurism of the aorta; but on this point the osseous symptoms rendered an exact diagnosis impossible. It was the opinion of both physicians that M. Valdemar would die about midnight on the morrow (Sunday). It was then seven o'clock on Saturday evening.

On quitting the invalid's bed-side to hold conversation with myself, Doctors D_____ and F_____ had bidden him a final farewell. It had not been their intention to return; but, at my request, they agreed to look in upon the patient about ten the next night.

When they had gone, I spoke freely with M. Valdemar on the subject of his approaching dissolution, as well as, more particularly, of the experiment proposed. He still professed himself quite willing and even anxious to have it made, and urged me to commence it at once. A male and a female nurse were in attendance; but I did not feel myself altogether at liberty to engage in a task of this character with no more reliable witnesses than these people, in case of sudden accident, might prove. I therefore postponed operations until about eight the next night, when the arrival of a medical student with whom I had some acquaintance, (Mr. Theodore L_____l) relieved me from farther embarrassment. It had been my design, originally, to wait for the physicians; but I was induced to proceed, first, by the urgent entreaties of M. Valdemar, and secondly, by my conviction that I had not a moment to lose, as he was evidently sinking fast.

Mr. L_____l was so kind as to accede to my desire that he would take notes of all that occurred; and it is from his memoranda that what I now have to relate is, for the most part, either condensed or copied verbatim.

It wanted about five minutes of eight when, taking the patient's hand, I begged him to state, as distinctly as he could, to Mr. L_____l whether he (M. Valdemar) was entirely willing that I should make the experiment of mesmerizing him in his then condition.

He relied feebly, yet quite audibly, "Yes, I wish to be mesmerized"—adding immediately afterwards, "I fear you have deferred it too long."

While he spoke thus, I commenced the passes which I had already found most effectual in subduing him. He was evidently influenced with the first lateral stroke of my hand across his forehead; but although I exerted all my powers, no farther perceptible effect was induced until some minutes after ten o'clock, when Doctors D_____ and F_____ called, according to appointment. I explained to them, in a few words, what I designed, and as they opposed no objection, saying that the patient was already in the death agony, I proceeded without hesitation—exchanging, however, the lateral passes for downward ones, and directing my gaze entirely into the right eye of the sufferer.

By this time his pulse was imperceptible and his breathing was stertorous, and at intervals of half a minute.

This condition was nearly unaltered for a quarter of an hour. At the expiration of this period, however, a natural although a very deep sigh escaped the bosom of the dying man, and the stertorous breathing ceased—that is to say, its stertorousness was no longer apparent; the intervals were undiminished. The patient's extremities were of an icy coldness.

At five minutes before eleven I perceived unequivocal signs of the mesmeric influence. The glassy roll of the eye was changed for that expression of uneasy *inward* examination which is never seen except in cases of sleep-waking, and which it is quite impossible to mistake. With a few rapid lateral passes I made the lids quiver, as in incipient sleep, and with a few more I closed them altogether. I was not satisfied, however, with this, but continued the manipulations vigorously, and with the fullest exertion of the will, until I had completely stiffened the limbs of the slumberer, after placing them in a seemingly easy position. The legs were at full length; the arms were nearly so, and reposed on the bed at a moderate distance from the loins. The head was very slightly elevated.

When I had accomplished this, it was fully midnight, and I requested the gentlemen present to examine M. Valdemar's condition. After a few experiments, they admitted him to be in an unusually perfect state of mesmeric trance. The curiosity of both the physicians was greatly excited. Dr. D_____ resolved at once to remain with the patient all night, while Dr. F_____ took leave with a promise to return at daybreak. Mr L_____l and the nurses remained.

We left M. Valdemar entirely undisturbed until about three o'clock in the morning, when I approached him and found him in precisely the same condition as when Dr. F_____ went away—that is to say, he lay in the same position; the pulse was imperceptible; the breathing was gentle (scarcely noticeable, unless through the application of a mirror to the lips); the eyes were closed naturally; and the limbs were as rigid and as cold as marble. Still, the general appearance was certainly not that of death.

As I approached M. Valdemar I made a kind of half effort to influence his right arm into pursuit of my own, as I passed the latter gently to and fro above his person. In such experiments with this patient I had never perfectly succeeded before, and assuredly I had little thought of succeeding now; but to my astonishment, his arm very readily, although feebly, followed every direction I assigned it with mine. I determined to hazard a few words of conversation.

"M. Valdemar," I said, "are you asleep?" He made no answer, but I perceived a tremor about the lips, and was thus induced to repeat the question, again and again. At its third repetition, his whole frame was agitated by a very slight shivering; the eyelids unclosed themselves so far as to display a white line of the ball; the lips moved sluggishly, and from between them, in a barely audible whisper, issued the words:

"Yes; asleep now. Do not wake me!—Let me die so!"

I here felt the limbs and found them as rigid as ever. The right arm, as before, obeyed the direction of my hand. I questioned the sleep-waker again:

"Do you still feel pain in the breast, M. Valdemar?"

The answer now was immediate, but even less audible than before:

"No pain—I am dying."

I did not think it advisable to disturb him farther just then, and nothing more was said or done until the arrival of Dr. F_____, who came a little before sunrise, and expressed unbounded astonishment at finding the patient still alive. After feeling the pulse and applying a mirror to the lips, he requested me to speak to the sleep-waker again. I did so, saying:

"M. Valdemar, do you still sleep?"

As before, some minutes elapsed ere a reply was made; and during the interval the dying man seemed to be collecting his energies to speak. At my fourth repetition of the question, he said very faintly, almost inaudibly:

"Yes; still asleep—dying."

It was now the opinion, or rather the wish, of the physicians, that M. Valdemar should be suffered to remain undisturbed in his present apparently tranquil condition, until death should supervene—and this, it was generally agreed, must now take place within a few minutes. I concluded, however, to speak to him once more, and merely repeated my previous question.

While I spoke, there came a marked change over the countenance of the sleep-waker. The eyes rolled themselves slowly open, the pupils disappearing upwardly; the skin generally assumed a cadaverous hue, resembling not so much parchment as white paper; and the circular hectic spots which, hitherto, had been strongly defined in the center of each cheek, *went out* at once. I use this expression, because the suddenness of their departure put me in mind of nothing so much as the extinguishment of a candle by a puff of the breath. The upper lip, at the same time, writhed itself away from the teeth, which it had previously covered completely; while the lower jaw fell with an audible jerk, leaving the mouth widely extended, and disclosing in full view the swollen and blackened tongue. I presume that no member of the party then present had been unaccustomed to death-bed horrors; but so hideous beyond conception was the appearance of M. Valdemar at this moment, that there was a general shrinking back from the region of the bed.

I now feel that I have reached a point of this narrative at which every reader will be startled into positive disbelief. It is my business, however, simply to proceed.

There was no longer the faintest sign of vitality in M. Valdemar; and concluding him to be dead, we were consigning him to the charge of the nurses, when a strong vibratory motion was observable in the tongue. This continued for perhaps a minute. At the expiration of this period, there issued from the distended and motionless jaws a voice—such as it would be madness in me to attempt describing. There are, indeed, two or three epithets which might be considered as applicable to it in part; I might say, for example, that the sound was harsh, and broken and hollow; but the hideous whole is indescribable, for the simple reason that no similar sounds have ever jarred upon the ear of humanity. There were two particulars, nevertheless, which I thought then, and still think, might fairly be stated as characteristic of the intonation—as well adapted to convey some idea of its unearthly peculiarity. In the first place, the voice seemed to reach our ears—at least mine—from a vast distance, or from some deep cavern within the earth. In the second place, it impressed me (I fear, indeed, that it will be impossible to make myself comprehended) as gelatinous or glutinous matters impress the sense of touch.

I have spoken both of "sound" and of "voice." I mean to say that the sound was one of distinct—of even wonderfully, thrillingly distinct—syllabification. Mr. Valdemar *spoke*—obviously in reply to the question I had propounded to him a few minutes before. I had asked him, it will be remembered, if he still slept. He now said:

"Yes—no—I *have been* sleeping—and now—now—*I am dead.*"

No person present even affected to deny, or attempted to repress, the unutterable, shuddering horror which these few words, thus uttered, were so well calculated to convey. Mr. L———l (the student) swooned. The nurses immediately left the chamber, and could not be induced to return. My own impressions I would not pretend to render intelligible to the reader. For nearly an hour we busied ourselves, silently—without the utterance of a word—in endeavors to revive Mr L————l. When he came to himself, we addressed ourselves again to an investigation of M. Valdemar's condition.

It remained in all respects as I have last described it, with the exception that the mirror no longer afforded evidence of respiration. An attempt to draw blood from the arm failed. I should mention, too, that this limb was no farther subject to my will. I endeavored in vain to make it follow the direction of my hand. The only read indication, indeed, of the mesmeric influence, was now found in the vibratory movement of the tongue, whenever I addressed M. Valdemar a question. He seemed to be making an effort to reply, but had no longer sufficient volition. To queries put to him by any other person than myself he seemed utterly insensible—although I endeavored to place each member of the company in mesmeric rapport with him. I believe that I have now related all that is necessary to an understanding of the sleep-waker's state at this epoch. Other nurses were procured; and at ten o'clock I left the house in company with the two physicians and Mr. L————l.

In the afternoon we all called again to see the patient. His condition remained precisely the same. We had now some discussion as to the propriety and feasibility of awakening him; but we had little difficulty in agreeing that no good purpose would be served by so doing. It was evident that, so far, death (or what is usually termed death) had been arrested by the mesmeric process. It seemed clear to us all that to awaken M. Valdemar would be merely to ensure his instant, or at least his speedy dissolution.

From this period until the close of last week—*an interval of nearly seven months*—we continued to make daily calls at M. Valdemar's house, accompanied, now and then, by medical and other friends. All this time the sleeper-waker remained *exactly* as I have last described him. The nurses' attentions were continual.

It was on Friday last that we finally resolved to make the experiment of awakening, or attempting to awaken him; and it is the (perhaps) unfortunate result of this latter experiment which has given rise to so much discussion in private circles—to so much of what I cannot help thinking unwarranted popular feeling.

For the purpose of relieving M. Valdemar from the mesmeric trance, I made use of the customary passes. These, for a time, were unsuccessful. The first indication of revival was afforded by a partial descent of the iris. It was observed, as especially remarkable, that this lowering of the pupil was accompanied by the profuse out-flowing of a yellowish ichor (from beneath the lids) of a pungent and highly offensive odor.

It was now suggested that I should attempt to influence the patient's arm, as heretofore. I made the attempt and failed. Dr. F_____ then intimated a desire to have me put a question. I did so, as follows:

"M. Valdemar, can you explain to us what are your feelings or wishes now?"

There was an instant return of the hectic circles on the cheeks; the tongue quivered, or rather rolled violently in the mouth (although the jaws and lips remained rigid as before;) and at length the same hideous voice which I have already described, broke forth:

"For God's sake!—quick!—quick!—put me to sleep—or, quick!—waken me!—quick!—*I say to you that I am dead!*"

I was thoroughly unnerved, and for an instant remained undecided what to do. At first I made an endeavor to re-compose the patient; but, failing in this through total abeyance of the will, I retraced my steps and as earnestly struggled to awaken him. In this attempt I soon saw that I should be successful—or at least I soon fancied that my success would be complete—and I am sure that all in the room were prepared to see the patient awaken.

For what really occurred, however, it is quite impossible that any human being could have been prepared.

As I rapidly made the mesmeric passes, amid ejaculations of "dead! dead!" absolutely *bursting* from the tongue and not from the lips of the sufferer, his whole frame at once—within the space of a single minute, or even less, shrunk—crumbled—absolutely *rotted* away beneath my hands. Upon the bed, before the whole company, there lay a nearly liquid mass of loathsome—of detestable putridity.

Exercises and Projects

CHECKING YOUR COMPREHENSION

1. Early in the story the narrator gives his reasons for wanting to hypnotize a dying man. What are they?

2. Why was Ernest Valdemar an ideal subject, according to the narrator?

3. Describe the reactions among those present to Valdemar's announcement that he was dead.

4. After Valdemar's self announced death, the mesmeric influence all but vanished. What was all that remained of it?

FOR DISCUSSION AND DEBATE

1. The narrator discusses Valdemar's physical condition in highly technical terms. Is this necessary? For what reason?

2. What is your impression of the narrator? Is he a man of conscience? Is enough revealed for you to make a sound judgment of his character?

3. How successful is the ending, in your opinion? What other parts of the story, if any, did you find particularly effective or ineffective?

FOR YOUR NOTEBOOK

1. Look into the earliest medical applications of hypnosis. Take notes, being sure to record important names and dates. Also remember to list your sources.

2. Poe's and Hawthorne's tales show science at the threshold of the supernatural. Do you see any examples of this in the real world?

FOR WRITING

1. Create a story in which a hypnotist places someone in a trance and takes him or her to a time before birth as a way of proving the existence of reincarnation.

2. Write an analytical essay of three- to five-pages on one of these topics involving hypnosis:
   a. the origins of mesmerism
   b. the medical benefits of hypnosis
   c. hypnosis and the supernatural

3. Research the uses, both medical and nonmedical, of hypnotism; then restrict your topic to one facet of medical or nonmedical hypnosis. What are the benefits? The dangers? The misconceptions?

4. For a term project, write an essay on Poe's attitude toward science. Consider tales such as "The Balloon-Hoax," "The Domain of Arnheim," and "Eureka," which may be found in several collections of Poe's work, such as *The Annotated Tales of Edgar Allan Poe,* edited by Stephan Peithman (1981). Also consider Poe's "Sonnet: To Science," which seems to contradict the attitude toward science reflected in the tales. But does it really?

Sonnet: To Science

Science! true daughter of Old Time thou art!
  Who alterest all things with thy peering eyes.
Why preyest thou thus upon the poet's heart,
  Vulture, whose wings are dull realities?
How should he love thee? or how deem thee wise?
  Who wouldst not leave him in his wandering
To seek for treasure in the jewelled skies,
  Albeit he soared with an undaunted wing?
Hast thou not dragged Diana from her car?
  And driven the Hamadryad from the wood
To seek a shelter in some happier star?
  Hast thou not torn the Naiad from her flood,
The Elfin from the green grass, and from me
The summer dream beneath the tamarind tree?

                 —*Edgar Allan Poe*

Diana: Roman goddess of the Moon, the forest, and chastity

car: chariot

Hamadryad: a wood nymph, or minor nature goddess

Naiad: a water nymph

tamarind tree: a tropical tree, yielding a fruit of the same name

When Walt Whitman proclaimed, in the opening line to his most celebrated poem, "Song of Myself,"

> I celebrate myself, and sing myself

he was not being an egoist in the narrow sense of the word; on the contrary, he was celebrating the freedom of selfhood to embrace the universe in all its diversity. Whitman's universe includes people from all walks of life, who engage in all kinds of activity, experiencing all that can be experienced.

> Agonies are one of my changes of garments.
> I do not ask the wounded person how he feels, I myself become the wounded person,
> My hurts turn livid upon me as I lean on a cane and observe.

The two poems that follow represent the range of Whitman's attitude toward science and technology. In one sense, technology (symbolized by the locomotive) possesses a fierce beauty and a nature all its own—a force to be marveled at, a force that can build a new nation. In another sense, the technology that permits close observation of nature—such as a telescope permitting close observation of heavenly bodies—tends to diminish the way we should experience nature. Is there any way to reconcile this apparent contradiction? Can the seemingly different attitudes be resolved?

TERMS TO LEARN

recitative: a type of song using the rhythms of spoken words, as in opera

panoply: a protective covering or shield

the Muse: the spirit of artistic and poetic inspiration. In Greek mythology, nine Muses presided over science, literature, and the fine arts.

WALT WHITMAN

 To a Locomotive in Winter

Thee for my recitative,
Thee in the driving storm even as now, the snow, the winter-day
    declining,
Thee in thy panoply, thy measur'd dual throbbing and thy beat
    convulsive,
Thy black cylindric body, golden brass and silvery steel,
Thy ponderous side-bars, parallel and connecting rods, gyrating,
    shuttling at thy sides,

Thy metrical, now swelling pant and roar, now tapering in the
    distance,
Thy great protruding head-light fix'd in front,
Thy long, pale, floating vapor-pennants, tinged with delicate purple,
The dense and murky clouds out-belching from thy smoke-stack,
Thy knitted frame, thy springs and valves, the tremulous twinkle of
    thy wheels,

Thy train of cars behind, obedient, merrily following,
Through gale or calm, now swift, now slack, yet steadily careering;
Type of the modern—emblem of motion and power—pulse of the
    continent,
For once come serve the Muse and merge in verse, even as here I
    see thee,
With storm and buffeting gusts of wind and falling snow,
By day thy warning ringing bell to sound its notes,
By night thy silent signal lamps to swing.

Fierce-throated beauty!
Roll through my chant with all thy lawless music, thy swinging
    lamps at night,
Thy madly-whistled laughter, echoing, rumbling like an earthquake,
    rousing all
Law of thyself complete, thine own track firmly holding,
(No sweetness debonair of tearful harp or glib piano thine),
Thy trills of shrieks by rocks and hills return'd,
Launch'd o'er the prairies wide, across the lakes,
To the free skies unpent and glad and strong.

WALT WHITMAN

 When I Heard the Learn'd Astronomer

When I heard the learn'd astronomer,
When the proofs, the figures, were ranged in columns before me,
When I was shown the charts and diagrams, to add, divide, and
    measure them,
When I sitting heard the astronomer where he lectured with much
    applause in the lecture-room,
How soon unaccountable I became tired and sick,
Till rising and gliding out I wander'd off by myself,
In the mystical moist night air, and from time to time,
Look'd up in perfect silence at the stars.

Exercises and Projects

CHECKING YOUR COMPREHENSION

1. In the first poem, the poet is addressing the locomotive directly.
   What is his request?

2. Describe the poet's essential feelings toward the locomotive.
   Toward the astronomer.

3. What does Whitman mean by the locomotive's "measur'd dual
   throbbing" and "beat convulsive"?

FOR DISCUSSION AND DEBATE

1. Why does the poet refer to the locomotive's sounds as "lawless
   music" (line 19)? Do the two words contradict each other?

2. What effect is achieved in "Locomotive" by setting the scene in
   winter? What, besides the obivous imagery, would change if the
   season were summer, autumn, or spring?

3. What is the significance of the word *recitative* in the opening line of "Locomotive"?

4. Why does Whitman refer to the locomotive as an emblem of motion and power?

5. What is the significance of the last line in "Astronomer"?

FOR YOUR NOTEBOOK

1. Observe people at work, say at a construction site, or in a factory. Try to capture the scene in free-verse form.

2. Observe a large, powerful machine, such as a pile driver, dynamo, or harvester, at close range. Capture the essence of the machine in a free-verse poem.

3. Read several of Whitman's poems and record your favorite lines. Do the same with Emily Dickinson's poems. What is it about the language that makes the lines so effective?

FOR WRITING

1. After reading several of the poems in Whitman's *Leaves of Grass*—for example, "Song of the Broad-Axe," "A Song for Occupations," "Birds of Passage," and "Song of Myself"—write an essay on Whitman's sense of the relationship between industrial growth and democracy in America. Is Whitman's attitude always clear or consistent? Is he profound or naive, or both?

2. Try your hand at writing a free-verse poem in Whitman's style in which you celebrate or denounce some facet of science or technology in contemporary American life.

3. Compare Whitman's "To a Locomotive in Winter" with Emily Dickinson's poem, "I Like to See It Lap the Miles" (number 585), reprinted below. Call attention to similarities and differences in the poets' attitudes toward locomotives. Also discuss the similarities and differences in language and style.

I Like to See It Lap the Miles

I like to see it lap the Miles—
And lick the Valleys up—
And stop to feed itself at Tanks—
And then—prodigious step

Around a Pile of Mountains—
And supercilious peer
In Shanties—by the sides of Roads
And then a Quarry pare

To fit its Ribs
And crawl between
Complaining all the while
In horrid—hooting stanza—
Then chase itself down Hill—

And neigh like Boanerges[1]—
Then—punctual as a Star
Stop—docile and omnipotent
At its own stable door—

—Emily Dickinson

[1]Boanerges: Literally "sons of thunder," Jesus's epithet for the apostles James and John. See Mark 3:17.

READING INTRODUCTION

Pick up a copy of Thoreau's *Walden* (1854), begin reading it anywhere at random, and within seconds you will feel Thoreau's almost fierce self-sufficiency and rare combination of philosophical insight and earthiness.

Thoreau's great purpose in life was to convince us, through his own example, that we cannot truly live until we return to nature. Now it is all too easy to misinterpret "return to nature" as an escapist withdrawal from the responsibilities of modern life or as a romantic gesture of a bygone age, when there still were wildernesses to escape to. Actually, even in Thoreau's day, wilderness areas were fast disappearing.

Thoreau makes clear his reasons for leaving civilization for two years: "I went to the woods because I wished to live deliberately, to front only the essential facts of life, and see if I could not learn what it had to teach." But what does Thoreau mean by "live deliberately" or "the essential facts of life"? Can human beings learn from nature how to be better? Reading the following excerpt from *Walden* should help us find the answer.

TERMS TO LEARN

tarn: a small mountain lake

freshet: a freshwater stream, often one that fills suddenly in a flood or from melting snow

point d'appui (pronounced pwan dapwee): a place of reinforcement (for example, for military purposes)

nilometer: originally, an instrument used by the ancient Egyptians for measuring the rise and fall of the Nile River. More generally, an instrument for measuring any river's height.

Where I Lived, and What I Lived For

I was seated by the shore of a small pond, about a mile and a half south of the village of Concord and somewhat higher than it, in the midst of an extensive wood between that town and Lincoln, and about two miles south of that our only field known to fame, Concord Battle Grounds; but I was so low in the woods that the opposite shore, half a mile off, like the rest, covered with wood, was my most distant horizon. For the first week, whenever I looked out on the pond it impressed me like a tarn high up on the side of a mountain, its bottom far above the surface of other lakes, and, as the sun arose, I saw it throwing off its nightly clothing of mist, and here and there, by degrees, its soft ripples or its smooth reflecting surface was revealed, while the mists, like ghosts, were stealthily withdrawing in every direction into the woods, as at the breaking up of some nocturnal conventicle. The very dew deemed to hang upon the trees later into the day than usual, as on the sides of mountains.

This small lake was of most value as a neighbor in the intervals of a gentle rain-storm in August, when, both air and water being perfectly still, but the sky overcast, mid-afternoon had all the serenity of evening, and the wood thrush sang around, and was heard from shore to shore. A lake like this is never smoother than at such a time; and the clear portion of the air above it being shallow and darkened by clouds, the water, full of light and reflections, becomes a lower heaven itself so much the more important. From a hill-top near by, where the wood had been recently cut off, there was a pleasing vista southward across the pond, through a wide indentation in the hills which form the shore there, where their opposite sides sloping toward each other suggested a stream flowing out in that direction through a wooded valley, but stream there was none. That way I looked between and over the near green hills to some distant and higher ones in the horizon, tinged with blue. Indeed, by standing on tiptoe I could catch a glimpse of some of the peaks of the still bluer and more distant mountain ranges in the northwest, those true-blue coins from heaven's own mint, and also of some portion of the village. But in other directions, even from this point, I could not see over or beyond the woods which surrounded me. It is well to have some water in your neighborhood, to give buoyancy to and float the earth. One value even of the smallest well is, that when you look into it you see that earth is not continent but insular. This is as important as that it keeps butter cool. When I looked across the pond from this peak toward the Sudbury meadows, which in time of flood I distinguished elevated perhaps by a mirage in their seething valley, like a coin in a basin, all the earth beyond the pond appeared like a thin crust insulated and floated even by this small sheet of intervening water, and I was reminded that this on which I dwelt was but *dry land.*

Though the view from my door was still more contracted, I did not feel crowded or confined in the least. There was pasture enough for my imagination. The low shrub oak plateau to which the opposite shore arose stretched away toward the prairies of the West and the steppes of Tartary, affording ample room for all the roving families of men. "There are none happy in the world but beings who enjoy freely a vast horizon," said Damodara,[1] when his herds required new and larger pastures.

Both place and time were changed, and I dwelt nearer to those parts of the universe and to those eras in history which had most attracted me. Where I lived was as far off as many a region viewed nightly by astronomers. We are wont to imagine rare and delectable places in some remote and more celestial corner of the system, behind the constellation of Cassiopeia's Chair, far from noise and disturbance. I discovered that my house actually had its site in such a withdrawn, but forever new and unprofaned, part of the universe. If it were worth the while to settle in those parts near to the Pleiades or the Hyades, to Aldebaran or Altair, then I was really there, or at an equal remoteness from the life which I had left behind, dwindled and twinkling with as fine a ray to my nearest neighbor, and to be seen only in moonless nights by him. Such was that part of creation where I had squatted;

> There was a shepherd that did live,
>   And held his thoughts as high
> As were the mounts whereon his flocks
>   Did hourly feed him by.[2]

What should we think of the shepherd's life if his flocks always wandered to higher pastures than his thoughts?

Every morning was a cheerful invitation to make my life of equal simplicity, and I may say innocence, with Nature herself. I have been as sincere a worshipper of Aurora as the Greeks. I got up early and

---

[1]Damodara: another name for Hindu god Krishna.

[2]Stanza from an anonymous seventeenth-century lyric. [Ed.]

bathed in the pond; that was a religious exercise, and one of the best things which I did. They say that characters were engraven on the bathing tub of King Tching-thang to this effect: "Renew thyself completely each day; do it again, and again, and forever again."[3] I can understand that. Morning brings back the heroic ages. I was as much affected by the faint hum of a mosquito making its invisible and unimaginable tour through my apartment at earliest dawn, when I was sitting with door and windows open, as I could be by any trumpet that ever sang of fame. It was Homer's requiem; itself an Iliad and Odyssey in the air, singing its own wrath and wanderings. There was something cosmical about it; a standing advertisement, till forbidden, of the everlasting vigor and fertility of the world. The morning, which is the most memorable season of the day, is the awakening hour. Then there is least somnolence in us; and for an hour, at least, some part of us awakes which slumbers all the rest of the day and night. Little is to be expected of that day, if it can be called a day, to which we are not awakened by our Genius, but by the mechanical nudgings of some servitor, are not awakened by our own newly acquired force and aspirations from within, accompanied by the undulations of celestial music, instead of factory bells, and a fragrance filling the air—to a higher life than we fell asleep from; and thus the darkness bear its fruit, and prove itself to be good, no less than the light. That man who does not believe that each day contains an earlier, more sacred, and auroral hour than he has yet profaned, has despaired of life, and is pursuing a descending and darkening way. After a partial cessation of his sensuous life, the soul of man, or its organs rather, are reinvigorated each day, and his Genius tries again what noble life it can make. All memorable events, I should say, transpire in morning time and in a morning atmosphere. The Vedas[4] say, "All intelligences awake with the morning." Poetry and art, and the fairest and most memorable of the actions of men, date from such an hour. All poets and heroes, like Memmon,[5] are the children of Aurora, and emit their music at sunrise. To him whose elastic and vigorous thought keeps pace with the sun, the day is a perpetual morning. It matters not what the clocks say or the attitudes and labors of men. Morning is when I am awake and there is a dawn in me. Moral reform is the effort to throw off sleep. Why is it that men give so poor an account of their day if they have not been slumbering? They are not such poor calculators. If they had not been overcome with drowsiness,

---

[3]From a commentary by Confucious. [Ed.]

[4]Sacred Hindu writings. [Ed.]

[5]Ethiopian king slain by Achilles during the Trojan war. [Ed.]

they would have performed something. The millions are awake enough for physical labor; but only one in a million is awake enough for effective intellectual exertion, only one in a hundred millions to a poetic or divine life. To be awake is to be alive. I have never yet met a man who was quite awake. How could I have looked him in the face?

We must learn to reawaken and keep ourselves awake, not by mechanical aids, but by an infinite expectation of the dawn, which does not forsake us in our soundest sleep. I know of no more encouraging fact than the unquestionable ability of man to elevate his life by a conscious endeavor. It is something to be able to paint a particular picture, or to carve a statue, and so to make a few objects beautiful; but it is far more glorious to carve and paint the very atmosphere and medium through which we look, which morally we can do. To affect the quality of the day, that is the highest of arts. Every man is tasked to make his life, even in its details, worthy of the contemplation of his most elevated and critical hour. If we refused, or rather used up, such paltry information as we get, the oracles would distinctly inform us how this might be done.

I went to the woods because I wished to live deliberately, to front only the essential facts of life, and see if I could not learn what it had to teach, and not, when I came to die, discover that I had not lived. I did not wish to live what was not life, living is so dear; nor did I wish to practice resignation, unless it was quite necessary. I wanted to live deep and suck out all the marrow of life, to live so sturdily and Spartanlike as to put to rout all that was not life, to cut a broad swath and shave close, to drive life into a corner, and reduce it to its lowest terms, and, if it proved to be mean, why then to get the whole and genuine meanness of it, and publish its meanness to the world; or if it were sublime, to know it by experience, and be able to give a true account of it in my next excursion. For most men, it appears to me, are in a strange uncertainty about it, whether it is of the devil or of God, and have *somewhat hastily* concluded that it is the chief end of man here to "glorify God and enjoy him forever."

Still we live meanly, like ants; though the fable tells us that we were long ago changed into men; like pygmies we fight with cranes; it is error upon error, and clout upon clout, and our best virtue has for its occasion a superfluous and evitable wretchedness. Our life is frittered away by detail. An honest man has hardly need to count more than his ten fingers, or in extreme cases he may add his ten toes, and lump the rest. Simplicity, simplicity, simplicity! I say, let your affairs be as two or three, and not a hundred or a thousand; instead of a million count half a dozen, and keep your accounts on your thumb-nail. In the midst of this chopping sea of civilized life, such are the clouds and storms and quicksands and thousand-and-one items to be allowed for, that a man has to live, if he would not founder and go to the bottom and not make his port at all, by dead reckoning, and he must be a great calculator indeed who succeeds. Simplify, simplify. Instead of three meals a day, if it be necessary eat but one; instead of a hundred dishes, five; and reduce other things in proportion. Our life is like a German Confederacy, made up of petty states, with its boundary forever fluctuating, so that even a German cannot tell you how it is bounded at any moment. The nation itself, with all its so-called internal improvements, which, by the way are all external and superficial, is just such an unwieldly and overgrown establishment, cluttered with furniture and tripped up by its own traps, ruined by luxury and heedless expense, by want of calculation and a worthy aim, as the million households in the land; and the only cure for it, as for them, is in a rigid economy, a stern and more than Spartan simplicity of life and elevation of purpose. It lives too fast. Men think that it is essential that the *Nation* have commerce, and export ice, and talk through a telegraph, and ride thirty miles an hour, without a doubt, whether *they* do or not; but whether we should live like baboons or like men, is a little uncertain. If we do not get out sleepers, and forge rails, and devote days and nights to the work, but go to tinkering upon our *lives* to improve *them,* who will build railroads? And if railroads are not built, how shall we get to heaven in season? But if we stay at home and mind our business, who will want railroads? We do not ride on the railroad; it rides upon us. Did you ever think what those sleepers are that underlie the railroad? Each one is a man, an Irishman, or a Yankee man. The rails are laid on them, and they are covered with sand, and the cars run smoothly over them. They are sound sleepers, I assure you. And every few years a new lot is laid down and run over; so that, if some have the pleasure of riding on a rail, others have the misfortune to be ridden upon. And when they run over a man that is walking in his sleep, a supernumerary sleeper in the wrong position, and wake him up, they suddenly stop the cars, and make a hue and cry about it, as if this were an exception. I am glad to know that it takes a gang of men for every five miles to keep the sleepers down and level in their beds as it is, for this is a sign that they may sometime get up again.

Why should we live with such hurry and waste of life? We are determined to be starved before we are hungry. Men say that a stitch in time saves nine, and so they take a thousand stitches to-day to save nine to-morrow. As for *work,* we haven't any of any consequence. We have the Saint Vitus' dance,[6] and cannot possibly keep our heads still. If I should only give a few pulls at the parish bell-rope, as for a fire, that is, without setting the bell, there is hardly a man on his farm in the outskirts of Concord, notwithstanding that press of engagements which was his excuse so many times this morning, nor a boy, nor a woman, I might almost say, but would forsake all and follow that sound, not mainly to save property from the flames, but, if we will confess the truth, much more to see it burn, since burn it must, and we, be it known, did not set it on fire—or to see it put out, and have a hand in it, if that is done as handsomely; yes, even if it were the parish church itself. Hardly a man takes a half-hour's nap after dinner, but when he wakes he holds up his head and asks, "What's the news?" as if the rest of mankind had stood his sentinels. Some give directions to be waked every half hour, doubtless for no other purpose; and then, to pay for it, they tell what they have dreamed. After a night's sleep the news is as indispensable as the breakfast. "Pray tell me anything new that has happened to a man anywhere on this globe"— and he reads it over his coffee and rolls, that a man has had his eyes gouged out this morning on the Wachito River; never dreaming the while that he lives in the dark unfathomed mammoth cave of this world, and has but the rudiment of an eye himself.

For my part, I could easily do without the post office. I think that there are very few important communications made through it. To speak critically, I never received more than one or two letters in my life—I wrote this some years ago—that were worth the postage. The penny-post is, commonly, an institution through which you seriously offer a man that penny for his thoughts which is so often safely offered in jest. And I am sure that I never read any memorable news in a newspaper. If we read of one man robbed, or murdered, or killed by accident, or one house burned, or one vessel wrecked, or one steamboat blown up, or one cow run over on the Western Railroad, or one mad dog killed, or one lot of grasshoppers in the winter—we never need read of another. One is enough. If you are acquainted with the principle, what do you care for a myriad instances and applications? To a philosopher all *news,* as it is called, is gossip, and they who edit and read it are old women over their tea. Yet not a few are greedy after this gossip. There was such a rush, as I hear, the other day at one of the offices to learn the foreign news by the last arrival, that several large squares of plate glass belonging to the establishment were broken by the pressure—news which I seriously

[6]A nervous disorder marked by spasmodic movement. [Ed.]

think a ready wit might write a twelve month, or twelve years, before-hand with sufficient accuracy. As for Spain, for instance, if you know how to throw in Don Carlos and the Infanta, and Don Pedro and Seville and Granada,[7] from time to time in the right proportions—they may have changed the names a little since I saw the papers—and serve up a bullfight when other entertainments fail, it will be true to the letter, and give us as good an idea of the exact state or ruin of things in Spain as the most succinct and lucid reports under this head in the newspapers: and as for England, almost the last significant scrap of news from that quarter was the revolution of 1649; and if you have learned the history of her crops for an average year, you never need attend to that thing again, unless your specula-tions are of a merely pecuniary character. If one may judge who rarely looks into the newspapers, nothing new does ever happen in foreign parts, a French revolution not excepted.

What news! how much more important to know what that is which was never old! "Kieou-he-yu (great dignitary of the state of Wei) sent a man to Khoung-tseu to know his news. Khoung-tseu caused the messenger to be seated near him, and questioned him in these terms: What is your master doing? The messenger answered with respect: My master desires to diminish the number of his faults, but he cannot come to the end of them. The messenger being gone, the philosopher remarked: What a worthy messenger! What a worthy messenger!"[8] The preacher, instead of vexing the ears of drowsy farmers on their day of rest at the end of the week—for Sunday is the fit conclusion of an ill-spent week, and not the fresh and brave beginning of a new one—with this one other draggle-tail of a sermon, should shout with thundering voice, "Pause! Avast! Why so seeming fast, but deadly slow?"

Shams and delusions are esteemed for soundest truths, while reality is fabulous. If men would steadily observe realities only, and not allow themselves to be deluded, life, to compare it with such things as we know, would be like a fairy tale and the Arabian Nights' Entertainments. If we respected only what is inevitable and has a right to be, music and poetry would resound along the streets. When we are unhurried and wise, we perceive that only great and worthy things have any permanent and absolute existence, that petty fears and petty pleasures are but the shadow of the reality. This is always exhilarating and sublime. By closing the eyes and slumbering, and

---

[7]Don Carlos . . . Grenada: references to popular melodramas of the day. [Ed.]

[8]"Kieou-he-yu . . . messenger!" From the *Dialects of Confucious* (Book 4, Chapter 26). [Ed.]

consenting to be deceived by shows, men establish and confirm their daily life of routine and habit everywhere, which still is built on purely illusory foundations. Children, who play life, discern its true law and relations more clearly than men, who fail to live it worthily, but who think that they are wiser by experience, that is, by failure. I have read in a Hindoo book, that "there was a king's son, who, being expelled in infancy from his native city, was brought up by a forester, and, growing up to maturity in that state, imagined himself to belong to the barbarous race with which he lived. One of his father's ministers having discovered him, revealed to him what he was, and the misconception of his character was removed, and he knew himself to be a prince. So soul," continues the Hindoo philosopher, "from the circumstances in which it is placed, mistakes its own character, until the truth is revealed to it by some holy teacher, and then it knows itself to be *Brahme*."[9] I perceive that we inhabitants of New England live this mean life that we do because our vision does not penetrate the surface of things. We think that that *is* which *appears* to be. If a man should walk through this town and see only the reality, where, think you, would the "Mill-dam" go to? If he should give us an account of the realities he beheld there, we should not recognize the place in his description. Look at a meetinghouse, or a court-house, or a jail, or a shop, or a dwellinghouse, and say what that thing really is before a true gaze, and they would all go to pieces in your account of them. Men esteem truth remote, in the outskirts of the system, behind the farthest star, before Adam and after the last man. In eternity there is indeed something true and sublime. But all these times and places and occasions are now and here. God himself culminates in the present moment, and will never be more divine in the lapse of all the ages. And we are enabled to apprehend at all what is sublime and noble only by the perpetual instilling and drenching of the reality that surrounds us. The universe constantly and obediently answers to our conceptions; whether we travel fast or slow, the track is laid for us. Let us spend our lives in conceiving then. The poet or the artist never yet had so fair and noble a design but some of his posterity at least could accomplish it.

Let us spend one day as deliberately as Nature, and not be thrown off the track by every nutshell and mosquito's wing that falls on the rails. Let us rise early and fast, or break fast, gently and without perturbation; let company come and let company go, let the bells ring and the children cry—determined to make a day of it. Why should we knock under and go with the stream? Let us not be upset

---

[9]Highest Hindu caste, usually a priest. [Ed.]

and overwhelmed in that terrible rapid and whirlpool called a dinner, situated in the meridian shallows. Weather this danger and you are safe, for the rest of the way is down hill. With unrelaxed nerves, with morning vigor, sail by it, looking another way, tied to the mast like Ulysses.[10] If the engine whistles, let it whistle till it is hoarse for its pains. If the bell rings, why should we run? We will consider what kind of music they are like. Let us settle ourselves, and work and wedge our feet downward through the mud and slush of opinion, and prejudice, and tradition, and delusion, and appearance, that alluvion which covers the globe, through Paris and London, through New York and Boston and Concord, through Church and State, through poetry and philosophy and religion, tell we come to a hard bottom and rocks in place, which we can call *reality,* and say, This is, and no mistake; and then begin, having a *point d'appui,* below freshet and frost and fire, a place where you might found a wall or a state, or set a lamp-post safely, or perhaps a gauge, not a Nilometer, but a Realometer, that future ages might know how deep a freshet of shams and appearances had gathered from time to time. If you stand right fronting and face to face to a fact, you will see the sun glimmer on both its surfaces, as if it were a cimeter,[11] and feel its sweet edge dividing you through the heart and marrow, and so you will happily conclude your mortal career. Be it life or death, we crave only reality. If we are really dying, let us hear the rattle in our throats and feel cold in the extremities; if we are alive, let us go about our business.

Time is but the stream I go a-fishing in. I drink at it; but while I drink I see the sandy bottom and detect how shallow it is. Its thin current slides away, but eternity remains. I would drink deeper; fish in the sky, whose bottom is pebbly with stars. I cannot count one. I know not the first letter of the alphabet. I have always been regretting that I was not as wise as the day I was born. The intellect is a cleaver; it discerns and rifts its way into the secret of things. I do not wish to be any more busy with my hands than is necessary. My head is hands and feet. I feel all my best faculties concentrated in it. My instinct tells me that my head is an organ for burrowing, as some creatures use their snout and fore paws, and with it I would mine and burrow my way through these hills. I think that the richest vein is somewhere hereabouts; so by the divining-rod and thin rising vapors I judge; and here I will begin to mine.

[10]In Book 12 of Homer's *Odyssey* Odysseus (Ulysses), in order to survive the Sirens (half-bird, half-woman sea nymphs who tempt sailors with their music in order to destroy them), stuffs wax into the ears of his crew; but being a seeker of knowledge, Ulysses orders his men to tie him to a mast so that he may hear the Sirens, yet not be able to harm himself. [Ed.]

[11]Scimitar, a saber with a curved blade. [Ed.]

Exercises and Projects

CHECKING YOUR COMPREHENSION

1. Why does Thoreau consider it so important to have a body of water "in one's neighborhood"?

2. Thoreau held a special regard for the early morning hours. Why?

3. What is Thoreau's reason for saying that he could easily do without the post office?

4. In what way, according to Thoreau, is the intellect a cleaver?

5. How is our life "like a German Confederacy"? What cure does Thoreau recommend for this problem?

FOR DISCUSSION AND DEBATE

1. Thoreau regarded his daily early morning bathing in the pond as a religious exercise. What do you suppose Thoreau means by this?

2. What are some of the trivial matters that keep us from the essentials of life? Do you agree that they are trivial or that they detract us from greater concerns?

3. What does Thoreau mean when he says, "I know not the first letter of the alphabet"?

4. Discuss what Thoreau has in mind when he writes, "Let us spend one day as deliberately as Nature."

FOR YOUR NOTEBOOK

1. The next time you go on a nature walk, or go camping or fishing, take along your notebook and record descriptions of your immediate surroundings, other person you are with, your activities, and any meditations that have been stimulated by your new surroundings.

2. How do people in an urban environment feel about nature? Are some content to cultivate a garden or houseplants? Do others feel a need "to get away from it all" every so often? Where do they go, and why?

FOR WRITING

1. This selection from *Walden* contains some of Thoreau's most famous sayings:
   a. "We must learn to reawaken and keep ourselves awake, not by mechanical aids, but by an infinite expectation of the dawn."
   b. "Simplicity, simplicity, simplicity."
   c. "We are determined to be starved before we are hungry."
   d. "Shams and delusions are esteemed for soundest truths, while reality is fabulous."
   e. "Time is but the stream I go a-fishing in."

   Select one of the above quotations and use it as the basis of a short essay. Draw from your own personal experiences, and also make some reference to Thoreau's experiences at Walden Pond.

2. Write a critical analysis of Thoreau's concept of nature as you see it expressed in this selection. You may also want to draw from other sections of *Walden*.

3. How do you or other persons you know experience wilderness? Write an essay about a modern-day Thoreau who loves to hike and camp out in the wilderness. In a short essay, describe this person's activities and attitude as fully as you can, comparing him or her to Thoreau.

Robert Frost is one of the few great American poets whose work appeals to people from all walks of life; he even read his poetry at President John F. Kennedy's inauguration. Frost was a farmer in Vermont, and he wrote about farming and about rural American life in general—about weary travelers and hired hands, apple picking and twin roads diverging in the woods. Beneath these simple, lyrical verses lies a deep concern for human destiny in a world that tends to estrange people from their ancient ties with the land. Frost is, in many ways, a latter-day Thoreau. In the following poem, Frost meditates on a common facet of mind-body dualism.

TERMS TO LEARN

atrophy: the degeneration of body tissue or limbs

vestigial: a no-longer functional body part, such as the human appendix

ROBERT FROST

 Etherealizing

A theory if you hold it hard enough
And long enough gets rated as a creed:
Such as that flesh is something we can slough
So that the mind can be entirely freed.
Then when the arms and legs have atrophied,
And the brain is all that's left of mortal stuff,
We can lie on the beach with the seaweed
And take our daily tide baths smooth and rough.
There once we lay as blobs of jellyfish
At evolution's opposite extreme.
But now as blobs of brain we'll lie and dream,
With only one vestigial creature wish:
Oh, may the tide be soon enough at high
To keep our abstract verse from being dry.

Exercises and Projects

CHECKING YOUR COMPREHENSION

1. How does Frost support his assertion that a theory can become a creed? What is undesirable about this?

2. Explain the comparison Frost is making between a jellyfish and a human brain.

3. State the theme of the poem in your own words.

FOR DISCUSSION AND DEBATE

1. In his "Essay on Criticism," Alexander Pope said of poetry that "the sound must be an echo to the sense." To what extent does the sound (tone of voice, rhyme, meter) of "Etherealizing" reflect its sense (meaning)?

2. What is Frost really satirizing in this poem? Do you feel that the satiric attack is warranted?

FOR YOUR NOTEBOOK

Read two or three of Frost's nature poems (for example, "The Mountain," "Wild Grapes," and "Spring Pools" from *The Complete Poems of Robert Frost*), and speculate on the attitude toward nature Frost is trying to convey in each of them.

FOR WRITING

1. Frost has written other poems on scientific topics, among them "The Demiurge's Laugh," "Riders," and "Why Wait for Science?" (*The Complete Poems of Robert Frost,* 1949). Write a critical essay on Frost's attitude toward science as manifested in his poetry.

2. Write an essay comparing Frost's attitude toward nature to Whitman's, Emily Dickinson's, and Thoreau's. Discuss such poems as "The Mountain," "After Apple-Picking," "The Wood-Pile," and "A Hillside Thaw."

3. Defend or challenge the argument in "Etherealizing" that "A theory if you hold it hard enough / And long enough gets rated as a creed."

READING INTRODUCTION

There are no quick or easy words to sum up Robinson Jeffers's poetry. Like Whitman he wrote expansively; his are rhythms rough hewn like the rugged northern California coast he loved to write about. But unlike Whitman, who mainly celebrates the human condition, Jeffers largely deplores it. Human egoism in general and greed in particular, for Jeffers, lead ultimately to loss of control, cruelty, and war.

Jeffers is by no means an "inspirational" poet as the term is usually defined, but it is a mistake to consider his work depressing or nihilistic. There is a way to avoid the pitfalls of human nature, Jeffers would say, and that is to understand and identify with the natural world, including animal life, and not to regard ourselves as apart from and superior to nature. After all, as Jeffers writes, "The tides are in our veins." We are, in other words, as much a part of nature as the salt in our blood and the calcium in our bones. (Notice how Loren Eiseley works with this same theme in his essay, "The Judgment of the Birds," later in part 4.) In "Star-Swirls," one of his last poems, published posthumously, Jeffers contemplates the impact that an awareness of geological ages can have on everyday concerns.

TERMS TO LEARN

star swirls: galaxies, often spiral shaped, like the great galaxy in Andromeda, and consisting of roughly 100 billion stars. We inhabit such a galaxy—the Milky Way.

glacier: a mass of slowly moving ice created when more snow accumulates than is able to melt. During the last ice age, which ended 10,000 years ago, much of the northern hemisphere, including the northern half of the United States, was glaciated.

ROBINSON JEFFERS

 Star-Swirls

The polar ice-caps are melting, the mountain glaciers
Drip into rivers; all feed the ocean;
Tides ebb and flow, but every year a little bit higher.
They will drown New York, they will drown London.
And this place, where I have planted tree and built a stone house,
Will be under sea. The poor trees will perish,
And little fish will flicker in and out the windows. I built it well,
Thick walls and Portland cement and gray granite,
The tower at least will hold against the sea's buffeting; it will
    become
Geological, fossil and permanent.
What a pleasure it is to mix one's mind with geological
Time, or with astronomical relax it.
There is nothing like astronomy to pull the stuff out of man.
His stupid dreams and red-rooster importance: let him count the
    star-swirls.

Exercises and Projects

CHECKING YOUR COMPREHENSION

1. State the theme of the poem in one or two sentences.

2. What does Jeffers think the study of astronomy can do for
    people?

3. Why does Jeffers begin with the allusion to the melting polar ice
    caps and glaciers?

4. Jeffers's stone tower (he actually built such a structure next to his
    Carmel oceanfront home) acquires a paradoxical nature in the
    poem. Explain.

FOR DISCUSSION AND DEBATE

1. Why does Jeffers call it a "pleasure" to contemplate geological time?

2. What significance does the stone tower have in the poem?

3. Defend or refute Jeffers's assertion, in line 13, that "There is nothing like astronomy to pull the stuff out of man." What does Jeffers mean by "stuff"?

FOR YOUR NOTEBOOK

After reading several poems by Jeffers and Frost, list what you consider to be the major similarities and differences between these two poets' attitudes toward nature.

FOR WRITING

1. In a three- to five-page essay, defend or challenge Jeffers's view of humanity as it is reflected in this and other short poems of his. Poems to consider are "Boats in a Fog," "Carmel Point," "Oh, Lovely Rock," and "Hurt Hawks," all of which can be found in *The Selected Poetry of Robinson Jeffers* (1938).

2. Many of Jeffers's poems are about animals, or contain references to animals. Write a critical essay on the significance of animals in Jeffers's poetry. Some poems to consider are "Roan Stallion," "The Purse-Seine," "The House Dog's Grave," "Original Sin," "Animals," and "Vulture," all of which can be found in *Selected Poems,* 1965.

3. The Nobel Prize-winning poet Czeslaw Milosz is an admirer of Jeffers but fundamentally disagrees with Jeffers's philosophy. Read Milosz's poem "To Robinson Jeffers" (*Selected Poems,* 1981) and argue, in a short essay, for or against Milosz's premise.

READING INTRODUCTION

Religion and science are often regarded as incompatible, yet scientists have typically been drawn by their religious beliefs to explore the universe. Isaac Newton is a good example: He felt that by understanding the physical laws that govern God's creation, one could better come to know God. The philosopher George Santayana believed that religion is an important vehicle for rational life "since the ends of rational life are attained by it."

In the following story the narrator, a Jesuit, once shared Newton's attitude, but as he laments at the beginning of the story, "Now I have seen that handiwork, and my faith is sorely troubled." The statement is not without its irony, as you will discover.

Arthur C. Clarke lives in Sri Lanka and is not only a distinguished science fiction writer *(2001: A Space Odyssey* [1968] and *Childhood's End* [1953]*)* but also a distinguished scientist as well. He is the inventor of the communications satellite (in 1945—nearly two decades before the first communications satellite was launched), has written many books on science for general readers, and is a member of the Royal Astronomical Society.

TERMS TO LEARN

light-year: the distance traversed in one year by a beam of light traveling at 186,200 miles per second. This comes to roughly 6 trillion miles, or 2000 times the distance between Earth and the outermost planet in the solar system, Pluto. The nearest star to us (Alpha Centauri) is 4.3 light-years away, a mere 26 trillion miles.

astrophysics: the aspect of astronomy that concentrates on the physical properties and dynamics of celestial objects

nebula: an interstellar "cloud" of debris. Galaxies used to be conceived of as nebulae before large telescopes resolved them into large accumulations of stars.

spectrophotometer: an instrument used to compare the intensities of color in spectra (bands of refracted light that reveal much about the chemical composition of its source)

spectrogram: the photograph of a spectrum

nova: an exploding star

ARTHUR C. CLARKE

 The Star

It is three thousand light-years to the Vatican. Once, I believed that space could have no power over faith, just as I believed that the heavens declared the glory of God's handiwork. Now I have seen that handiwork, and my faith is sorely troubled. I stare at the crucifix that hangs on the cabin wall above the Mark VI Computer, and for the first time in my life I wonder if it is no more than an empty symbol.

I have told no one yet, but the truth cannot be concealed. The facts are there for all to read, recorded on the countless miles of magnetic tape and the thousands of photographs we are carrying back to Earth. Other scientists can interpret them as easily as I can, and I am not one who would condone that tampering with the truth which often gave my order a bad name in the olden days.

The crew are already sufficiently depressed: I wonder how they will take this ultimate irony. Few of them have any religious faith, yet they will not relish using this final weapon in their campaign against me—that private, good-natured, but fundamentally serious, war which lasted all the way from Earth. It amused them to have a Jesuit as chief astrophysicist: Dr. Chandler, for instance, could never get over it (why are medical men such notorious atheists?). Sometimes he would meet me on the observation deck, where the lights are always low so that the stars shine with undiminished glory. He would come up to me in the gloom and stand staring out of the great oval port, while the heavens crawled slowly around us as the ship turned end over end with the residual spin we had never bothered to correct.

"Well, Father," he would say at last, "it goes on forever and forever, and perhaps *Something* made it. But how you can believe that Something has a special interest in us and our miserable little world— that just beats me." Then the argument would start, while the stars and nebulae would swing around us in silent, endless arcs beyond the flawlessly clear plastic of the observation port.

It was, I think, the apparent incongruity of my position that caused most amusement to the crew. In vain I would point to my three papers in the *Astrophysical Journal,* my five in the *Monthly Notices of the Royal Astronomical Society.* I would remind them that my order has long been famous for its scientific works. We may be few now, but ever since the eighteenth century we have made contributions to astronomy and geophysics out of all proportion to our numbers. Will my report on the Phoenix Nebula end our thousand years of history? It will end, I fear, much more than that.

I do not know who gave the nebula its name, which seems to me a very bad one. If it contains a prophecy, it is one that cannot be verified for several billion years. Even the word nebula is misleading: this is a far smaller object than those stupendous clouds of mist—the stuff of unborn stars—that are scattered throughout the length of the Milky Way. On the cosmic scale, indeed, the Phoenix Nebula is a tiny thing—a tenuous shell of gas surrounding a single star.

Or what is left of a star...

The Reubens engraving of Loyola[1] seems to mock me as it hangs there above the spectrophotometer tracings. What would *you,* Father, have made of this knowledge that has come into my keeping, so far from the little world that was all the universe you knew? Would your faith have risen to the challenge, as mine has failed to do?

You gaze into the distance, Father, but I have traveled a distance beyond any that you could have imagined when you founded our order a thousand years ago. No other survey ship has been so far from Earth: we are at the very frontiers of the explored universe. We set out to reach the Phoenix Nebula, we succeeded, and we are homeward bound with our burden of knowledge. I wish I could lift that burden from my shoulders, but I call to you in vain across the centuries and the light-years that lie between us.

On the book you are holding the words are plain to read. *Ad maiorem dei gloriam,*[2] the message runs, but it is a message I can no longer believe. Would you still believe it, if you could see what we have found?

We knew, of course, what the Phoenix Nebula was. Every year, in our galaxy alone, more than a hundred stars explode, blazing for a few hours or days with thousands of times their normal brilliance before they sink back into death and obscurity. Such are the ordinary novae—the commonplace disasters of the universe. I have recorded the spectrograms and light curves of dozens since I started working at the Lunar Observatory.

But three or four times in every thousand years occurs something beside which even a nova pales into total insignificance.

When a star becomes a *supernova,* it may for a little while outshine all the massed suns of the galaxy. The Chinese astronomers watched this happen in A.D. 1054, not knowing what it was they saw. Five

[1]Ignatius Loyola, 1491–1556, founder of the Society of Jesus (Jesuit Order). [Ed.]
[2]"For the greater glory of God." [Ed.]

centuries later, in 1572, a supernova blazed in Cassiopeia so brilliantly that it was visible in the daylight sky. There have been three more in the thousand years that have passed since then.

Our mission was to visit the remnants of such a catastrophe, to reconstruct the events that led up to it, and, if possible, to learn its cause. We came slowly in through the concentric shells of gas that had been blasted out six thousand years before, yet were expanding still. They were immensely hot, radiating even now with a fierce violet light, but were far too tenuous to do us any damage. When the star had exploded, its outer layers had been driven upward with such speed that they had escaped completely from its gravitational field. Now they formed a hollow shell large enough to engulf a thousand solar systems, and at its center burned the tiny, fantastic object which the star had now become—a White Dwarf, smaller than the Earth, yet weighing a million times as much.

The glowing gas shells were all around us, banishing the normal night of interstellar space. We were flying into the center of a cosmic bomb that had detonated millennia ago and whose incandescent fragments were still hurtling apart. The immense scale of the explosion, and the fact that the debris already covered a volume of space many billions of miles across, robbed the scene of any visible movement. It would take decades before the unaided eye could detect any motion in these tortured wisps and eddies of gas, yet the sense of turbulent expansion was overwhelming.

We had checked our primary drive hours before, and were drifting slowly toward the fierce little star ahead. Once it had been a sun like our own, but it had squandered in a few hours the energy that should have kept it shining for a million years. Now it was a shrunken miser, hoarding its resources as if trying to make amends for its prodigal youth.

No one seriously expected to find planets. If there had been any before the explosion, they would have been boiled into puffs of vapor, and their substance lost in the greater wreckage of the star itself. But we made the automatic search, as we always do when approaching an unknown sun, and presently we found a single small world circling the star at an immense distance. It must have been the Pluto of this vanished solar system, orbiting on the frontiers of the night. Too far from the central sun ever to have known life, its remoteness had saved it from the fate of all its lost companions.

The passing fires had seared its rocks and burned away the mantle of frozen gas that must have covered it in the days before the disaster. We landed, and we found the Vault.

Its builders had made sure that we should. The monolithic marker that stood above the entrance was now a fused stump, but even the first long-range photographs told us that here was the work of intelligence. A little later we detected the continent-wide pattern of radioactivity that had been buried in the rock. Even if the pylon above the Vault had been destroyed, this would have remained, an immovable and all but eternal beacon calling to the stars. Our ship fell toward this gigantic bull's-eye like an arrow into its target.

The pylon must have been a mile high when it was built, but now it looked like a candle that had melted down into a puddle of wax. It took us a week to drill through the fused rock, since we did not have the proper tools for a task like this. We were astronomers, not archaeologists, but we could improvise. Our original purpose was forgotten: this lonely monument, reared with such labor at the greatest possible distance from the doomed sun, could have only one meaning. A civilization that knew it was about to die had made its last bid for immortality.

It will take us generations to examine all the treasures that were placed in the Vault. They had plenty of time to prepare, for their sun must have given its first warnings many years before the final detonation. Everything that they wished to preserve, all the fruit of their genius, they brought here to this distant world in the days before the end, hoping that some other race would find it and that they would not be utterly forgotten. Would we have done as well, or would we have been too lost in our own misery to give thought to a future we could never see or share?

If only they had had a little more time! They could travel freely enough between the planets of their own sun, but they had not yet learned to cross the interstellar gulfs, and the nearest solar system was a hundred light-years away. Yet even had they possessed the secret of the Transfinite Drive, no more than a few millions could have been saved. Perhaps it was better thus.

Even if they had not been so disturbingly human as their sculpture shows, we could not have helped admiring them and grieving for their fate. They left thousands of visual records and the machines for projecting them, together with elaborate pictorial instructions from which it will not be difficult to learn their written language. We have examined many of these records, and brought to life for the first time in six thousand years the warmth and beauty of a civilization that in many ways must have been superior to our own. Perhaps they only showed us the best, and one can hardly blame them. But their worlds were very lovely, and their cities were built with a grace that matches anything of man's. We have watched them at work and play, and listened to their musical speech sounding across the centuries. One scene is still before my eyes—a group of children on a beach of strange blue sand, playing in the waves as children play on Earth. Curious whiplike trees line the shore, and some very large animal is wading in the shallows yet attracting no attention at all.

And sinking into the sea, still warm and friendly and life-giving, is the sun that will soon turn traitor and obliterate all this innocent happiness.

Perhaps if we had not been so far from home and so vulnerable to loneliness, we should not have been so deeply moved. Many of us had seen the ruins of ancient civilizations on other worlds, but they had never affected us so profoundly. This tragedy was unique. It is one thing for a race to fail and die, as nations and cultures have done on Earth. But to be destroyed so completely in the full flower of its achievement, leaving no survivors—how could that be reconciled with the mercy of God?

My colleagues have asked me that, and I have given what answers I can. Perhaps you could have done better, Father Loyola, but I have found nothing in the *Exercitia Spiritualia*[3] that helps me here. They were not an evil people: I do not know what gods they worshiped, if indeed they worshiped any. But I have looked back at them across the centuries, and have watched while the loveliness they used their last strength to preserve was brought forth again into the light of their shrunken sun. They could have taught us much: why were they destroyed?

I know the answers that my colleagues will give when they get back to Earth. They will say that the universe has no purpose and no plan, that since a hundred suns explode every year in our galaxy, at this very moment some race is dying in the depths of space. Whether that race has done good or evil during its lifetime will make no difference in the end: there is no divine justice, for there is no God.

Yet, of course, what we have seen proves nothing of the sort. Anyone who argues thus is being swayed by emotion, not logic. God has no need to justify His actions to man. He who built the universe can destroy it when He chooses. It is arrogance—it is perilously near blasphemy—for us to say what He may or may not do.

This I could have accepted, hard though it is to look upon whole worlds and peoples thrown into the furnace. But there comes a point when even the deepest faith must falter, and now, as I look at the calculations lying before me, I know I have reached that point at last.

---

[3]*The Spiritual Exercises,* the handbook written by Loyola; used by Jesuits for training the mind and spirit. [Ed.]

We could not tell, before we reached the nebula, how long ago the explosion took place. Now, from the astronomical evidence and the record in the rocks of that one surviving planet, I have been able to date it very exactly. I know in what year the light of this colossal conflagration reached our Earth. I know how brilliantly the supernova whose corpse now dwindles behind our speeding ship once shone in terrestrial skies. I know how it must have blazed low in the east before sunrise, like a beacon in that oriental dawn.

There can be no reasonable doubt: the ancient mystery is solved at last. Yet, oh God, there were so many stars you could have used. What was the need to give these people to the fire, that the symbol of their passing might shine above Bethlehem?

Exercises and Projects

CHECKING YOUR COMPREHENSION

1. The Jesuit narrator feels mocked by the engraving of St. Loyola. Why?

2. On what kind of a mission were the narrator and his crew?

3. "The Star" includes considerable information about supernovas. Summarize the essential nature of this bizarre phenomenon, as it is presented in the story.

4. Explain why the narrator was so greatly disturbed by what his calculations revealed about the supernova.

FOR DISCUSSION AND DEBATE

1. What different examples of irony can you find in this story? In what way is the subject of irony itself a part of the story?

2. How does Clarke prepare his readers for the full impact of the ending? In other words, what essential information does he include in the story so the ending will work?

3. What is the significance of the opening sentence?

4. Describe the conflict between faith and knowledge that the narrator is experiencing. How successful is he in resolving the conflict?

5. Compare and contrast the narrator in Clarke's story with Hawthorne's Aylmer and with the narrator in Poe's story.

FOR YOUR NOTEBOOK

Write a profile of someone, real or imaginary, who experiences an inner conflict between religious faith and scientific understanding. How does he or she resolve this inner conflict?

FOR WRITING

1. Write a short story in which a deeply religious person makes a scientific discovery that severely challenges his or her faith in God. What will your character do in an effort to resolve the conflict? Will he or she make any intellectual or emotional sacrifice?

2. Write a personal essay in which you attempt to reconcile your scientific understanding of things with your religious beliefs.

3. For the first time in nearly 400 years, astronomers witnessed, on February 23, 1987, a supernova—an exploding star—in one of our satellite galaxies called the Large Magellanic Cloud, 170,000 light-years away. Read the story of this discovery, which was widely reported during the months of March and April, 1987 (see *Time,* March 23, 1987, pp. 60–69). Also read about supernovas and stellar evolution in general. Once you are familiar with the subject, write an essay for young readers on the nature and importance of supernovas.

A scientist is frequently thought of as a researcher, hunched over an intricate arrangement of laboratory equipment. However, perhaps it would be more accurate to think of a scientist as a searcher, one who is wonderstruck by new discoveries and new possibilities that involve not only the future but also the past. The great physicist Max Planck says, in *The New Science* (1959), "Scientific discovery and scientific knowledge have been achieved only by those who have gone in pursuit of it without any practical purpose whatsoever in view." What keeps the archaeologist, the paleontologist, and the anthropologist from becoming overwhelmed by the tedium of routine digging and notation is the possibility of exciting discovery for its own sake—that the next turn of the shovel will yield an artifact or fossil that could change our perception of who we are.

Loren Eiseley was that kind of searcher. A lifetime of delving into the mysteries of the human past as an anthropologist (Eiseley was a professor of anthropology and curator of early man at the University of Pennsylvania) deepened rather than diminished his aesthetic and spiritual perceptions. In the following essay, Eiseley relates four strange encounters with birds: pigeons outside a Manhattan hotel at midnight, a crow disoriented in the fog, a flight of birds across the Badlands of South Dakota, and a group of small birds reacting to an attacking raven. Together these encounters weave a vision of life that is full of mystery and profundity.

Perhaps more than any other scientist/writer in this anthology, Eiseley shows us that the quest for knowledge, rather than distancing us from the human spirit, can take us into its very domain, bringing us face to face with the miraculous.

TERMS TO LEARN

gorge: a narrow and deep passage, often cut by a stream, between steep walls of rock

badlands: barren, heavily eroded stretches of land, often rich in fossils

titanotheres: a generic reference to large primitive mammals that lived about 50 million years ago

LOREN EISELEY

 # The Judgment of the Birds

It is a commonplace of all religious thought, even the most primitive, that the man seeking visions and insight must go apart from his fellows and live for a time in the wilderness. If he is of the proper sort, he will return with a message. It may not be a message from the god he set out to seek, but even if he has failed in that particular, he will have had a vision or seen a marvel, and these are always worth listening to and thinking about.

The world, I have come to believe, is a very queer place, but we have been part of this queerness for so long that we tend to take it for granted. We rush to and fro like Mad Hatters upon our peculiar errands, all the time imagining our surroundings to be dull and ourselves quite ordinary creatures. Actually, there is nothing in the world to encourage this idea, but such is the mind of man, and this is why he finds it necessary from time to time to send emissaries into the wilderness in the hope of learning of great events, or plans in store for him, that will resuscitate his waning taste for life. His great news services, his worldwide radio network, he knows with a last remnant of healthy distrust will be of no use to him in this matter. No miracle can withstand a radio broadcast, and it is certain that it would be no miracle if it could. One must seek, then, what only the solitary approach can give—a natural revelation.

Let it be understood that I am not the sort of man to whom is entrusted direct knowledge of great events or prophecies. A naturalist, however, spends much of his life alone, and my life is no exception. Even in New York City there are patches of wilderness, and a man by himself is bound to undergo certain experiences falling into the class of which I speak. I set mine down, therefore: a matter of pigeons, a flight of chemicals, and a judgment of birds, in the hope that they will come to the eye of those who have retained a true taste for the marvelous, and who are capable of discerning in the flow of ordinary events the point at which the mundane world gives way to quite another dimension.

New York is not, on the whole, the best place to enjoy the downright miraculous nature of the planet. There are, I do not doubt, many remarkable stories to be heard there and many strange sights to be seen, but to grasp a marvel fully it must be savored from all aspects. This cannot be done while one is being jostled and hustled along a crowded street. Nevertheless, in any city there are true wildernesses where a man can be alone. It can happen in a hotel room, or on the high roofs at dawn.

One night on the twentieth floor of a midtown hotel I awoke in the dark and grew restless. On an impulse I climbed upon the broad old-fashioned window sill, opened the curtains, and peered out. It was the hour just before dawn, the hour when men sigh in their sleep or, if awake, strive to focus their wavering eyesight upon a world emerging from the shadows. I leaned out sleepily through the open window. I had expected depths, but not the sight I saw.

I found I was looking down from that great height into a series of curious cupolas or lofts that I could just barely make out in the darkness. As I looked, the outlines of these lofts became more distinct because the light was being reflected from the wings of pigeons who, in utter silence, were beginning to float outward upon the city. In and out through the open slits in the cupolas passed the white-winged birds on their mysterious errands. At this hour the city was theirs, and quietly, without the brush of a single wing tip against stone in that high, eerie place, they were taking over the spires of Manhattan. They were pouring upward in a light that was not yet perceptible to human eyes, while far down in the black darkness of the alleys it was still midnight.

As I crouched half-asleep across the sill, I had a moment's illusion that the world had changed in the night, as in some immense snowfall, and that, if I were to leave, it would have to be as these other inhabitants were doing, by the window. I should have to launch out into that great bottomless void with the simple confidence of young birds reared high up there among the familiar chimney pots and interposed horrors of the abyss.

I leaned farther out. To and fro went the white wings, to and fro. There were no sounds from any of them. They knew man was asleep and this light for a little while was theirs. Or perhaps I had only dreamed about man in this city of wings—which he could surely never have built. Perhaps I, myself, was one of these birds dreaming unpleasantly a moment of old dangers far below as I teetered on a window ledge.

Around and around went the wings. It needed only a little courage, only a little shove from the window ledge, to enter that city of light. The muscles of my hands were already making little premonitory lunges. I wanted to enter that city and go away over the roofs in the first dawn. I wanted to enter it so badly that I drew back carefully into the room and opened the hall door. I found my coat on the chair, and it slowly became clear to me that there was a way down through the floors, that I was, after all, only a man.

I dressed then and went back to my own kind, and I have been rather more than usually careful ever since not to look into the city of light. I had seen, just once, man's greatest creation from a strange inverted angle, and it was not really his at all. I will never forget how those wings went round and round, and how, by the merest pressure of the fingers and a feeling for air, one might go away over the roofs. It is a knowledge, however, that is better kept to oneself. I think of it sometimes in such a way that the wings, beginning far down in the black depths of the mind, begin to rise and whirl till all the mind is lit by their spinning, and there is a sense of things passing away, but lightly, as a wing might veer over an obstacle.

To see from an inverted angle, however, is not a gift allotted merely to the human imagination. I have come to suspect that within their degree it is sensed by animals, though perhaps as rarely as among men. The time has to be right; one has to be, by chance or intention, upon the border of two worlds. And sometimes these two borders may shift or interpenetrate and one sees the miraculous.

I once saw this happen to a crow.

This crow lives near my house, and though I have never injured him, he takes good care to stay up in the very highest trees and, in general, to avoid humanity. His world begins at about the limit of my eyesight.

On the particular morning when this episode occurred, the whole countryside was buried in one of the thickest fogs in years. The ceiling was absolutely zero. All planes were grounded, and even a pedestrian could hardly see his outstretched hand before him.

I was groping across a field in the general direction of the railroad station, following a dimly outlined path. Suddenly out of the fog, at about the level of my eyes, and so closely that I flinched, there flashed a pair of immense black wings and a huge beak. The whole bird rushed over my head with a frantic cawing outcry of such hideous terror as I have never heard in a crow's voice before and never expect to hear again.

He was lost and startled, I thought, as I recovered my poise. He ought not to have flown out in this fog. He'd knock his silly brains out.

All afternoon that great awkward cry rang in my head. Merely being lost in a fog seemed scarcely to account for it—especially in a tough, intelligent old bandit such as I knew that particular crow to be. I even looked once in the mirror to see what it might be about me that had so revolted him that he had cried out in protest to the very stones.

Finally, as I worked my way homeward along the path, the solution came to me. It should have been clear before. The borders of our worlds had shifted. It was the fog that had done it. That crow, and I knew him well, never under normal circumstances flew low near men. He had been lost all right, but it was more than that. He had thought he was high up, and when he encountered me looming gigantically through the fog, he had perceived a ghastly and, to the crow mind, unnatural sight. He had seen a man walking on air, desecrating the very heart of the crow kingdom, a harbinger of the most profound evil a crow mind could conceive of—air-walking men. The encounter, he must have thought, had taken place a hundred feet over the roofs.

He caws now when he sees me leaving for the station in the morning, and I fancy that in that note I catch the uncertainty of a mind that has come to know things are not always what they seem. He has seen a marvel in his heights of air and is no longer as other crows. He has experienced the human world from an unlikely perspective. He and I share a viewpoint in common: our worlds have interpenetrated, and we both have faith in the miraculous.

It is a faith that in my own case has been augmented by two remarkable sights. I once saw some very odd chemicals fly across a waste so dead it might have been upon the moon, and once, by an even more fantastic piece of luck, I was present when a group of birds passed a judgment upon life.

On the maps of the old voyageurs it is called *Mauvaises Terres,* the evil lands, and, slurred a little with the passage through many minds, it has come down to us anglicized as the badlands. The soft shuffle of moccasins has passed through its canyons on the grim business of war and flight, but the last of those slight disturbances of immemorial silences died out almost a century ago. The land, if one can call it a land, is a waste as lifeless as that valley in which lie the kings of Egypt. Like the Valley of the Kings, it is a mausoleum, a place of dry bones in what once was a place of life. Now it has silences as deep as those in the moon's airless chasms.

Nothing grows among its pinnacles; there is no shade except under great toadstools of sandstone whose bases have been eaten to the shape of wine glasses by the wind. Everything is flaking, cracking, disintegrating, wearing away in the long, imperceptible weather of time. The ash of ancient volcanic outbursts still sterilizes its soil, and its colors in that waste are the colors that flame in the lonely sunsets on dead planets. Men come there but rarely, and for one purpose only, the collection of bones.

It was a late hour on a cold, wind bitten autumn day when I climbed a great hill spined like a dinosaur's back and tried to take my bearings. The tumbled waste fell away in waves in all directions. Blue air was darkening into purple along the bases of the hills. I shifted my knapsack, heavy with the petrified bones of long-vanished creatures, and studied my compass. I wanted to be out of there by nightfall, and already the sun was going sullenly down in the west.

It was then that I saw the flight coming on. It was moving like a little close-knit body of black specks that danced and darted and closed again. It was pouring from the north and heading toward me with the undeviating relentlessness of a compass needle. It streamed through the shadows rising out of monstrous gorges. It rushed over towering pinnacles in the red light of the sun or momentarily sank from sight within their shade. Across that desert of eroding clay and wind-worn stone they came with a faint wild twittering that filled all the air about me as those tiny living bullets hurtled past into the night.

It may not strike you as a marvel. It would not, perhaps, unless you stood in the middle of a dead world at sunset, but that was where I stood. Fifty million years lay under my feet, fifty million years of bellowing monsters moving in a green world now gone so utterly that its very light was traveling on the farther edge of space. The chemicals of all that vanished age lay about me in the ground. Around me still lay the shearing molars of dead titanotheres, the delicate sabers of soft-stepping cats, the hollow sockets that had held the eyes of many a strange, outmoded beast. Those eyes had looked out upon a world as real as ours; dark, savage brains had roamed and roared their challenges into the steaming night.

Now they were still here, or, put it as you will, the chemicals that made them were here about me in the ground. The carbon that had driven them ran blackly in the eroding stone. The stain of iron was in the clays. The iron did not remember the blood it had once moved within, the phosphorus had forgot the savage brain. The little individual moment had ebbed from all those strange combinations of chemicals as it would ebb from our living bodies into the sinks and runnels of oncoming time.

I had lifted up a fistful of that ground. I held it while that wild flight of south-bound warblers hurtled over me into the oncoming dark. There went phosphorus, there went iron, there went carbon, there beat the calcium in those hurrying wings. Alone on a dead planet I watched that incredible miracle speeding past. It ran by some true compass over field and waste land. It cried its individual ecstasies into the air until the gullies rang. It swerved like a single body, it knew itself, and, lonely, it bunched close in the racing darkness, its individual entities feeling about them the rising night.

And so, crying to each other their identity, they passed away out of my view.

I dropped my fistful of earth. I heard it roll inanimate back into the gully at the base of the hill: iron, carbon, the chemicals of life. Like men from those wild tribes who had haunted these hills before me seeking visions, I made my sign to the great darkness. It was not a mocking sign, and I was not mocked. As I walked into my camp late that night, one man, rousing from his blankets beside the fire, asked sleepily, "What did you see?"

"I think, a miracle," I said softly, but I said it to myself. Behind me that vast waste began to glow under the rising moon.

I have said that I saw a judgment upon life, and that it was not passed by men. Those who stare at birds in cages or who test minds by their closeness to our own may not care for it. It comes from far away out of my past, in a place of pouring waters and green leaves. I shall never see an episode like it again if I live to be a hundred, nor do I think that one man in a million has ever seen it, because man is an intruder into such silences. The light must be right, and the observer must remain unseen. No man sets up such an experiment. What he sees, he sees by chance.

You may put it that I had come over a mountain, that I had slogged through fern and pine needles for half a long day, and that on the edge of a little glade with one long, crooked branch extending across it, I had sat down to rest with my back against a stump. Through accident I was concealed from the glade, although I could see into it perfectly.

The sun was warm there, and the murmurs of forest life blurred softly away into my sleep. When I awoke, dimly aware of some commotion and outcry in the clearing, the light was slanting down through the pines in such a way that the glade was lit like some vast cathedral. I could see the dust motes of wood pollen in the long shaft of light, and there on the extended branch sat an enormous raven with a red and squirming nestling in his beak.

The sound that awoke me was the outraged cries of the nestling's parents, who flew helplessly in circles about the clearing. The sleek black monster was indifferent to them. He gulped, whetted his beak on the dead branch a moment, and sat still. Up to that point the little tragedy had followed the usual pattern. But suddenly, out of all that area of woodland, a soft sound of complaint began to rise. Into the glade fluttered small birds of half a dozen varieties drawn by the anguished outcries of the tiny parents.

No one dared to attack the raven. But they cried there in some instinctive common misery, the bereaved and the unbereaved. The glade filled with their soft rustling and their cries. They fluttered as though to point their wings at the murderer. There was a dim intangible ethic he had violated, that they knew. He was a bird of death.

And he, the murderer, the black bird at the heart of life, sat on there, glistening in the common light, formidable, unmoving, unperturbed, untouchable.

The sighing died. It was then I saw the judgment. It was the judgment of life against death. I will never see it again so forcefully presented. I will never hear it again in notes so tragically prolonged. For in the midst of protest, they forgot the violence. There, in that clearing, the crystal note of a song sparrow lifted hesitantly in the hush. And finally, after painful fluttering, another took the song, and then another, the song passing from one bird to another, doubtfully at first, as though some evil thing were being slowly forgotten. Till suddenly they took heart and sang from many throats joyously together as birds are known to sing. They sang because life is sweet and sunlight beautiful. They sang under the brooding shadow of the raven. In simple truth they had forgotten the raven, for they were the singers of life, and not of death.

I was not of that airy company. My limbs were the heavy limbs of an earthbound creature who could climb mountains, even the mountains of the mind, only by a great effort of will. I knew I had seen a marvel and observed a judgment, but the mind which was my human endowment was sure to question it and to be at me day by day with its heresies until I grew to doubt the meaning of what I had seen. Eventually darkness and subtleties would ring me round once more.

And so it proved until, on the top of a stepladder, I made one more observation upon life. It was cold that autumn evening, and, standing under a suburban street light in a spate of leaves and beginning snow, I was suddenly conscious of some huge and hairy shadows dancing over the pavement. They seemed attached to an odd, globular shape that was magnified above me. There was no mistaking it. I was standing under the shadow of an orb-weaving spider. Gigantically projected against the street, she was about her spinning when everything was going underground. Even her cables were magnified upon the sidewalk and already I was half-entangled in their shadows.

"Good Lord," I thought, "she has found herself a kind of minor sun and is going to upset the course of nature."

I procured a ladder from my yard and climbed up to inspect the situation. There she was, the universe running down around her, warmly arranged among her guy ropes attached to the lamp supports—a great black and yellow embodiment of the life force, not giving up to either frost or stepladders. She ignored me and went on tightening and improving her web.

I stood over her on the ladder, a faint snow touching my cheeks, and surveyed her universe. There were a couple of iridescent green beetle cases turning slowly on a loose strand of web, a fragment of luminescent eye from a moth's wing and a large indeterminable object, perhaps a cicada, that had struggled and been wrapped in silk. There were also little bits and slivers, little red and blue flashes from the scales of anonymous wings that had crashed there.

Some days, I thought, they will be dull and gray and the shine will be out of them; then the dew will polish them again and drops hang on the silk until everything is gleaming and turning in the light. It is like a mind, really, where everything changes but remains, and in the end you have these eaten-out bits of experience like beetle wings.

I stood over her a moment longer, comprehending somewhat reluctantly that her adventure against the great blind forces of winter, her seizure of this warming globe of light, would come to nothing and was hopeless. Nevertheless it brought the birds back into my mind, and that faraway song which had traveled with growing strength around a forest clearing years ago—a kind of heroism, a world where even a spider refuses to lie down and die if a rope can still be spun on to a star. Maybe man himself will fight like this in the end, I thought, slowly realizing that the web and its threatening yellow occupant had been added to some luminous store of experience, shining for a moment in the fogbound reaches of my brain.

The mind, it came to me as I slowly descended the ladder, is a very remarkable thing; it has gotten itself a kind of courage by looking at a spider in a street lamp. Here was something that ought to be passed on to those who will fight our final freezing battle with the void. I thought of setting it down carefully as a message to the future: *In the days of the frost seek a minor sun.*

But as I hesitated, it became plain that something was wrong. The marvel was escaping—a sense of bigness beyond man's power to grasp, the essence of life in its great dealings with the universe. It was better, I decided, for the emissaries returning from the wilderness, even if they were merely descending from a stepladder, to record their marvel, not to define its meaning. In that way it would go echoing on through the minds of men, each grasping at that beyond out of which the miracles emerge, and which, once defined, ceases to satisfy the human need for symbols.

In the end I merely made a mental note: One specimen of Epeira observed building a web in a street light. Late autumn and cold for spiders. Cold for men, too. I shivered and left the lamp glowing there in my mind. The last I saw of Epeira she was hauling steadily on a cable. I stepped carefully over her shadow as I walked away.

Exercises and Projects

CHECKING YOUR COMPREHENSION

1. What idea does Eiseley hope to give readers by sharing his unusual encounters with birds?

2. Describe the sensations Eiseley experienced when he peered out his Manhattan hotel window late at night and observed the pigeons.

3. Why did the crow appear to be so startled?

4. In your own words, describe the miracle Eiseley experienced in the South Dakota Badlands.

5. What constituted the "judgment" made by the small birds?

FOR DISCUSSION AND DEBATE

1. At the end of the essay, Eiseley describes an encounter with a spider spinning a web beneath a streetlight one winter evening. How does this incident fit in with the others (which are all encounters with birds)? What significance does it have for the essay as a whole?

2. The British poet W. H. Auden, a great admirer of Loren Eiseley, once wrote that he suspected Eiseley of being melancholic. Do you agree or disagree, based on your reading of "The Judgment of the Birds"?

3. This essay, written by a scientist, is filled with allusions to religion and mythology. What connections do you think Eiseley is trying to make between, say, a scientist searching for fossils and one who ventures into the wilderness in search of spiritual fulfillment?

4. Comment on the significance of the following passages from the essay:
   a. "The muscles of my hands were already making little premonitory lunges."
   b. "For in the midst of protest they forgot the violence. There, in that clearing, the crystal note of a song sparrow lifted hesitantly in the hush."
   c. "The mind . . . has gotten itself a kind of courage by looking at a spider in a street lamp."

FOR YOUR NOTEBOOK

1. Go on a bird-watching excursion, taking along a guidebook, a pair of binoculars, a camera, and your notebook. Take detailed notes of every species of bird you encounter.

2. If you have a pet, make a list of every behavioral trait you observe. How many new traits have you discovered as a result of conducting this observation?

FOR WRITING

1. Compare Loren Eiseley's venture into the Badlands with Thoreau's sojourn at Walden Pond. What are the similarities and differences between Eiseley's and Thoreau's attitudes toward nature?

2. Eiseley has given us examples of the "queerness" of the world— a queerness that becomes apparent to us only when we look beyond our usual routines. Write an essay in which you relate, through specific incidents, your own sense of the world's queerness.

3. Animals play an important role in Loren Eiseley's essays (just as they do in Robinson Jeffers's poetry). Write a critical essay that examines the themes generated by encounters with animals in Eiseley's work. Among the additional essays you will want to read are "The Innocent Fox" and "The Bird and the Machine," from *The Star Thrower* (1978).

Like Thoreau and Eiseley, Annie Dillard is a literary naturalist who also manages to fuse scientific fact with imaginative insight. She uses a prose style that is richly evocative and filled with a sense of wonder similar to that of a child who for the first time discovers nature's strange secrets.

In the following excerpt from her highly popular first collection of essays, *Pilgrim at Tinker Creek,* which won a Pulitzer Prize in 1974, Dillard recalls a strangely disturbing incident that reveals both the fierce endurance and the acute sensitivity of new life.

TERMS TO LEARN

Polyphemus moth: a large yellow-brown moth found in the United States, so named because of the eye-like spots on its wings. (In Homer's *The Odyssey,* Polyphemus is the cyclops whom Odysseus blinds.)

chitin (pronounced KITE-n): the tough secretion that forms much of the outer covering of insects and crustaceans

ANNIE DILLARD

 The Moth Cocoon

Once, when I was ten or eleven years old, my friend Judy brought in a Polyphemus moth cocoon. It was January; there were doily snowflakes taped to the schoolroom panes. The teacher kept the cocoon in her desk all morning and brought it out when we were getting restless before recess. In a book we found what the adult moth would look like; it would be beautiful. With a wingspread of up to six inches, the Polyphemus is one of the few huge American silk moths, much larger than, say, a giant or tiger swallowtail butterfly. The moth's enormous wings are velveted in a rich, warm brown, and edged in bands of blue and pink delicate as a watercolor wash. A startling "eyespot," immense, and deep blue melding to an almost translucent yellow, luxuriates in the center of each hind wing. The effect is one of a masculine splendor foreign to the butterflies, a fragility unfurled to strength. The Polyphemus moth in the picture looked like a mighty wraith, a beating essence of the hardwood forest, alien-skinned and brown, with spread, blind eyes. This was the giant moth packed in the faded cocoon. We closed the book and turned to the cocoon. It was an oak leaf sewn into a plump oval bundle; Judy had found it loose in a pile of frozen leaves.

We passed the cocoon around; it was heavy. As we held it in our hands, the creature within warmed and squirmed. We were delighted, and wrapped it tighter in our fists. The pupa began to jerk violently, in heart-stopping knocks. Who's there? I can still feel those thumps, urgent through a muffling of spun silk and leaf, urgent through the swaddling of many years, against the curve of my palm. We kept passing it around. When it came to me again it was hot as a bun; it jumped half out of my hand. The teacher intervened. She put it, still heaving and banging, in the ubiquitous Mason jar.

It was coming. There was no stopping it now, January or not. One end of the cocoon dampened and gradually frayed in a furious battle. The whole cocoon twisted and slapped around in the bottom of the jar. The teacher fades, the classmates fade, I fade: I don't remember anything but that thing's struggle to be a moth or die trying. It emerged at last, a sodden crumple. It was a male; his long antennae were thickly plumed, as wide as his fat abdomen. His body was very thick, over an inch long, and deeply furred. A gray, furlike plush covered his head; a long, tan furlike hair hung from his wide thorax over his brown-furred, segmented abdomen. His multijointed legs, pale and powerful, were shaggy as a bear's. He stood still, but he breathed.

He couldn't spread his wings. There was no room. The chemical that coated his wings like varnish, stiffening them permanently, dried, and hardened his wings as they were. He was a monster in a Mason jar. Those huge wings stuck on his back in a torture of random pleats and folds, wrinkled as a dirty tissue, rigid as leather. They made a single nightmare clump still wracked with useless, frantic convulsions.

The next thing I remember, it was recess. The school was in Shadyside, a busy residential part of Pittsburgh. Everyone was playing dodgeball in the fenced playground or racing around the concrete schoolyard by the swings. Next to the playground a long delivery drive sloped downhill to the sidewalk and street. Someone—it must have been the teacher—had let the moth out. I was standing in the driveway, alone, stock-still, but shivering. Someone had given the Polyphemus moth his freedom, and he was walking away.

He heaved himself down the asphalt driveway by infinite degrees, unwavering. His hideous crumpled wings lay glued and rucked on his back, perfectly still now, like a collapsed tent. The bell rang twice; I had to go. The moth was receding down the driveway, dragging on. I went; I ran inside. The Polyphemus moth is still crawling down the driveway, crawling down the driveway hunched, crawling down the driveway on six furred feet, forever.

Exercises and Projects

CHECKING YOUR COMPREHENSION

1. What caused the moth to hatch prematurely?

2. Why does Dillard refer to it as "the monster in the Mason jar"?

3. Describe the mixed feelings that Dillard has toward the school-teachers who first taught her about the natural world.

FOR DISCUSSION AND DEBATE

1. Discuss the purpose, as well as the effectiveness, of the last sentence. Why does Dillard shift to present tense?

2. Should the teacher have conducted the cocoon observation lesson differently? If yes, how? If no, why not?

3. What purpose is served by Dillard's detailed description of the adult Polyphemus moth?

FOR YOUR NOTEBOOK

Insects are as fascinating as they are abundant. Over the next few days, keep an "insect journal"—write a detailed description of an ant (by itself and with other ants), a moth, a fly, a spider (spiders are actually arachnids, not insects), and any other insects you happen to encounter.

FOR WRITING

1. The theme of curiosity leading to monstrosity or catastrophe is a common one in science fiction, beginning with Mary Shelley's *Frankenstein* (1818). Write an essay on the dangers, as well as the virtues, of curiosity in science.

2. Write an essay on the importance of teaching science to elementary school children. What topics and procedures should be stressed first? What, if anything, should be avoided, and why?

3. Go on a nature walk, making sure you bring along your notebook. Record what you encounter—but try to avoid sweeping generalizations ("the mountains were majestic"). Instead, focus on the minute, the easily overlooked. Take your time, as if you were an artist doing sketches. After your walk, go through your notes and select those items that can provide you with a sharp focus, such as "The Wildflowers of Central Park," or "Spiders of the Mojave," and write an essay with this as the topic.

READING INTRODUCTION

Medicine, because it alleviates human suffering and maintains health and well-being, has an especially high status among the sciences. Physicians and surgeons are "healers" and "miracle workers." And despite our complaints about the outrageous prices for their services, physicians and surgeons are the most highly esteemed of professionals except, perhaps, for the clergy.

The link between healer and holy person has a long ancestry; in primitive societies these persons are often one—the shaman. Richard Selzer, a practicing surgeon and a member of the faculty at the Yale School of Medicine, as well as a distinguished essayist, reinvokes this ancient association and, in so doing, allows us to realize just how intertwined modern medical science is with the darkest recesses of the human soul.

TERMS TO LEARN

Vesalius: Andreas Vesalius (1514–1564), a Belgian physician, was a pioneering anatomist who corrected the many misconceptions about the human body that persisted in ancient texts. His seven-volume *De Humani Corporis Fabrica* (On the Structure of the Human Body), published in 1543, laid the foundations of modern anatomical science.

hierophant: an ancient high priest

peritoneum: the membrane covering the abdominal cavity, protecting the visceral organs

cilia: tiny hairlike growths of certain cells (for instance, of arterial walls) that aid in the movement of fluids

meningitis: inflammation of the membranes (meninges) that wrap around the brain or spinal cord

Peloponnesus: the large peninsula that forms the southern portion of Greece

RICHARD SELZER

The Surgeon as Priest

In the foyer of a great medical school there hangs a painting of Vesalius. Lean, ascetic, possessed, the anatomist stands before a dissecting table upon which lies the naked body of a man. The flesh of the two is silvery. A concentration of moonlight, like a strange rain of virus, washes them. The cadaver has dignity and reserve; it is distanced by its death. Vesalius reaches for his dissecting knife. As he does so, he glances over his shoulder at a crucifix on the wall. His face wears an expression of guilt and melancholy and fear. He knows that there is something wrong, forbidden in what he is about to do, but he cannot help himself, for he is a fanatic. He is driven by a dark desire. To see, to feel, to discover is all. His is a passion, not a romance.

I understand you, Vesalius. Even now, after so many voyages within, so much exploration, I feel the same sense that one must not gaze into the body, the same irrational fear that it is an evil deed for which punishment awaits. Consider. The sight of our internal organs is denied us. To how many men is it given to look upon their own spleens, their hearts, and live? The hidden geography of the body is a Medusa's head one glimpse of which would render blind the presumptuous eye. Still, rigid rules are broken by the smallest inadvertencies: I pause in the midst of an operation being performed under spinal anesthesia to observe the face of my patient, to speak a word or two of reassurance. I peer above the screen separating his head from his abdomen, in which I am most deeply employed. He is not asleep, but rather stares straight upward, his attention riveted, a look of terrible discovery, of wonder upon his face. Watch him. This man is violating a taboo. I follow his gaze upward, and see in the great operating lamp suspended above his belly the reflection of his viscera. There is the liver, dark and turgid above, there the loops of his bowel winding slow, there his blood runs extravagantly. It is that which he sees and studies with so much horror and fascination. Something primordial in him has been aroused—a fright, a longing. I feel it, too, and quickly bend above his open body to shield it from his view. How dare he look within the Ark! Cover his eyes! But it is too late; he has already *seen;* that which no man should; he has trespassed. And I am no longer a surgeon, but a hierophant who must do magic to ward off the punishment of the angry gods.

I feel some hesitation to invite you to come with me into the body. It seems a reckless, defiant act. Yet there is more than dread reflected from these rosy coasts, these restless estuaries of pearl. And it is time to share it, the way the catbird shares the song which must be a joy to him and is a living truth to those who hear it. So shall I make of my fingers, words; of my scalpel, a sentence; of the body of my patient, a story.

One enters the body in surgery, as in love, as though one were an exile returning at last to his hearth, daring uncharted darkness in order to reach home. Turn sideways, if you will, and slip with me into the cleft I have made. Do not fear the yellow meadows of fat, the red that sweats and trickles where you step. Here, give me your hand. Lower between the beefy cliffs. Now rest a bit upon the peritoneum. All at once, gleaming, the membrane parts . . . and you are *in.*

It is the stillest place that ever was. As though suddenly you are struck deaf. Why, when the blood sluices fierce as Niagara, when the brain teems with electricity, and the numberless cells exchange their goods in ceaseless commerce—why is it so quiet? Has some priest in charge of these rites uttered the command "Silence"? This is no silence of the vacant stratosphere, but the awful quiet of ruins, of rainbows, full of expectation and holy dread. Soon you shall know surgery as a Mass served with Body and Blood, wherein disease is assailed as though it were sin.

Touch the great artery. Feel it bound like a deer in the might of its lightness, and know the thunderless boil of the blood. Lean for a bit against this bone. It is the only memento you will leave to the earth. Its tacitness is everlasting. In the hush of the tissue wait with me for the shaft of pronouncement. Press your ear against this body, the way you did as a child holding a seashell and heard faintly the half-remembered, longed-for sea. Now strain to listen *past* the silence. In the canals, cilia paddle quiet as an Iroquois canoe. Somewhere nearby a white whipslide of tendon bows across a joint. Fire burns here but does not crackle. Again, listen. Now there *is* sound—small splashings, tunneled currents of air, slow gaseous bubbles ascend through dark, unlit lakes. Across the diaphragm and into the chest . . . here at last it is all noise; the whisper of the lungs, the *lubdup, lubdup* of the garrulous heart.

But it is good you do not hear the machinery of your marrow lest it madden like the buzzing of a thousand coppery bees. It is frightening to lie with your ear in the pillow, and hear the beating of your heart. Not that it beats . . . but that it might stop, even as you listen. For anything that moves must come to rest; no rhythm is endless but must one day lurch . . . then halt. Not that it is a disservice to a man to be made mindful of his death, but—at three o'clock in the morning it is less than philosophy. It is Fantasy, replete with dreadful images forming in the smoke of alabaster crematoria. It is then that one thinks of the bristlecone pines, and envies them for having lasted. It is their slowness, I think. Slow down, heart, and drub on.

What is to one man a coincidence is to another a miracle. It was one or the other of these that I saw last spring. While the rest of nature was in flux, Joe Riker remained obstinate through the change of seasons. "No operation," said Joe. "I don't want no operation."

Joe Riker is a short-order cook in a diner where I sometimes drink coffee. Each week for six months he had paid a visit to my office, carrying his affliction like a pet mouse under his hat. Every Thursday at four o'clock he would sit on my examining table, lift the fedora from his head, and bend forward to show me the hole. Joe Riker's hole was as big as his mouth. You could have dropped a plum in it. Gouged from the tonsured top of his head was a mucky puddle whose meaty heaped edge rose above the normal scalp about it. There was no mistaking the announcement from this rampart.

The cancer had chewed through Joe's scalp, munched his skull, then opened the membranes underneath—the dura mater, the pia mater, the arachnoid—until it had laid bare this short-order cook's brain, pink and gray, and pulsating so that with each beat a little pool of cerebral fluid quivered. Now and then a drop would manage the rim to run across his balding head, and Joe would reach one burry hand up to wipe it away, with the heel of his thumb, the way such a man would wipe away a tear.

I would gaze then upon Joe Riker and marvel. How dignified he was, as though that tumor, gnawing him, denuding his very brain, had given him a grace that a lifetime of good health had not bestowed.

"Joe," I say, "let's get rid of it. Cut out the bad part, put in a metal plate, and you're cured." And I wait.

"No operation," says Joe. I try again.

"What do you mean, 'no operation'? You're going to get meningitis. Any day now. And die. That thing is going to get to your brain."

I think of it devouring the man's dreams and memories. I wonder what they are. The surgeon knows all the parts of the brain, but he does not know his patient's dreams and memories. And for a moment I am tempted . . . to take the man's head in my hands, hold it to my ear, and listen. But his dreams are none of my business. It is his flesh that matters.

"No operation," says Joe.

"You give me a headache," I say. And we smile, not because the joke is funny anymore, but because we've got something between us, like a secret.

"Same time next week?" Joe asks. I wash out the wound with peroxide, and apply a dressing. He lowers the fedora over it.

"Yes," I say, "same time." And the next week he comes again.

There came the week when Joe Riker did not show up; nor did he the week after that, nor for a whole month. I drive over to his diner. He is behind the counter, shuffling back and forth between the grill and the sink. He is wearing the fedora. He sets a cup of coffee in front of me.

"I want to see your hole," I say.

"Which one?" he asks, and winks.

"Never mind that," I say. "I want to see it." I am all business.

"Not here," says Joe. He looks around, checking the counter, as though I have made an indecent suggestion.

"My office at four o'clock," I say.

"Yeah," says Joe, and turns away.

He is late. Everyone else has gone for the day. Joe is beginning to make me angry. At last he arrives.

"Take off your hat," I say, and he knows by my voice that I am not happy. He does, though, raise it straight up with both hands the way he always does, and I see . . . that the wound has healed. Where once there had been a bitten-out excavation, moist and shaggy, there is now a fragile bridge of shiny new skin.

"What happened?" I manage.

"You mean that?" He points to the top of his head. "Oh well," he says, "the wife's sister, she went to France, and brought me a bottle of water from Lourdes. I've been washing it out with that for a month."

"Holy water?" I say.

"Yeah," says Joe. "Holy water."

I see Joe now and then at the diner. He looks like anything but a fleshly garden of miracles. Rather, he has taken on a terrible ordinariness— Eden after the Fall, and minus its most beautiful creatures. There is a certain slovenliness, a dishevelment of the tissues. Did the disease ennoble him, and now that it is gone, is he somehow diminished? Perhaps I am wrong. Perhaps the only change is just the sly wink with which he greets me, as though to signal that we have shared something furtive. Could such a man, I think as I sip my coffee, could such a man have felt the brush of wings? How often it seems that the glory leaves as soon as the wound is healed. But then it is only saints who bloom in martyrdom, becoming less and less the flesh that pains, more and more ghost-colored weightlessness.

It was many years between my first sight of the living human brain and Joe Riker's windowing. I had thought then, long ago: Could this one-pound loaf of sourdough be the pelting brain? *This,* along whose busy circuitry run Reason and Madness in perpetual race—a race that most often ends in a tie? But the look deceives. What seems a fattish snail drowzing in its shell, in fact lives in quickness, where all is dart and stir and rapids of electricity.

Once again to the operating room . . .

How to cut a paste that is less solid than a cheese—Brie, perhaps? And not waste any of it? For that would be a decade of remembrances and wishes lost there, wiped from the knife. Mostly it is done with cautery, burning the margins of the piece to be removed, coagulating with the fine electric current these blood vessels that course everywhere. First a spot is burned, then another alongside the first, and the cut is made between. One does not stitch—one cannot sew custard. Blood is blotted with little squares of absorbent gauze. These are called patties. Through each of these a long black thread has been sewn, lest a blood-soaked patty slip into some remote fissure, or flatten against a gyrus like a starfish against a coral reef, and go unnoticed come time to close the incision. A patty abandoned brainside does not benefit the health, or improve the climate of the intelligence. Like the bodies of slain warriors, they must be retrieved from the field, and carried home, so they do not bloat and mortify, poisoning forever the plain upon which the battle was fought. One pulls them out by their black thread and counts them.

Listen to the neurosurgeon: "Patty, buzz, suck, cut," he says. Then "Suck, cut, patty, buzz." It is as simple as a nursery rhyme.

The surgeon knows the landscape of the brain, yet does not know how a thought is made. Man has grown envious of this mystery. He would master and subdue it electronically. He would construct a computer to rival or surpass the brain. He would harness Europa's bull to a plow. There are men who implant electrodes into the brain, that part where anger is kept—the rage center, they call it. They press a button, and a furious bull halts in mid-charge, and lopes amiably to nuzzle his matador. Anger has turned to sweet compliance. Others sever whole tracts of brain cells with their knives, to mollify the insane. Here is surgery grown violent as rape. These men cannot know the brain. They have not the heart for it.

I last saw the brain in the emergency room. I wiped it from the shoulder of a young girl to make her smashed body more presentable to her father. Now I stand with him by the stretcher. We are arm in arm, like brothers. All at once there is that terrible silence of discovery. I glance at him, follow his gaze and see that there is more brain upon her shoulder, newly slipped from the cracked skull. He bends forward a bit. He must make certain. It *is* her brain! I watch the knowledge expand upon his face, so like hers. I, too, stare at the fragment flung wetly, now drying beneath the bright lights of the emergency room, its cargo of thoughts evaporating from it, mingling for this little time with his, with mine, before dispersing in the air.

On the east coast of the Argolid, in the northern part of the Peloponnesus, lies Epidaurus. O bury my heart there, in that place I have never seen, but that I love as a farmer loves his home soil. In a valley nearby, in the fourth century B.C., there was built the temple of Asclepius, the god of medicine. To a great open colonnaded room, the abaton, come the sick from all over Greece. Here they lay down on pallets. As night fell, the priests, bearing fire for the lamps, walked among them, commanding them to sleep. They were told to dream of the god, and that he would come to them in their sleep in the form of a serpent, and that he would heal them. In the morning they arose cured. . . .

Walk the length of the abaton; the sick are in their places, each upon his pallet. Here is one that cannot sleep. See how his breath rises and falls against some burden that presses upon it. At last, he dozes, only to awaken minutes later, unrefreshed. It is toward dawn. The night lamps flicker low, casting snaky patterns across the colonade. Already the chattering swallows swoop in and out among the pillars. All at once the fitful eyes of the man cease their roving, for he sees between the candle-lamp and the wall the shadow of an upraised serpent, a great yellow snake with topaz eyes. It slides closer. It is arched and godlike. It bends above him, swaying, the tongue and the lamplight flickering as one. Exultant, he raises himself upon one arm, and with the other, reaches out for the touch that heals.

On the bulletin board in the front hall of the hospital where I work, there appeared an announcement. "Yeshi Dhonden," it read, "will make rounds at six o'clock on the morning of June 10." The particulars were then given, followed by a notation:"Yeshi Dhonden is Personal Physician to the Dalai Lama." I am not so leathery a skeptic that I would knowingly ignore an emissary from the gods. Not only might such sangfroid be inimical to one's earthly well-being, it could take care of eternity as well. Thus, on the morning of June 10, I join the clutch of whitecoats waiting in the small conference room adjacent to the ward selected for the rounds. The air in the room is heavy with ill-concealed dubiety and suspicion of bamboozlement. At precisely six o'clock, he materializes, a short, golden, barrelly man dressed in a sleeveless robe of saffron and maroon. His scalp is shaven, and the only visible hair is a scanty black line above each hooded eye.

He bows in greeting while his young interpreter makes the introduction. Yeshi Dhonden, we are told, will examine a patient selected by a member of the staff. The diagnosis is as unknown to Yeshi Dhonden as it is to us. The examination of the patient will take place in our presence, after which we will reconvene in the conference room where Yeshi Dhonden will discuss the case. We are further informed that for the past two hours Yeshi Dhonden has purified himself by bathing, fasting, and prayer. I, having breakfasted well, performed only the most desultory of ablutions, and given no thought at all to my soul, glance furtively at my fellows. Suddenly, we seem a soiled, uncouth lot.

The patient had been awakened early and told that she was to be examined by a foreign doctor, and had been asked to produce a fresh specimen of urine, so when we enter her room, the woman shows no surprise. She has long ago taken on that mixture of compliance and resignation that is the facies of chronic illness. This was to be but another in an endless series of tests and examinations. Yeshi Dhonden steps to the bedside while the rest stand apart, watching. For a long time he gazes at the woman, favoring no part of her body with his eyes, but seeming to fix his glance at a place just above her supine form. I, too, study her. No physical sign nor obvious symptom gives a clue to the nature of her disease.

At last he takes her hand, raising it in both of his own. Now he bends over the bed in a kind of crouching stance, his head drawn down into the collar of his robe. His eyes are closed as he feels for her pulse. In a moment he has found the spot, and for the next half hour he remains thus, suspended above the patient like some exotic golden bird with folded wings, holding the pulse of the woman beneath his fingers, cradling her hand in his. All the power of the man seems to have been drawn down into this one purpose. It is palpation of the pulse raised to the state of ritual. From the foot of the bed, where I stand, it is as though he and the patient have entered a special place of isolation, of apartness, about which a vacancy hovers, and across which no violation is possible. After a moment the woman rests back upon her pillow. From time to time, she raises her head to look at the strange figure above her, then sinks back once more. I cannot see their hands joined in a correspondence that is exclusive, intimate, his fingertips receiving the voice of her sick body through the rhythm and throb she offers at her wrist. All at once I am envious—not of him, not of Yeshi Dhonden for his gift of beauty and holiness, but of her. I want to be held like that, touched so, *received*. And I know that I, who have palpated a hundred thousand pulses, have not felt a single one.

At last Yeshi Dhonden straightens, gently places the woman's hand upon the bed, and steps back. The interpreter produces a small wooden bowl and two sticks. Yeshi Dhonden pours a small portion of the urine specimen into the bowl, and proceeds to whip the liquid with the two sticks. This he does for several minutes until a foam is raised. Then, bowing above the bowl, he inhales the odor three times. He sets down the bowl and turns to leave. All this while, he has not uttered a single word. As he nears the door, the woman raises her head and calls out to him in a voice at once urgent and serene. "Thank you, doctor," she says, and touches with her other hand the place he had held on her wrist, as though to recapture something that had visited there. Yeshi Dhonden turns back for a moment to gaze at her, then steps into the corridor. Rounds are at an end.

We are seated once more in the conference room. Yeshi Dhonden speaks now for the first time, in soft Tibetan sounds that I have never heard before. He has barely begun when the young interpreter begins to translate, the two voices continuing in tandem—a bilingual fugue, the one chasing the other. It is like the chanting of monks. He speaks of winds coursing through the body of the woman, currents that break against barriers, eddying. These vortices are in her blood, he says. The last spendings of an imperfect heart. Between the chambers of her heart, long, long before she was born, a wind had come and blown open a deep gate that must never be opened. Through it charge the full waters of her river, as the mountain stream cascades in the springtime, battering, knocking loose the land, and flooding her breath. Thus he speaks, and is silent.

"May we now have the diagnosis?" a professor asks.

The host of these rounds, the man who knows, answers.

"Congenital heart disease," he says. "Interventricular septal defect, with resultant heart failure."

A gateway in the heart, I think. That must not be opened. Through it charge the full waters that flood her breath. So! Here then is the doctor listening to the sounds of the body to which the rest of us are deaf. He is more than doctor. He is priest.

I know... I know... the doctor to the gods is pure knowledge, pure healing. The doctor to man stumbles, must often wound; his patient must die, as must he.

Now and then it happens, as I make my own rounds, that I hear   53
the sounds of his voice, like an ancient Buddhist prayer, its meaning
long since forgotten, only the music remaining. Then a jubilation
possesses me, and I feel myself touched by something divine.

Exercises and Projects

CHECKING YOUR COMPREHENSION

1. What associations do the various internal organs and tissues have
   for Selzer?

2. Why, according to Selzer, can it be fearful to listen to the beating
   of one's own heart?

3. What unusual qualities (by Western standards at least) did Yeshi
   Dhonden possess?

4. Selzer marvels at the dignity of one of his cancer patients, Joe
   Riker. What was it that made Joe appear so dignified?

FOR DISCUSSION AND DEBATE

1. Why does Selzer see himself as "no longer a surgeon, but a
   hierophant who must do magic to ward off the punishment of
   the angry gods"? Do you see this as hyperbole (exaggeration) or
   a literal statement? If the former, then what is its purpose? If the
   latter, how thoroughly does Selzer convince you of his
   "priestliness"?

2. Why does Selzer begin the essay by invoking Vesalius?

3. Selzer is often admired for the uncanny way in which he fuses
   highly subjective, poetic images with highly precise, technical
   details. Point out three or four passages in the essay that
   accomplish this, in your opinion. What does such a fusion
   accomplish?

FOR YOUR NOTEBOOK

1. Do some freewriting on various parts of the body. What comes to mind when you see the words *stomach, liver, uterus (womb),* or *rib?*

2. Describe a recent visit to a doctor. What made it particularly pleasant or unpleasant?

FOR WRITING

1. Someone once asked Selzer why a surgeon would write. His answer was, "because I wish to be a doctor." Write an essay that explores the implications of Selzer's answer. First, examine the etymology (origins) of the word *doctor* (consult an unabridged dictionary), then draw particulars from Selzer's essay, "The Exact Location of the Soul," from which the above anecdote is taken. (The essay is in *Mortal Lessons: Notes on the Art of Surgery,* 1976.)

2. Write an essay on what qualities make an ideal physician. How involved with patients should he or she be? What breadth of learning, in addition to medical learning, should the physician possess? Should he or she be "religious"? In what way, and how should that religiousness be evident?

3. Compare selected essays of Richard Selzer to those of neurologist Oliver Sacks, whose book, *The Man Who Mistook His Wife for a Hat and Other Clinical Tales* (1985), has won high acclaim. Possible focus: "The Importance of Compassion for Patients in the Essays of Selzer and Sacks." You may wish to focus on two of Sacks's essays from his book: the title essay and "The Disembodied Lady."

We may think of the lands north of the Arctic Circle as utterly barren, as a moonscape of ice and snow, where only the hardiest explorers venture. While living is indeed harsh there, these arctic regions, Barry Lopez reveals, are full of beauty, and the cultural diversity of many Eskimo settlements is centuries old and virtually undisturbed by outsiders.

A contributing editor to *Harper's* magazine and winner of the John Burroughs Medal for his book, *Of Wolves and Men* (1979), Barry Lopez dramatizes the anxiety he experiences when observing the Yup'ik men of St. Lawrence Island (in the Bering Sea) hunting walrus. The selection is taken from *Arctic Dreams* (1986).

TERMS TO LEARN

auklets: seabirds indigenous to the north Pacific Ocean and Alaska

murres: seabirds similar to the auklets, known for their diving abilities

Gilgamesh: the hero king of the oldest extant epic in literature, the Sumerian *Epic of Gilgamesh* (cuneiform script, ca. 2000 B.C.). Because of Gilgamesh's oppressive rule over his people, the gods send the wildman, Enkidu, to vanquish him in a wrestling match. But nobody wins, and the two men become close friends and embark on a series of adventures together.

Albert Schweitzer (1875–1965): an Alsace-French theologian, organist, musical theorist, and medical missionary to French Equatorial Africa (now Gabon), where he built a hospital. Schweitzer, whose philosophy was based on reverence for life, received the Nobel Peace Prize in 1952.

longspur: a finchlike bird with long hind claws

glaucous gull: a common gray and white Arctic seagull

phalarope: a small wading bird, resembling a sandpiper

oldsquaw: a sea duck, usually black and white

cormorant: a large diving bird with a hooked beak

BARRY LOPEZ

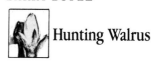 Hunting Walrus

The mountain in the distance is called Sevuokuk. It marks the northwest cape of Saint Lawrence Island in the Bering Sea. From where we are on the ice, this eminence defines the water and the sky to the east as far as we can look. Its western face, a steep wall of snow-streaked basalt, rises above a beach of dark cobbles, riven, ice-polished, ocean-rolled chips of Sevuokuk itself. The village of Gambell is there, the place I have come from with the Yup'ik men, to hunt walrus in the spring ice.

We are, I believe, in Russian waters; and also, by a definition to them even more arbitrary, in "tomorrow," on the other side of the international date line. Whatever political impropriety might be involved is of little importance to the Yup'ik, especially while they are hunting. From where blood soaks the snow, then, and piles of meat and slabs of fat and walrus skin are accumulating, from where ivory tusks have been collected together like exotic kindling, I stare toward the high Russian coast. The mental categories, specific desires, and understanding of history among the people living there are, I reflect, nearly as different from my own as mine are from my Yup'ik companions'.

I am not entirely comfortable on the sea ice butchering walrus like this. The harshness of the landscape, the vulnerability of the boat, and the great size and power of the hunted animal combine to increase my sense of danger. The killing jars me, in spite of my regard for the simple elements of human survival here.

We finish loading the boats. One of the crews has rescued two dogs that have either run off from one of the Russian villages or been abandoned out here on the ice. Several boats gather gunnel to gunnel to look over the dogs. They have surprisingly short hair and seem undersize to draw a sled, smaller than Siberian huskies. But the men assure me these are typical Russian sled dogs.

We take our bearing from the far prominence of Sevuokuk and turn home, laden with walrus meat, with walrus hides and a few seals, with crested auklets and thick-billed murres, with ivory and Russian dogs. When we reach shore, the four of us put our shoulders to the boat to bring it high up on the beach. A young man in the family I am staying with packs a sled with what we have brought back. He pulls it away across the snow behind his Honda three-wheeler, toward the house. Our meals. The guns and gear, the harpoons and floats and lines, the extra clothing and portable radios are all secured and taken away. I am one of the last to leave the beach, still turning over images of the hunt.

No matter what sophistication of mind you bring to such events, no matter what breadth of anthropological understanding, no matter your fondness for the food, your desire to participate, you have still seen an animal killed. You have met the intertwined issues—What is an animal? What is death?—in those large moments of blood, violent exhalation, and thrashing water, with the acrid odor of burned powder in the fetid corral smells of a walrus haul-out. The moments are astounding, cacophonous, also serene. The sight of men letting bits of meat slip away into the dark green water with mumbled benedictions is as stark in my memory as the suddenly widening eyes of the huge, startled animals.

I walk up over the crest of the beach and toward the village, following a set of sled tracks. There is a narrow trail of fresh blood in the snow between the runners. The trail runs out at a latticework of drying racks for meat and skins. The blood in the snow is a sign of life going on, of other life going on. Its presence is too often confused with cruelty.

I rest my gloved fingers on the driftwood meat rack. It is easy to develop an affection for the Yup'ik people, especially when you are invited to participate in events still defined largely by their own traditions. The entire event—leaving to hunt, hunting, coming home, the food shared in a family setting—creates a sense of well-being easy to share. Viewed in this way, the people seem fully capable beings, correct in what they do. When you travel with them, their voluminous and accurate knowledge, their spiritual and technical confidence, expose what is insipid and groundless in your own culture.

I brood often about hunting. It is the most spectacular and succinct expression of the Eskimo's relationship with the land, yet one of the most perplexing and disturbing for the outsider to consider. With the compelling pressures of a cash-based economy to contend with, and the ready availability of modern weapons, hunting practices have changed. Many families still take much of their food from the land, but they do it differently now. "Inauthentic" is the criticism most often made of their methods, as though years ago time had stopped for the Yup'ik.

But I worry over hunting for another reason—the endless reconciliation that must be made of Jacob with his brother Esau. The anguish of Gilgamesh at the death of his companion Enkidu. We do not know how exactly to bridge this gap between civilized man and the society of the hunter. The Afrikaner writer Laurens van der Post, long familiar with Kalahari hunting peoples as archetypal victims of our prejudice, calls the gap between us "an abyss of deceit and murder" we have created. The existence of such a society alarms us. In part this is a trouble we have with writing out our history. We adjust our histories in order to elevate ourselves in the creation that surrounds us; we cut ourselves off from our hunting ancestors, who make us uncomfortable. They seem too closely aligned with insolent, violent predatory animals. The hunting cultures are too barbaric for us. In condemning them, we see it as "inevitable" that their ways are being eclipsed. Yet, from the testimony of sensitive visitors among them, such as van der Post and others I have mentioned in the Arctic, we know that something of value resides with these people.

I think of the Eskimos compassionately as *hibakusha*—the Japanese word for "explosion-affected people," those who continue to suffer the effects of Hiroshima and Nagasaki. Eskimos are trapped in a long, slow detonation. What they know about a good way to live is disintegrating. The sophisticated, ironic voice of civilization insists that their insights are only trivial, but they are not.

I remember looking into a herd of walrus that day and thinking: do human beings make the walrus more human to make it comprehensible or to assuage loneliness? What is it to be estranged in this land?

It is in the land, I once thought, that one searches out and eventually finds what is beautiful. And an edge of this deep and rarefied beauty is the acceptance of complex paradox and the forgiveness of others. It means you will not die alone.

I looked at the blood in the snow for a long time, and then turned away from the village. I walked north, toward the spot where the gravel spit on which the houses stand slips under the sea ice. It is possible to travel in the Arctic and concentrate only on the physical landscape—on the animals, on the realms of light and dark, on movements that excite some consideration of the ways we conceive of time and space, history, maps, and art. One can become completely isolated, for example, in the intricate life of the polar bear. But the ethereal and timeless power of the land, that union of what is beautiful with what is terrifying, is insistent. It penetrates all cultures, archaic and modern. The land gets inside us; and we must decide one way or another what this means, what we will do about it.

One of our long-lived cultural differences with the Eskimo has been over whether to accept the land as it is or to exert the will to change it into something else. The great task of life for the traditional

Eskimo is still to achieve congruence with a reality that is already given. The given reality, the real landscape, is "horror within magnificence, absurdity with intelligibility, suffering within joy," in the words of Albert Schweitzer. We do not esteem as highly these lessons in paradox. We hold in higher regard the land's tractability, its alterability. We believe the conditions of the earth can be changed to ensure human happiness, to provide jobs and to create material wealth and ease. Each culture, then, finds a different sort of apotheosis, of epiphany, and comfort in the land.

Any latent wisdom there might be in the Eskimo position is overwhelmed for us by our ability to alter the land. The long pattern of purely biological evolution, however, strongly suggests that a profound collision of human will with immutable aspects of the natural order is inevitable. This, by itself, seems reason enough to inquire among aboriginal cultures concerning the nature of time and space and other (invented) dichotomies; the relationship between hope and the exercise of will; the role of dreams and myths in human life; and the therapeutic aspects of long-term intimacy with a landscape.

We tend to think of places like the Arctic, the Antarctic, the Gobi, the Sahara, the Mojave, as primitive, but there are in fact no primitive or even primeval landscapes. Neither are there permanent landscapes. And nowhere is the land empty or underdeveloped. It cannot be improved upon with technological assistance. The land, an animal that contains all other animals, is vigorous and alive. The challenge to us, when we address the land, is to join with cosmologists in their ideas of continuous creation, and with physicists with their ideas of spatial and temporal paradox, to see the subtle grace and mutability of the different landscapes. They are crucibles of mystery, precisely like the smaller ones that they contain—the arctic fox, the drawf birch, the pi-meson; and the larger ones that contain them, side by side with such seemingly immutable objects as the Horsehead Nebula in Orion. These are not solely arenas for human invention. To have no elevated conversation with the land, no sense of reciprocity with it, to rein it in or to disparage conditions not to our liking, shows a certain lack of courage, too strong a preference for human devising.

The farther I got from the village below Sevuokuk, the more exposed I was to the wind. I pulled my face farther into my parka. Snow squeaked beneath my boots. As I crossed from patches of wind-slabbed snow to dark cobbles, I wobbled over my footing. The beach stones clattered in the wet cold. The violet and saffron streaks of the sunset had long been on the wane. They had gone to pastels, muted, like slow water or interstellar currents, rolling over. They had become the colors of sunrise. The celestial light on an arctic cusp.

I stood with my feet squared on the stones at the edge of the ice and looked north into Bering Strait, the real Estrecho de Anian. To the east was America, the Seward Peninsula; to the west the Magadan Region of Siberia, the Chukchi Peninsula. On each were the burial grounds of archaic Bering Sea-culture people, the richest of all the prehistoric arctic cultures. In the summer of 1976, a Russian group led by M. A. Chlenov discovered a 500-year-old monument on the north shore of Yttygran Island, on Seniavin Strait, off the southeast Chukchi coast. The complex consists of a series of bowhead whale skulls and jawbones set up in a line on the beach that is about 2500 feet long. The monument is associated with several stone and earth structures and also with meat pits. Many of the skulls are still standing up vertically in the ground, in a strict geometric pattern. Chlenov and his colleagues regard the area as a "sacred precinct" and link it to the ceremonial lives of a select group of highly skilled whale hunters, whose culture was continuous with Cape Dezhnev in the north to Providence Bay and included Saint Lawrence Island, where the cultural phase has been named Punuk.

Perhaps the Punuk hunters at Whalebone Alley, as it is known, lived, some of them, exemplary lives. Perhaps they knew exactly what words to say to the whale so they would not go off in dismay or feel the weight of its death. I remember the faces of the walrus we killed, and do not know what words to say to them.

No culture has yet solved the dilemma each has faced with the growth of a conscious mind: how to live a moral and compassionate existence when one is fully aware of the blood, the horror inherent in all life, when one finds darkness not only in one's own culture but within oneself. If there is a stage at which an individual life becomes truly adult, it must be when one grasps the irony in its unfolding and accepts responsibility for a life lived in the midst of such paradox. One must live in the middle of contradiction because if all contradiction were eliminated at once life would collapse. There are simply no answers to some of the great pressing questions. You continue to live them out, making your life a worthy expression of a leaning into the light.

I stood for a long time at the tip of Saint Lawrence Island, regarding the ice, the distant dark leads of water. In the twilight and wind and the damp cold, memories of the day were like an aura around me, unresolved, a continuous perplexity pierced here and there by sharp rays of light—other memories, coherence. I thought of the layers of it—the dying walrus moving through the chill green water, through the individual minds of the hunters, the mind of an observer. Of the very idea of the walrus living on, even as I ate its flesh. Lines in books about the walrus; walrus-hide lines tied to harpoons, dragging walrus-skin boats over the sea. The curve and weight of a tusk in my mind, from a head as dense with bone as a boulder. Walrus-meat stew is waiting back at the house, hot now, while I stand in this cold, thickening wind. At the foot of Sevuokuk, Lapland longspurs build their nests in the walrus's abandoned crania.

Glaucous gulls fly over. In the shore lead are phalaropes, with their twiglike legs. In the distance I can see flocks of oldsquaw against the sky, and a few cormorants. A patch of shadow that could be several thousand crested auklets—too far away to know. Out there are whales—I have seen six or eight gray whales as I walked this evening. And the ice, pale as the dove-colored sky. The wind raises the surface of the water. Wake of a seal in the shore lead, gone now. I bowed. I bowed to what knows no deliberating legislature or parliament, no religion, no competing theories of economics, an expression of allegiance with the mystery of life.

I looked out over the Bering Sea and brought my hands folded to the breast of my parka and bowed from the waist deeply toward the north, that great strait filled with life, the ice and the water. I held the bow to the pale sulphur sky at the northern rim of the earth. I held the bow until my back ached, and my mind was emptied of its categories and designs, its plans and speculations. I bowed before the simple evidence of the moment in my life in a tangible place on the earth that was beautiful.

When I stood I thought I glimpsed my own desire. The landscape and the animals were like something found at the end of a dream. The edges of the real landscape became one with the edges of something I had dreamed. But what I had dreamed was only a pattern, some beautiful pattern of light. The continuous work of the imagination, I thought, to bring what is actual together with what is dreamed is an expression of human evolution. The conscious desire is to achieve a state, even momentarily, that like light is unbounded, nurturing, suffused with wisdom and creation, a state in which one has absorbed that very darkness which before was the perpetual sign of defeat.

Whatever world that is, it lies far ahead. But its outline, its adumbration, is clear in the landscape, and upon this one can actually hope we will find our way.

I bowed again, deeply, toward the north, and turned south to retrace my steps over the dark cobbles to the home where I was staying. I was full of appreciation for all that I had seen.

Exercises and Projects

CHECKING YOUR COMPREHENSION

1. Why does Lopez think of the Eskimos as "explosion-affected people" (*hibakusha*)?

2. How does Lopez justify to himself the investigation of aboriginal cultures by more advanced cultures?

3. Describe Lopez's reaction to the walrus killings.

4. What relevance to Gilgamesh and Enkidu, Jacob and Esau, have for Lopez in the context of this essay?

FOR DISCUSSION AND DEBATE

1. Lopez's essay is filled with philosophical reflections stemming from his effort to appreciate the Eskimos' way of life. For example:
   a. "Any latent wisdom there might be in the Eskimo position is overwhelmed for us by our ability to alter the land."
   b. "We adjust our histories in order to elevate ourselves in the creation that surrounds us; we cut ourselves off from our hunting ancestors, who make us uncomfortable."
   c. "The long pattern of purely biological evolution . . . suggests that a profound collision of human will with immutable aspects of the natural order is inevitable."
   Use one or more of these assertions to spark a class debate on the right of an "advanced" culture to exert its influence on a "primitive" one.

2. Lopez wonders, "Do human beings make the walrus more human to make it comprehensible or to assuage loneliness?" How would you answer?

3. Why do you suppose Lopez tells us that "Walrus-meat stew is waiting for me back at the house, hot now, while I stand in this cold, thickening wind"?

FOR YOUR NOTEBOOK

Spend a few days reading about so-called "primitive" people: the Inuit (Eskimos), any of the North American Indian peoples, or

Australian aboriginals, for example. Take notes on their social organization, their foods, their religious beliefs, their arts and crafts.

FOR WRITING

1. Write an essay in which you attempt to resolve the dilemma between protecting animals like the walrus and seal pup and protecting the culture of a native people like the Yup'ik in which the hunting of such animals is a tradition.

2. Choose a locale that you consider evocative in some way—a mountain lake, a pine forest, a desert plateau, small farm town, a ski resort, and so on—and try to describe it in as much sensory detail as possible. Include a description of the locale's inhabitants—human or animal.

3. Write an essay about a hunting experience—one of your own or that of someone you know. Try to capture any conflicting feelings you or your friend may have experienced with regard to killing an animal, even for food. Or, if conflicting feelings were not a problem, provide a detailed account of the hunt from beginning to end.

Ever since Walt Whitman, poets have discovered that anything can be the subject of a poem—that there is really no such thing as "poetic language" or a "poetic subject." Good poetry is marked by its startling freshness of imagery and association, by its ability to pull an idea out of its strictly literal context and give it universal human meaning.

It used to be thought that the sciences, dealing as they do with abstract concepts, had little to do with such traditionally human concerns as love and hate, melancholy and spiritual bliss, betrayal and injustice. However, as the following poems reveal, a scientific perspective can illuminate some obscure corners of human experience.

Siv Cedering, a Swedish-American poet, has written many poems on astronomical themes. Her latest collection of poems, *Letters from the Floating World* (1984), has been published by the University of Pittsburgh Press.

R. H. W. Dillard directs the writing program at Hollins College in Virginia. His collection of poems, *The First Man on the Sun,* was published in 1983.

May Swenson has published several volumes of poetry, such as *To Mix with Time* (1963) and *New and Selected Things Taking Place* (1979). The latter contains several poems on scientific themes, including the selection that follows.

Cory Wade, who received her Ph.D. in English from the University of Washington, teaches creative writing and medieval literature at Santa Clara University. Her poetry has appeared in many journals, including *The Southern Review.* Wade, an animal rights activist, has written "The Lethal Dose 50: Dermal Version" especially for this anthology.

SIV CEDERING

 Letter from Caroline Herschel (1750–1848)

William is away, and I am minding
the heavens. I have discovered
eight new comets and three nebulae
never before seen by man,
and I am preparing an Index to
Flamsteed's observations, together with
a catalogue of 560 stars omitted from
the British Catalogue, plus a list of errata
in that publication. William says

I have a way with numbers, so I handle
all the necessary reductions and
calculations. I also plan
every night's observation
schedule, for he says my intuition
helps me turn the telescope to discover
star cluster after star cluster.

I have helped him polish the mirrors
and lenses of our new telescope. It is
the largest in existence. Can you imagine
the thrill of turning it to some new
corner of the heavens to see
something never before seen
from earth? I actually like

that he is busy with the Royal society
and his club, for when I finish my other work
I can spend all night sweeping
the heavens.

Sometimes when I am alone
in the dark, and the universe reveals
yet another secret, I say the names
of my long, lost sisters, forgotten
in the books that record
our science—
Aganice of Thessaly,
Hyptia,

Hildegard,
Catherina Hevelius,
Maria Agnesi

—as if the stars themselves could

remember. Did you know that Hildegard
proposed a heliocentric universe
300 years before Copernicus? that she
wrote of universal gravitation 500 years
before Newton? But who would listen
to her? She was just a nun, a woman.
What is our age, if that age was dark?
As for my name, it will also be
forgotten, but I am not accused
of being a sorceress, like Aganice,
and the Christians do not threaten to
drag me to church, to murder me, like they did
Hyptia of Alexandria, the eloquent, young
woman who devised the instruments
used to accurately measure the position
and motion of

heavenly bodies.
However long we live, life is short, so I
work. And however important man becomes,
he is nothing compared to the stars.
There are secrets, dear sister, and it is
for us to reveal them. Your name, like mine,
is a song. Write soon,
                              Caroline

R. H. W. DILLARD

 How Einstein Started It Up Again

*"It should be possible to explain the laws of
physics to a barmaid."*
  —*Ernest Rutherford*

"Oh, Albert," she said,
Shaking her head
And falling back
On the rumpled and unmade bed,
"You make everything
So dizzy." And he did.

It was Albert and his equations—
This equals that,
And it's all the same—
Knocked it all out of line,
Curved space, bent time,
Cosmos like a wrinkled sheet.

He made it all so energetic
And so odd, made attraction
Seem so natural,
Just like rolling off a log:
The up and down, the in and out,
First you're still, then you move about.

And the sun is all
In how you see it,
Boiling overhead,
Moving by, or the one
Still point
In the moving sky.

She found it hard,
How this could be that
And still be this,
How it's here and then there,
Or then there or then here,
Or then here and there, hit or miss.

She curved up like space
And then rolled in a ball,
Looking back
To just where she had been,
When Albert rolled in
And began to begin again.

Sun and still sky,
Red clouds that veer
And drift by, the day's demise
Or sunrise (depending
On where you are or were),
And Albert's continuing surprise.

"Oh, Albert," she said,
Shaking her head
And falling back again
On the rumpled and unmade bed,
"You make everything
So dizzy." And he did.

MAY SWENSON

 The DNA Molecule

The DNA Molecule is The Nude Descending a Staircase[1],
a circular one. See the undersurfaces of the spiral
treads and the spaces in between. She is descending
and, at the same time, ascending, and she moves
around herself. For she is the staircase, "a proto-
plasmic framework that twists and turns." She is a
double helix, mounting and dismounting around the
swivel of her imaginary spine.

The Nude named DNA can be constructed as a model with
matches and a ribbon of tape. Be sure to use only
four colors on two white strands of twistable tape.
"Only matches of complementary colors may be placed
opposite each other. The pairs are to be Red and Green,
and Yellow and Blue." Make your model as high as the
Empire State Building, and you have an acceptable
replica of The Nude. But (and this is harder) you
must make her move in a continuous coil, an alpha helix,
a double spiral downward and upward at once, and you
must make her increase while, at the same time, occupy-
ing the same field. She must be made to maintain
"a basic topography," changing, yet remaining stable,
if she is to perform her function, which is to produce
and reproduce the microsphere.

Such a sphere is invisible to, but omnipresent in, the
naked eye of The Nude. It contains a "central region
and an outer membrane," making it both able to divide
and to make exact copies of itself without limit.
The Nude "has the capacity for replication and trans-
cription" of all genesis. She ingests and regurgitates
the genetic material, it being the material of her own
cell-self. From single she become double, and from
double single. As a woman ingests the demon sperm and,
with the same membrane, regurgitates the mitotic double
of herself upon the slide of time, so The DNA Molecule

---

[1]The title of a famous painting by Marcel Duchamp (1887–1968). See p. 342. [Ed.]

produces, with a little pop, at the waistline of its
viscous drop, a new microsphere the same size as herself,
which proceeds singly to grow in order to divide and
double itself. So, from single to double and double to
single, and mounting while descending, she expands
while contracts, she proliferates while disappearing,
at both of her ends.

Remember that Red can only be opposite Green, and Blue
opposite Yellow. Remember that the complementary pairs
of matches must differ slightly in length, "for nature's
pairs can be made only with units whose structures
permit an interplay of forces between the partners."

I fixed a Blue match opposite a Red match of the same
length, pointed away from the center on the double strand
of tape. I saw laid a number of eggs on eggs on the
sticky side of a twig. I saw a worm with many feet
grow out of an egg. The worm climbed the twig, a single
helix, and gobbled the magnified edge of a leaf in quick
enormous bites. It then secreted out of itself a gray
floss with which it wrapped itself, tail first, and
so on, until it had completely muffled and encased
itself, head too, as in a mummy sack.

I saw plushy, iridescent wings push moistly out of the
pouch. At first glued together, they began to part.
On each wing I saw a large blue eye, open forever
in the expression of resurrection. The new Nude
released the flanges of her wings, stretching herself
to touch at all points the outermost rim of the
noösphere.[2] I saw that, for her body, from which the
wings expanded, she had retained the worm.

---

[2] A term coined by Jesuit anthropologist Teilhard de Chardin referring to "the sphere
of mind" in contrast to nature itself (the biosphere). [Ed.]

CORY WADE

 The Lethal Dose 50: Dermal Version

*"When 50% of test animals have died from a dose
applied directly to the skin, the product may be
considered hazardous."*
          —*Instruction Manual for the LD50*
          (minimum number of test animals: 40)

He thinks about the grant he needs to win.
He pulls rabbit Eighteen from its tiny cage.
He sighs with some relief it's not his skin,

shaved then burned with a compound of chlorine,
death by chemical fire. But it's not the pain
he thinks about: the grant he needs to win

could be reduced by the outcry there has been—
though funding's not shaky yet, despite public rage;
he sighs with some relief it's not. His skin

itches from holding the restraint strap tightly in:
rabbit Eighteen is convulsing. As he waits,
he thinks about the grant he needs. To win,

he'll dismiss all this talk of ends and means and sin . . .
(though he'd hate being Head of Testing in such an age;
he sighs with some relief—it's not his skin!)

Rabbit Eighteen is dead. He shaves the thinned
fur from Nineteen's neck. It's a decent wage,
he thinks. About the grant he needs to win,
he sighs with some relief. It's not his skin.

Exercises and Projects

CHECKING YOUR COMPREHENSION

1. Describe Herschel's attitude toward her husband, William.

2. How does the speaker in Cedering's poem support her assertion that she has "a way with numbers"?

3. What does the speaker in Dillard's poem include as examples of how Albert [Einstein] makes "everything so dizzy"?

4. Summarize the content of Swenson's "The DNA Molecule" in one paragraph.

5. Wade's "The Lethal Dose 50: Dermal Vision" narrates an incident. Summarize it in one or two sentences.

FOR DISCUSSION AND DEBATE

1. Why do you suppose Cedering presented Herschel's point of view in the form of a letter to her sister? What connotations does the word *sister* acquire in the poem?

2. There are many ironical utterances in Cedering's poem. How many you can identify? Do they point to a central irony?

3. Dillard's poem is a humorous view of relativity. What is the basis for the humor?

4. What is the significance of the Rutherford quotation that prefaces Dillard's poem?

5. Relativity has become very much a part of popular lore. Using Dillard's poem and your own experiences, suggest ways in which the original theory of relativity gets distorted in the process.

6. What does Swenson mean when she says of the figure in Duchamp's painting, "She is descending / and, at the same time, ascending"?

7. Although "the Nude" is a convenient way of referring to the Duchamp painting, it may also carry symbolic weight in the poem. Discuss.

8. The last two stanzas of "The DNA Molecule" describe the metamorphosis of a caterpillar into a moth or butterfly. How is this relevant to the poem as a whole?

9. "The Lethal Dose 50: Dermal Version" follows a traditional French poetic form known as a villanelle: five three-line stanzas (tercets), each rhymed a-b-a, and a concluding four-line stanza, a-b-a-a. Thus, only two rhymes operate in a villanelle. Why do you suppose Wade chose this pattern for her poem?

10. Why does Wade preface the poem with a quotation from the experimenters' Instruction Manual? (This is a verbatim quotation from an actual manual.)

11. To what extent is the experimenter in the poem representative of animal experimenters in general? You may wish to read and review the animal rights articles in Part 3.

FOR YOUR NOTEBOOK

Create your own gallery of favorite science-related poems. Browse through anthologies of contemporary poetry such as *The Morrow Anthology of Contemporary American Poets,* edited by Dave Smith and David Bottoms (William Morrow, 1985), or *Songs from Unsung Worlds: Science in Poetry,* edited by Bonnie Gordon (Birkhauser, 1985). Write a brief response to each poem you select.

FOR WRITING

1. Choose one of the poems and discuss it in terms of the scientific ideas it contains. Points to consider: How accurate are the scientific allusions? How do these allusions serve to illuminate an important facet of human experience?

2. Compose your own poem, using a traditional form or free form, on a theme in astronomy, animal rights, relativity, molecular biology, or in any other scientific area.

3. Write a detailed two-page explication of one of the poems. Begin with an overview of the poem's theme and technique, then analyze each stanza (not necessarily in sequence), trying to establish a reason for every detail included.

Suggestions for Further Reading

I. SEVENTEENTH AND EIGHTEENTH CENTURIES

Donne, John. *The Anatomy of the World (The First Anniversary).* (Originally published 1611.)

Donne reflects on the impact of new scientific discoveries on the established world picture. Contains the famous lines: "[The] new philosophy calls all indoubt / The element of fire is quite put out; / The Sun is lost, and th'earth, and no man's wit / Can well direct him where to looke for it."

Pope, Alexander. *An Essay on Man*. (Originally published 1733–34)

Swift, Jonathan. *Gulliver's Travels*. (Originally published 1726.)
In book 3, Gulliver journeys to the floating, completely circular island of Laputa, where the people devote themselves to mathematics and astronomy (working from the Astronomer's cave deep in the ground!), then to Balnibarbi, where members of the Academy in the capital city of Lagado conduct disgusting experiments. Swift is attacking the scientists of his day, who seemed to him more involved with sorcery than truth seeking.

Thomson, James. *A Poem Sacred to the Memory of Sir Isaac Newton*. (Originally published 1727.)

II. NINETEENTH CENTURY

Bellamy, Edward. *Looking Backward, 2000–1887.* (Originally published 1888.)
Presents a vision of a socialist utopia.

Dickens, Charles. *Hard Times*. (Originally published 1854.)
A darkly satirical novel about the effects of the industrial revolution on human conduct.

Emerson, Ralph Waldo. *Nature*. (Originally published 1836.)
The great transcendentalist "manifesto" on the correspondences between the natural world and human nature.

Muir, John. *The Mountains of California*. (Originally published 1894.)

Shelley, Mary. *Frankenstein: Or, the Modern Prometheus*. (Originally published 1818.)

Thoreau, Henry David. *The Natural History Essays*. Salt Lake City: Peregine-Smith, 1980.
Includes well-known essays such as "Walking" (1862) and "A Winter Walk" (1842), as well as lesser-known essays.

Twain, Mark. *A Connecticut Yankee in King Arthur's Court*. (Originally published 1883.)

Yankee scientific savvy is both praised and satirized in this entertaining novel about a nineteenth-century man who is bumped on the head and wakes up a thousand years in the past.

Wells, H. G. *The Time Machine*. (Originally published 1894.)

Allegorical tale of a nineteenth-century time traveler who journeys into the distant future to encounter the utopian Eloi and the bestial Morlocks.

III. TWENTIETH CENTURY

Ackerman, Diane. *The Planets: A Cosmic Pastoral*. New York: William Morrow, 1976.

Ackerman's poetry is rich in astronomical as well as mythic imagery. She devotes a poem to each planet in the solar system, including earth and the asteroids.

Appleman, Philip. *Darwin's Ark*. Bloomington: Indiana University Press, 1984.

Includes poems on the theme of biological evolution.

Benford, Gregory. *Timescape*. New York: Simon & Schuster, 1980.

A science fiction novel about ecological catastrophe; as much science as fiction—Benford is a professor of physics.

Calvino, Italo. *Cosmicomics*. Translated by William Weaver. New York: Harcourt Brace Jovanovich, 1968.

Includes parablelike tales on creation and evolution.

Čapek, Karel. *R.U.R.* (Rossum's Universal Robots) Translated by P. Selver. Oxford: Oxford University Press, 1923.

This play satirizes the mechanization of work. Čapek coined the word *robot* (from the Czech word *robota,* meaning work), meaning forced labor.

Clarke, Arthur C. *2001: A Space Odyssey*. New York: New American Library, 1968.

Presents a startling vision of human destiny that is at once scientific and religious in treatment.

Dillard, Annie. *Teaching a Stone to Talk: Expeditions and Encounters*. New York: Harper & Row, 1982.

Eiseley, Loren. *Darwin's Century*. New York: Anchor Books, 1959.

Eiseley's award-winning centennial study of Charles Darwin.

Eiseley, Loren. *All the Strange Hours: The Excavation of a Life.* New York: Scribner's, 1975.

Eiseley's autobiography.

Eiseley, Loren. *The Star Thrower.* New York: Harcourt Brace Jovanovich, 1978.

A selection of Eiseley's finest essays, along with some of his early poetry; published posthumously.

Gordon, Bonnie, ed. *Songs from Unsung Worlds: Science in Poetry.* Boston: Birkhauser, 1985.

Levi, Primo. *The Periodic Table.* Translated by Raymond Rosenthal. New York: Schocken Books. 1984.

Levi's memoir of survival as a chemist in war-torn Europe. Each chapter is title with a chemical element, and that element acquires both literal and symbolic importance.

Lem, Stanislaw. *The Cyberiad: Fables for the Cybernetic Age.* Translated by Michael Kandel. New York: Seabury Press, 1974.

McPhee, John. *Basin and Range.* New York: Farrar, Straus & Giroux, 1980.

A geological tour of America. McPhee's prose is lyrical, vigorous, factual.

Pirsig, Robert. *Zen and the Art of Motorcycle Maintenance: An Inquiry into Values.* New York: William Morrow, 1974.

Pynchon, Thomas. *The Crying of Lot 49.* New York: Lippincott, 1966.

The Uncertainty Principle applied to modern society! A weird novel.

Pynchon, Thomas. "Entropy." From *Slow Learner: Early Stories.* Boston: Little, Brown, 1984.

Raymo, Chet. *The Soul of the Night: An Astronomical Pilgrimage.* Englewood Cliffs, N.J.: Prentice-Hall, 1985.

Lyrical and meditative reflections on astronomical phenomena in the context of our earthly experiences.

Sacks, Oliver. *The Man Who Mistook His Wife for a Hat and Other Clinical Tales.* New York: Summit Books, 1985.

Selzer, Richard. *Confessions of a Knife.* New York: Simon & Schuster, 1978.

Selzer, Richard. *Letters to a Young Doctor.* New York: Simon & Schuster, 1982.

Sinclair, Upton. *The Jungle.* (Originally published 1906.)
Somewhat melodramatic but nonetheless highly influential novel about animal abuses and unsanitary conditions in the meat packing industry. Its publication helped lead to passage of the Pure Food and Drug Act.

Vonnegut, Kurt. *Cat's Cradle.* New York: Dell, 1963.
Mad religion and mad atomic science in a mad, mad world.

Researching a Scientific Topic

Nearly all writing requires research to some extent, but most of the time this research is regarded as "background reading." If you are writing a personal essay about a nature walk in Yosemite, you may want to refresh your memory about the trees native to the area, the geological formations, the climate, and so on. You will not "footnote" your personal essay, of course; instead, you may make a passing reference to an author, using a phrase like "according to," as, for example, "According to John Muir in his classic work, *The Mountains of California*...".

But in what is called a "research paper," otherwise known as a scholarly or professional article by the specialized journals that publish them, authors must carefully document their sources, using a simple, consistent format. This enables the readers, typically specialists in the subject, to examine the sources for themselves.

Documentation aside, it makes sense to be methodical in conducting a library research task. Begin by writing out a list of what you already know about the topic; this will alert you to knowledge gaps as well as get you involved quickly. Second, make sure you have a sound overview of the topic by reading a few encyclopedia articles (the *McGraw-Hill Encyclopedia of Science and Technology* is ideal); pay attention to cross references and bibliographies. Third, locate items in the bibliographies as well as in the periodical indexes (*General Science Index; Applied Science and Technology Index,* and so on) that seem promising and jot down relevant passages on index cards. Fourth, locate abstracts (summaries) of articles, collected in a variety of periodicals such as *Chemical Abstracts.* It makes good sense to begin a rough draft or outline fairly early, before you've completed the research. The act of "writing it out" can give you a better sense of direction as well as call attention to any more knowledge gaps.

It is important to remember that even the most scholarly papers still must be readable and engaging. As you read the following research paper, written by a college junior, try to pinpoint what the author has done to make her paper read well.

TERMS TO LEARN

enzyme: a group of amino acids that catalyzes important metabolic reactions in organisms

osteosclerosis: abnormal hardening of bone tissue

amide: a type of ammonia compound in which a hydrogen atom has been replaced by an acid radical (two atoms acting as a single atom) *phosphate:* the product of a phosphoric acid in which the hydrogen atoms are replaced by atoms of a metal such as sodium. Phosphates are important in plant and animal metabolism.

fluorosis: a disorder caused by excessive ingestion of fluorine

caries: tooth decay

goiter: a disease of the thyroid gland, characterized by enlargement; usually caused by iodine deficiency

KARLA SWATEK

 Artificial Fluoridation: How Safe?

To the townspeople of Grand Rapids, Michigan, it seemed a wonderful idea. By adding a small amount of cheap chemical called fluoride to their water supply, they could control and maybe even eliminate common tooth decay. For a few extra dollars per year, modern dentistry could be practiced in the home. But that was back in 1945. Forty years later we are in a state of controversy. Is artificial fluoridation really safe? Are large numbers of people now ingesting too much fluoride from an increasing number of sources? Recent studies indicate that too much fluoride is flooding our digestive systems. Although the chemical is beneficial in small doses, too much of a good thing has been shown to cause maladies ranging from enzyme poisoning to dental fluorosis and osteosclerosis.

Chemical Effects: Disrupted Bonding

Fluoride is a potent poison of enzymes. Since the chemical boasts a powerful hydrogen bonding capacity, it often interferes with the vital hydrogen bonding between the molecules of an enzyme. By attracting groups of ions that can form strong hydrogen bonds to themselves, fluoride changes the molecular conformation and thus inactivates an enzyme. Hydrogen bonds are weak connections between the hydrogen ions in O-H and N-H chemical bonds, and a second oxygen, nitrogen, or fluoride atom. The fluoride ion is particularly good at forming these weak bonds because of its small size and negative charge (*New Scientist* 94: 20). Although these bonds are weak, they hold complex systems together, like the double helix system of DNA.

But hydrogen bonds are no less important to enzymes such as amides—organic salts or ammonia. Many components within living cells contain amide groups, and the hydrogen bonds formed between amides are the most important weak hydrogen bonds in biological systems. Disruption of these bonds by fluoride in the formation of much stronger bonds may explain how the chemically inert fluoride ion interferes in the normal operations of living systems. Many enzymes are inhibited by fluoride even when this is present only in levels of a few parts per million.

Biological Effects: Disease

A healthy individual can easily cope with tiny doses of fluoride, and at low dosages the chemical does strengthen bones and aid the mineralization of tooth enamel. But at the same time, other parts of our metabolism are threatened. Fluoride causes maladies ranging from dental fluorosis to cancer. According to a study in the *British Dental Journal* (140: 307) dental fluorosis, no matter how minor, is an irreversible disease whose mottled discoloration is recognized by experts as the first detectable symptom of chronic fluoride poisoning. The primary target cells for fluoride poisoning are bone cells. Fluoride is absorbed into the body by the intestinal mucous membrane. While at least 50% of all fluoride absorbed is excreted in the urine on the same day, a small residue is retained in the skeleton. Continuous intake may lead to osteosclerosis. Furthermore, fluoride can disrupt the physiological function of the thyroid gland and lead to pathological developments such as goiter. Fluoride also causes allergies, premature aging, and isolated incidents of cancer through the disrupted hydrogen bonding of genetic material (DNA).

Causal Factors: Multiple Fluoride Sources

As formerly stated, too much fluoride can be harmful. When fluoridation projects first began, scientists envisaged that drinking about one liter of fluoridated water per day would provide 1 milligram of fluoride, an effective yet limited daily dosage. However, people are now ingesting fluoride from many more everyday sources; the amount received by the individual can no longer be controlled.

Ground water itself shows a content of between .05 and .8 mg. of fluoride, and the fluoride content has been found to increase with depth; underground wells serve as the main water supply for many communities. The daily fluoride intake with food by humans is approximately .2 to .5 mg., as reported in *Critical Reviews in Environmental Control* (9: 10). Foods and beverages rich in fluoride, such as tuna, salmon, and tea, can contribute anywhere from .8 to 1.3 mg. of fluoride per day. More than 90% of all toothpaste now sold contains high concentrations of fluoride, often more than 1000 parts per million. These toothpastes add another .3 to .5 mg. to daily fluoride intake, based on twice-a-day brushings. Many health experts still recommend the use of fluoride tablets and drops for pregnant women and for children from birth, and dental surgery often involves use of gels with fluoride concentrations of up to 60 mg. as a means of reinforcing tooth enamel. Such applications triple the recommended daily intake of fluoride. Finally, the air we beathe can add anywhere from .4 to 2 mg. of fluoride intake per day—the highest readings coming from areas that contain aluminum or phosphate manufacturing plants.

The Elimination of Artificial Fluoridation from Water Supplies: A Possible Solution

The quantities of fluoride needed to protect against dental caries and those that lead to disease are separated by a narrow margin. One milligram of fluoride per day is thought to be a positive amount, while dental fluorosis and other maladies can occur from the ingestion of 2 or more milligrams per day. So how can we reduce the potentially dangerous levels of fluoride that we consume? One feasible solution is the elimination of artificially induced fluoride from our water supplies. As dental caries are caused by dietary problems or inadequate dental care, tooth decay is not a fluoride deficiency disease in the sense that fluoridation of drinking water is a medication. It is merely a preventative measure. And while fluoride ingested from drinking water cannot be considered in isolation from other sources, the artificial fluoridation of a water supply does have negative consequences in that it raises the average daily fluoride intake by a considerable amount. It is crucial, therefore, that we stop fluoridating our water supplies.

At present, over 7000 communities in the United States have fluoridated water. The Department of Health, Education, and Welfare has recently launched a major campaign to fluoridate 535 new community and school district water systems, and hopes to make fluoride treatments mandatory by 1989 (*American City and County* 94: 13). In the absence of a feasible way to monitor individual fluoride intake, we should halt the induction of fluoride treatments to our water supplies. While the chemical seems beneficial, its long-term consequences are not worth the prevention of a few minor dental caries. What is beneficial to a part should be beneficial to the whole.

WORKS CITED

"Computer Reveals How Model Molecules Rearrange Themselves." *New Scientist* 94 (1 April 1982): 20.

"Daily Fluoride Intake." *Critical Reviews in Environmental Control* 9 (1979): 7–10.

"Dental Fluorosis." *British Dental Journal* 140 (1976): 307.

"Government Begins Campaign to Fluoridate the Nation's Water Supplies." *American City and County* 94 (October 1979): 13.

Exercises and Projects

CHECKING YOUR COMPREHENSION

1. When was fluoride first added to public water supplies?

2. How does fluoride interfere with the body's enzymes?

3. What effect can fluoride have on the thyroid gland? On bones?

4. According to the author, people are overdosing on fluoride. Why?

5. What would be the best countermeasure to excessive fluoride intake?

FOR DISCUSSION AND DEBATE

1. Discuss the appropriateness and effectiveness (in the context of a formal research paper) of the author's opening paragraph.

2. Swatek divides her article with subheads. How effective are they? Would the piece be just as readable without them? Explain.

3. How might fluoridation of water be better controlled?

4. Argue for or against Swatek's assertion that "we should halt the induction of fluoride treatments to our water supplies."

5. How successfully does Swatek define her technical terms? Are some terms defined more clearly than others?

FOR YOUR NOTEBOOK

Begin an ongoing series of notebook entries that focus on public response to a public health issue such as AIDS prevention, the effects of smoking, or fad dieting.

FOR WRITING

1. Gather information about the fluoridation of your local water supply and determine the safety factor in light of Swatek's assertions.

2. Write an essay on dental health programs. How might they be improved? What are their outstanding as well as problematic features?

3. Investigate a chemical contamination problem in your community and prepare a research study based on your findings. Plan to use interviews as your principal source of external evidence. Possible topics to investigate:
   a. contamination of drinking water by industrial pollutants
   b. oil spills in rivers, lakes, or oceans
   c. sewage contamination
   d. insecticide pollution (particularly of farm crops)
   e. use of preservatives in foods, such as red dyes in meat (Note: you will first need to establish that the preservative in question is a contaminant)

Important Scientists in History

ARCHIMEDES 287–212 B.C.

A Greek mathematician, Archimedes defined the principle of the lever, as well as the principle of hydrostatics (Archimedes' principle): The amount of fluid a body displaces is equal to the volume of that body.

AVICENNA 980–1037

A Persian physician, Avicenna's richly informative medical text, *The Canon of Medicine,* was widely used throughout the Middle East and Europe for centuries.

AVOGADRO, AMEDEO 1776–1856

An Italian chemist and physicist, Avogadro is famous for "Avogadro's hypothesis" (which later became a law) that under identical conditions of pressure and temperature, equal volumes of gases contain equal numbers of molecules. The number of molecules that exist in one gram molecular weight of a given substance is known as Avogadro's number.

BACON, ROGER 1214–1294

English philosopher, Franciscan friar, and scientist. Bacon stressed the importance of accurate observation and delved deeply into the study of alchemy.

BANNEKER, BENJAMIN 1731–1806

A black American mathematician, surveyor, and astronomer, Banneker in 1789 was appointed by President Washington to a commission established to plan the city of Washington, D.C.; Banneker became well known for his yearly almanacs.

BECQUEREL, ANTOINE HENRI 1852–1908

A French physicist, Becquerel discovered radioactivity in 1896.

BERNARD, CLAUDE 1813–1878

French physiologist and pioneer in experimental medicine. Bernard made pioneering studies of the human digestive process.

BETHE, HANS 1906–

An American physicist, Bethe postulated the means by which stars, including the sun, produce their energy (thermonuclear fusion). The work brought him the Nobel Prize in 1967. He worked on the atomic bomb project in Los Alamos and later fought to curb proliferation of nuclear arms.

BOAS, FRANZ 1858–1942

An American anthropologist, Boas pioneered the use of strict scientific procedures to anthropology and stressed the need for an in-depth study of a culture before drawing any conclusions. *Race, Language, and Culture* (1940) is one of his important books.

BOHR, NIELS 1885–1962

Danish physicist and formulator of the quantum theory, Bohr received the Nobel Prize in physics in 1922 for his work on atomic structure.

BOYLE, ROBERT 1627–1691

British physicist and chemist, Boyle was one of the founders of modern chemistry. He helped establish rigorous methods of laboratory procedure and was the first to observe that metals gained weight when they oxidized and the first to isolate a gas. The famous law that bears his name states that a gas's volume and pressure are inversely proportional.

BRAGG, SIR WILLIAM HENRY 1862–1942

A British physicist, Bragg pioneered the study of crystal structure using x-ray diffraction techniques. This work brought him the Nobel Prize for physics in 1915, which he shared with his son, Sir William Lawrence Bragg (1890–1971).

CARVER, GEORGE WASHINGTON 1864–1953

A black American botanist and agricultural scientist, Carver developed new ways to improve soil and new uses for peanuts, soybeans, and sweet potatoes.

COPERNICUS, NICHOLAS 1473–1543

Copernicus, a Polish astronomer, developed the heliocentric theory that the earth revolved around the sun.

CURIE, MARIE 1867–1934

Polish chemist who, along with her husband, Pierre, did pioneering work in the study of radioactive substances. Curie received two Nobel Prizes: one in physics (1903) and the other in chemistry (1911).

CUVIER, GEORGES 1769–1832

A French naturalist, Cuvier was the first to present a systematic classification of the animal kingdom; he also pioneered the study of comparative anatomy.

DALTON, JOHN 1766–1844

A British chemist and physicist, Dalton was the developer of modern atomic theory and the first to compute atomic weights (published in his *New System of Chemical Philosophy,* 1803). He also advanced the science of meteorology.

DARWIN, CHARLES ROBERT 1809–1882

Darwin is the English naturalist whose detailed observations of life forms around the world were assimilated into his masterwork, *On the Origin of Species* (1859).

DAVY, SIR HUMPHREY 1778–1829

A British chemist, Davy studied the effects of electricity on chemical compounds and developed the electrolyte method for isolating hitherto undiscovered elements, such as potassium and sodium. He also experimented with anesthetics.

DEMOCRITUS 460–370 B.C.

First to develop the atomic theory of matter. Democritus, a Greek philosopher, thought that all material objects were composed of indivisible particles, all identical to each other, called atoms (from *atomos,* indivisible).

DIRAC, PAUL 1902–1984

A British physicist, Dirac contributed to quantum theory and in 1930 discovered the positron (antielectron).

DREW, CHARLES R. 1904–1950

A black American physician, Drew developed a method for storing blood plasma.

EDISON, THOMAS 1847–1931

An American inventor of electrical products fundamental to the modern age, Edison introduced the phonograph (1877), the incandescent lamp and the dynamo (1879), the first centralized electric power station (New York City, 1882), and the kinetescope, or motion picture projector (1888). In 1928 Edison was awarded the Congressional Gold Medal for his revolutionary inventions.

EINSTEIN, ALBERT 1879–1959

The American theoretical physicist who revolutionized physics with his theories of relativity. Einstein received the Nobel Prize in physics in 1921.

EUCLID 290 B.C.

In addition to his famous thirteen-volume *Elements,* which included plane and solid geometry and the properties of numbers, Euclid, a Greek mathematician, also wrote a description of the universe (the *Phenomena*) and a description of music (*Division of the Scale*).

FARADAY, MICHAEL 1791–1867

A British chemist and physicist and a pioneer in electrochemistry and magnetism, Faraday discovered the principles of electrolysis and electromagnetic induction. His best-known work is *Experimental Researches in Chemistry and Physics* (1859).

FERMI, ENRICO 1901–1954

An American physicist, Fermi designed the first sustained nuclear reaction in December 1942. He won a Nobel Prize in 1938 for his research into the production of artificial radioactivity using neutron bombardment.

FLEMING, SIR ALEXANDER 1881–1955

A British bacteriologist and immunologist, Fleming is renowned for his discovery of penicillin.

FOUCAULT, JEAN 1819–1868

A French physicist, Foucault demonstrated the earth's rotation with a pendulum and studied magnetic fields.

FRANKLIN, BENJAMIN 1706–1790

An American inventor and statesman, Franklin distinguished himself in pure and applied science as much as he did in politics, diplomacy, and public education. His Franklin stove radiated more heat and burned less fuel than conventional fireplaces; he researched the nature of light and electricity and demonstrated, through his legendary kite flying experiment, that lightning was an electrical phenomenon; he then went on to invent the lightning rod. His *Autobiography* (1788) is a classic of American literature.

FREUD, SIGMUND 1856–1939

An Austrian neurologist, Freud is the founder of psychoanalysis.

GALEN A.D. 130–200

Galen was one of the greatest physicians of ancient Greece and among the first to use animal dissection and experimentation to obtain anatomical and medicinal knowledge.

GALILEI, GALILEO 1564–1642

An Italian astronomer, physicist, and mathematician who built the first astronomical telescope and discovered the four largest moons of Jupiter, as well as craters on Earth's moon.

GALTON, SIR FRANCIS 1822–1911

A British founder of the science of eugenics (improving humanity through control of hereditary factors), Galton also established modern statistical methods.

GÖDEL, KURT 1906–1978

A Czech-American mathematician and logician, Gödel became famous for his theorem, which states that no mathematical proposition can be proven by the system that produced it. Gödel also contributed to relativity theory.

HALLEY, EDMUND 1656–1743

A British astronomer, Halley developed the principles of cometary astronomy. He plotted the orbit of a major comet (Halley's comet) and predicted its return—which proved that comets are part of the solar system.

HARVEY, WILLIAM 1578–1657

A British physician, Harvey discovered and described the circulation of the blood. His revolutionary treatise, *De Motu Cordis et Sanguinis in Animalibus* (The Motion of the Heart and Blood in Animals) was published in 1628.

HAWKING, STEPHEN 1942–

A British astrophysicist, Hawking was the principal investigator of black holes (collapsed stars with no mass at all, which generate a gravitational field so great that it drastically distorts space; when diagrammed, black holes resemble a funnel hole).

HEISENBERG, WERNER 1901–1976

Heisenberg, a German physicist, is one of the founders of the quantum theory. He is best known for his uncertainty principle.

HERSCHEL, CAROLINE 1750–1848

A British astronomer, Caroline Herschel greatly assisted her brother, William. She was awarded the Gold Medal of the Royal Astronomical Society. (See the poem by Siv Cedering in Part 4.)

HERSCHEL, WILLIAM 1738–1822

A British astronomer, William Herschel discovered the seventh planet, Uranus; he systematically surveyed the heavens with the help of his sister, Caroline.

HIPPOCRATES 450–370 B.C.

The greatest physician of ancient Greece, Hippocrates developed the techniques of prognosis and preventative medicine.

HUMBOLDT, ALEXANDER VON 1769–1859

A German naturalist, Humboldt is best known for his contributions to the science of geophysics.

HUTTON, JAMES 1726–1797

Hutton, a Scottish geologist, investigated the processes of gradual and uniform changes in nature, which he theorized to have been at work throughout vast periods of geological time (hence refuting the theory of catastrophism that major changes came about through violent disruption).

JAMES, WILLIAM 1842–1910

An American physiologist and philosopher, James developed the field of cognitive psychology. His *Principles of Psychology* (1890) helped establish psychology as a science instead of a branch of philosophy.

JENNER, EDWARD 1749–1823

An English physician and pioneer immunologist, Jenner developed the smallpox vaccine.

JOLIOT-CURIE, IRENE 1897–1956

A French physicist, Joliot-Curie investigated artificial radioactivity and helped discover the neutron. (See the section on Marie Curie in part 2.)

JUNG, CARL GUSTAV 1875–1961

A Swiss psychiatrist, Jung is best known for his theory of universal archetypes.

KELVIN, LORD (WILLIAM THOMSON) 1824–1907

Lord Kelvin advanced the knowledge of mechanical and heat energy. He is famous for his absolute temperature scale, developed in 1848.

KEPLER, JOHANNES 1571–1630

A German astronomer, Kepler formulated the laws of planetary motion (Kepler's laws), drawing from Copernicus's heliocentric theory.

LAMARCK, JEAN-BAPTISTE DE 1744–1829

A French evolutionary theorist and naturalist, Lamarck lived half a century before Darwin. He was first to propose, following an in-depth study of mollusks and other organisms, that species increase in complexity over great spans of time and that they acquire traits based on environmental factors.

LEAKEY, LOUIS 1903–1972

A British paleontologist and anthropologist, Leakey's remarkable findings at Olduvai Gorge in Tanzania greatly advanced our knowledge of human origins.

LEAKEY, MARY 1913–

British anthropologist and wife of Louis Leakey, Mary Leakey discovered the 2-million-year-old skull of *Australopithecus bosei*—one of the earliest hominids.

LEEUWENHOEK, ANTON VAN 1632–1723

A Dutch inventor of the microscope, Leeuwenhoek pioneered the study of microorganisms and blood.

LINNAEUS, CAROLUS 1707–1778

A Swedish botanist, Linnaeus founded the modern binomial system (genus name plus species name) of classifying life forms.

LORENTZ, HENDRIK 1853–1928

A Dutch physicist, Lorentz developed the electromagnetic theory of light and also helped formulate what is known as the Lorentz-FitzGerald contraction—that a body changes shape as its velocity increases. This concept became a cornerstone of relativity theory.

LORENTZ, KONRAD 1903–

A German scientist, Lorentz helped establish the science of ethology (animal behavior) and suggested that human aggression is genetic in origin. The concept is explained in his book *On Aggression* (1966).

LYELL, SIR CHARLES 1797–1875

A British geologist, Lyell advanced the work of James Hutton.

MAXWELL, JAMES CLERK 1831–1879

A Scottish physicist, Maxwell was the first to theorize that light is an electromagnetic phenomenon (experimentally confirmed by Helmich Hertz [1857–1894], who detected electromagnetic waves in 1887).

MEAD, MARGARET 1901–1978

American social anthropologist Mead's observations of cultures in New Guinea and Samoa led to important new insights into the nature of child rearing, sexual behavior, and adolescence. Mead was a strong opponent of the view that behavior is genetically predetermined. Among her most important works are *Coming of Age in Samoa* (1928), *Sex and Temperament in Three Primitive Societies* (1935), and her autobiography, *Blackberry Winter* (1972).

MENDEL, GREGOR 1822–1884

An Austrian pioneering geneticist, Mendel observed the traits of two generations of pea plants (involving more than 28,000 species)— observations that led to Mendel's laws of hereditary transmission. Mendel, a monk, conducted his research at the Augustinian monastery in Brünn, Austria (what is now Brno, Czechoslovakia), where he lived.

MENDELEYEV, DMITRI 1834–1907

A Russian chemist, Mendeleyev developed the periodic law of chemical elements, a classification of the elements according to their atomic weights. This he first represented as a table in 1869. His later version (1872) included gaps in the table for yet-undiscovered elements.

MESMER, FRANZ FRIEDRICH 1734–1815

Mesmer, an Austrian physician, discovered a trancelike state now called hypnotism but then known as mesmerism. Mesmer regarded this state as proof of "animal magnetism," a mysterious force generated by the body, analogous to natural magnetism. (See the section on Poe in Part 4.)

MÖBIUS, AUGUST FERDINAND 1790–1868

A German mathematician, Möbius developed the study of topology. He is famous for his "Möbius strip," a one-sided figure created by twisting a rectangular strip 90 degrees and tying the ends together.

NEUMANN, JOHN VON 1903–1957

An American mathematician, Neumann designed some of the earliest electronic computers, including MANIAC I (1952), which was the first computer to use a stored program. Neumann also developed game theory—the mathematical analysis of situations involving conflicting goals and the selection of the best strategies under the circumstances.

NEWTON, SIR ISAAC 1643–1727

The English physicist and mathematician who created calculus, developed the laws of motion and of gravitation. Newton also developed the modern theory of colors.

NIGHTINGALE, FLORENCE 1820–1910

English founder of professional nursing, Nightingale changed nursing's image from that of a menial chore to a worthy profession. She insisted on thorough schooling and founded the Nightingale School and Home for Nurses at St. Thomas's Hospital, London, in 1860. In the same year she published *Notes on Nursing,* the first nursing textbook. During the Crimean War (1854–1860), she greatly reduced the mortality rate through her reforms in sanitation and in care of the wounded.

OPPENHEIMER, J. ROBERT 1904–1967

An American physicist, Oppenheimer directed the atomic bomb project at Los Alamos, New Mexico. In 1947 he was appointed chair of the Atomic Energy Commission's Advisory Committee.

PAPANICOLAOU, GEORGE 1883–1962

An American physician, Papanicolaou developed a method of early cancer detection in women, using what is called the Pap Test.

PASTEUR, LOUIS 1822–1895

French founder of the science of microbiology, Pasteur developed vaccines for rabies, anthrax, and other diseases. Most notably, he developed the technique of pasteurization, whereby harmful bacteria in milk and other fluids are destroyed.

PAULING, LINUS 1901–

An American chemist, Pauling investigated the structure of molecules and the nature of chemical bonding. His work on the molecular nature of proteins helped lead to the discovery of the structure of DNA. Pauling is also noted for his controversial research into the role of vitamin C in combatting disease.

PAVLOV, IVAN 1849–1936

Pavlov, a Russian physiologist, is famous for his investigation of reflexes, conditioned and unconditioned, using dogs. Pavlov's findings were important in the development of behavioral psychology.

PIAGET, JEAN 1869–1980

A Swiss psychologist, Piaget studied the cognitive growth of children. His identification of discrete stages of mental development has had a profound influence on modern education.

POINCARÉ, JULES HENRI 1854–1912

French physicist and mathematician Poincaré's work spanned several scientific disciplines. He made important contributions to electromagnetic theory, calculus, thermodynamics, and relativity. He was also an esteemed philosopher of science. Among his many books are *The Value of Science* (1905) and *Science and Method* (1908).

PRIESTLY, JOSEPH 1733–1804

An English clergyman and chemist, Priestly helped found modern chemistry and is famous for his discovery and isolation of oxygen in 1774. Priestly also studied the properties of ammonia, carbon monoxide, and other gases.

PTOLEMY (CLAUDIUS PTOLEMAEUS) A.D. 100–170

Accepting the Aristotelian model of a geocentric (earth-centered) universe, the Greek astronomer Ptolemy undertook a detailed geometric description of that model in his treatise, the *Almagest.*

REED, WALTER 1851–1902

A U.S. Army surgeon, Reed traced the sources of such devastating epidemics as typhoid and yellow fever. He tracked down the cause of the latter disease—a single species of mosquito.

RÖNTGEN, WILLIAM 1845–1923

A German physicist, Röntgen discovered x-rays in 1901.

RUTHERFORD, ERNEST 1871–1937

A British physicist, Rutherford classified radiation as either alpha, beta, or gamma rays. He also investigated atomic structure and produced the familiar model of the atom as a nucleus of positive charge, orbited by negatively charged electrons. In 1919 Rutherford produced the first artificial nuclear reaction by bombarding nitrogen with alpha particles to create oxygen and beta rays.

SALK, JONAS 1914–

An American physician, Salk developed the first polio vaccine in 1952.

SKINNER, B. F. 1914–

An American behavioral psychologist, Skinner is known for his development of programmed instruction—a method of learning that requires units of information to be learned one at a time, in sequence. Skinner's important books include *The Technology of Teaching* (1968), *Beyond Freedom and Dignity* (1971), and *Reflections on Behaviorism and Society* (1978).

TURING, ALAN 1912–1954

A British mathematician and logician, Turing was a pioneering theorist in machine intelligence.

WATSON, JAMES D. 1928–

An American biologist who co-discovered the structure of the DNA molecule.

WATSON, JOHN B. 1878–1958

An American psychologist, Watson was the founder of behavioral psychology, which restricts the description of behavior to observable phenomena, experimentally based. Watson developed a theory of stimulus-response behavior whereby external stimuli lead to specific and often predictable behavior (response).

VON BRAUN, WERNHER 1912–1977

An American engineer, von Braun developed the liquid fuel rocket that was used for the voyages to the moon in 1969–1971, including the *Saturn V*, which served as the launch vehicle for the Apollo spacecraft.

WÖHLER, FRIEDRICH 1800–1882

German chemist—the first (in 1828) to create an organic compound, urea, in the laboratory.

ZENO OF ELEA 490–430 B.C.

Greek philosopher, famous for his paradoxes of motion.

Acknowledgments

Aristotle, "Science, Art, and Wisdom" is from *Nicomachean Ethics* in *The Ethics of Aristotle,* Book Six, translated by J. A. K. Thomson (London: Penguin, 1953), pp. 174–180.

Sir Francis Bacon, "The Four Idols" is from *Novum Organum,* Book I, 1620.

W. I. B. Beveridge, "The Powers of Observation" is from *The Art of Scientific Investigation,* Revised Edition, Chapter 8, pp. 98–105 (Norton Edition). Copyright © 1957. All rights reserved. Reprinted with permission of W. W. Norton & Company, Inc. and Heinemann Professional Publishing (London).

J. David Bolter, "From Socrates to Faust to Turing" is from *Turing's Man: Western Culture in the Computer Age,* pp. 216–222. © 1984 The University of North Carolina Press. Reprinted with permission of The University of North Carolina Press and J. David Bolter.

Jacob Bronowski, "The Reach of Imagination" is from *The American Scholar,* Spring 1967, pp. 193–201. The essay was originally delivered as the Blashfield Address to the American Academy of Arts and Letters, May 1967, and appears in Jacob Bronowski, *A Sense of the Future: Essays in Natural Philosophy,* edited by Piero Ariotti and Rita Bronowski (Cambridge, Ma.: MIT Press, 1977). Reprinted with permission of the American Academy and Institute of Arts and Letters and Rita Bronowski.

Siv Cedering, "Letter from Caroline Herschel (1750–1848)" is a poem that originally appeared as "Caroline Herschel (1750–1848)," Part IV of "Letters from the Astronomers," in *Letters from the Floating World.* © 1984 by Siv Cedering. Reprinted with permission of the University of Pittsburgh Press.

Arthur C. Clarke, "The Star" is from *The Other Side of the Sky,* pp. 179–186. Copyright © 1955 by Royal Publications, Inc. Reprinted with permission of Harcourt Brace Jovanovich, Inc.

Denis Collins, "Animal Rights vs. Medical Research" is from the *San Jose Mercury News,* August 7, 1987, pp. 1F–2F. Reprinted with permission of the *San Jose Mercury News.*

Barry Commoner, "The Dangers of Nuclear–Waste Disposal" is from *The Poverty of Power: Energy and the Economic Crisis,* pp. 89–94. Copyright © 1976 by Barry Commoner. Reprinted with permission of Alfred A. Knopf, Inc.

Marie Curie, "The Energy and Nature of Radiation" is from *Radio-active Substances,* 1903.

Charles Darwin, "Understanding Natural Selection" is from *On the Origin of Species by Means of Natural Selection, or the Preservation of Favoured Races in the Struggle for Life,* 1859.

Emily Dickinson, "I Like to See It Lap the Miles" is Miss Dickinson's poem number 585.

Annie Dillard, "The Moth Cocoon," is from *Pilgrim at Tinker Creek,* pp. 61–63. Copyright © 1974 by Annie Dillard. Reprinted with permission of Harper & Row, Publishers, Inc.

R. H. W. Dillard, "How Einstein Started It Up Again" is a poem from *The First Man on the Sun.* Copyright © 1983 by R. H. W. Dillard. Reprinted with permission of Louisiana State University Press.

Marcel Duchamp, *Nude Descending a Staircase No. 2.* 1912. Oil on canvas. 58″ × 35″. Philadelphia Museum of Art: Louise and Walter Arensberg Collection. Photo of the painting is reprinted with permission of the Philadelphia Museum of Art.

Albert Einstein, "The General Theory of Relativity" is from *Relativity: the Special and the General Theory,* pp. 63–69, translated by Robert Lawson. © MCMLXI by The Estate of Albert Einstein. Reprinted with permission of Crown Publishers, Inc.

Loren Eiseley, "The Judgment of the Birds" is from *The Immense Journey,* pp. 163–178. Copyright © 1956 by Loren Eiseley. Reprinted with permission of Random House, Inc.

Sigmund Freud, "The Dream–Censorship" is from "The Censorship of Dreams" (Ninth Lecture) in *Introductory Lectures on Psychoanalysis,* pp. 136–148, translated and edited by James Strachey. Copyright © 1966 by W. W. Norton & Company, Inc. Copyright © 1965, 1964, 1963 by James Strachey. Copyright © 1920, 1935 by Edward L. Bernays. Reprinted with permission of Liveright Publishing Corporation.

Robert Frost, "Etherealizing," copyright 1947, © 1969 by Holt, Rinehart and Winston, Inc., copyright © 1975 by Lesley Frost Ballantine, is a poem from *The Poetry of Robert Frost,* edited by Edward Connery Lathem. Reprinted with permission of Henry Holt and Company, Inc.

Galileo Galilei, "Observations of the Planet Jupiter" is from *The Starry Messenger* (1610) in *Discoveries and Opinions of Galileo,* pp. 51–57, translated by Stillman Drake. Copyright © 1957 by Stillman Drake. Reprinted with permission of Doubleday, a division of Bantam, Doubleday, Dell Publishing Group, Inc.

Martin Gardner, "The Amazing Code" is from *aha! Gotcha: Paradoxes to Puzzle and Delight,* pp. 48–49. Drawings by Scott Kim. Copyright © 1975 by Scientific American, Inc., and 1982 W. H. Freeman and Company. Reprinted with permission of W. H. Freeman and Company.

Victor Gilinsky, "A Common-Sense Approach to Nuclear Waste" is from *Technology Review,* January 1985, pp. 14, 59. Copyright 1985. Reprinted with permission of *Technology Review.*

Duane Gish and Isaac Asimov, "The Genesis War" (Debate) is from *Science Digest,* October 1981, pp. 82–87. Reprinted with permission of Duane Gish and Isaac Asimov.

Vivian Gornick, "Two Women of Science: Carol Steiner and Sharlene George" is from *Women in Science: Portraits from a World in Transition,* pp. 42–47. Copyright © 1983 by Vivian Gornick. Reprinted with permission of Simon & Schuster, Inc.

Stephen Jay Gould, "SETI and the Wisdom of Casey Stengel" is from *Discover,* March 1983. Reprinted with permission of Family Media.

Nathaniel Hawthorne, "The Birthmark" (1843) is from *Mosses from an Old Manse,* 1846.

Werner Heisenberg, "The Uncertainty Principle" is from *Physics and Philosophy,* pp. 89–91; Volume Nineteen in World Perspectives, planned and edited by Ruth Nanda Anshen. Copyright © 1958 by Werner Heisenberg. Reprinted with permission of Harper & Row, Publishers, Inc.

Robinson Jeffers, "Star–Swirls," copyright © 1963 by Garth Jeffers and Donnan Jeffers, is a poem from *The Beginning and the End and Other Poems.* Reprinted with permission of Random House, Inc.

Lewis H. Lapham, Nancy Neveloff Dubler, Thomas H. Murray, Jeremy Rifkin, and Lee Salk, "Ethics in Embryo" (Forum) is from *Harper's Magazine,* September 1987, pp. 38–47. Copyright © 1987 by *Harper's Magazine.* All rights reserved. Reprinted with permission of *Harper's Magazine.*

Barry Lopez, "Hunting Walrus" is from *Arctic Dreams,* pp. 407–415. Copyright © 1986 Barry Holstun Lopez. Reprinted with permission of Charles Scribner's Sons, an imprint of Macmillan Publishing Company.

John R. Mastalski, "Animal Rights in Perspective" is from *The Santa Clara,* April 30, 1987. The slightly revised version that appears in this volume is reprinted with permission of John R. Mastalski.

Sir Isaac Newton, "The Nature of Planetary Orbits" is from *A Treatise of the System of the World,* Second Edition, 1731.

William Oldendorf, "Should We Seek Out Alien Life?" is from *Science Digest,* November 1984, pp. 94, 115. Reprinted with permission of William Oldendorf.

Robert Ornstein and Richard F. Thompson, "Learning and Brain Growth" is from Robert Ornstein, Richard Thompson, and David Macaulay, *The Amazing Brain,* pp. 165–168. Text copyright © 1984 by Robert Ornstein and Richard F. Thompson. Illustrations by David Macaulay. Reprinted with permission of Houghton Mifflin Company.

Edgar Allen Poe, "The Facts in the Case of M. Valdemar," 1845.

Edgar Allen Poe, "Sonnet: To Science" (1829) is from *Poems,* 1831.

Carl Sagan, "Extraterrestrial Life: An Idea Whose Time Has Come" is from Carl Sagan and Jerome Agel, *The Cosmic Connection,* pp. 195–198. Copyright © 1973 by Carl Sagan and Jerome Agel. Reprinted with permission of Doubleday, a division of Bantam, Doubleday, Dell Publishing Group, Inc.

Richard Selzer, "The Surgeon as Priest" is from *Mortal Lessons: Notes on the Art of Surgery,* pp. 24–36. Copyright © 1974, 1975, 1976 by Richard Selzer. Reprinted with permission of Simon & Schuster, Inc.

Peter Singer, "When Are Experiments on Animals Justifiable?" is from *Animal Liberation* (New York: Avon Books, 1977), pp. 74–79. Reprinted with permission of Peter Singer.

Karla Swatek, "Artificial Fluoridation: How Safe?" is a student research paper published with permission of Karla Swatek.

May Swenson, "The DNA Molecule," copyright © 1968 by May Swenson, is a poem from *New and Selected Things Taking Place,* 1979, p. 92. Reprinted with permission of May Swenson.

Lewis Thomas, "Computers" is from *The Lives of a Cell,* pp. 111–114. Copyright © 1974 by Lewis Thomas. All rights reserved. Reprinted with permission of Viking Penguin Inc.

Henry David Thoreau, "Where I Lived, and What I Lived For" is from *Walden.* 1854.

Cory Wade, "The Lethal Dose 50: Dermal Version." Copyright © 1989 by Cory Wade. The poem is published in this volume with permission of Cory Wade.

James D. Watson, "The DNA Puzzle: Finding How the Pieces Fit" is from *The Double Helix,* pp. 123, 125–126. Copyright © 1968 James D. Watson. Reprinted with permission of Atheneum Publishers, an imprint of Macmillan Publishing Company.

Alfred North Whitehead, "The Essence of a Liberal Education" is from *The Aims of Education,* pp. 55–59 (Mentor Edition). Copyright 1929 by Macmillan Publishing Company; renewed 1957 by Evelyn Whitehead. Reprinted with permission of Macmillan Publishing Company.

Walt Whitman, "To a Locomotive in Winter" is a poem from *Leaves of Grass,* 1891.

Walt Whitman, "When I Heard the Learn'd Astronomer" is a poem from *Leaves of Grass,* 1891.

Index